Tornado

Multi-Role Combat Aircraft

Jon Lake
& Mike Crutch

TORNADO
Multi-Role Combat Aircraft
ISBN 1 85780 096 6   Copyright 2000
The RAF Benevolent Fund Enterprises

Written by Jon Lake and Mike Crutch
Edited by Peter R. March
Appendices by Howard Curtis
Design by Graham Finch Design

First published in 2000 by Midland Publishing
(an imprint of Ian Allan Publishing Ltd)
24 The Hollow, Earl Shilton
Leicester, LE9 7NA, England
Tel: 01455 847 815 Fax: 01455 841 805
E-mail: midlandbooks@compuserve.com

Worldwide distribution (except North America):
Midland Counties Publications
Unit 3 Maizefield, Hinckley Fields
Hinckley, Leics., LE10 1YF, England
Tel: 01455 233 747 Fax: 01455 233 737
E-mail: midlandbooks@compuserve.com

North America trade distribution:
Specialty Press Publishers & Wholesalers Inc,
11605 Kost Dam Road,
North Branch, MN 55056, USA
Tel: 651 583 3239 Fax: 651 583 2023
Toll free telephone: 800 895 4585

Printed by Ian Allan Printing Limited
Molesey Road, Riverdene Business Park
Hersham, Surrey, KT12 4RG, England

Cover photograph:
No II (AC) Squadron Tornado GR1A ZA401 on a low level training sortie. Sgt Rick Brewell, RAF Public Relations

Frontispiece:
A No 12 Squadron Tornado GR1B based at RAF Lossiemouth, armed with a pair of Sea Eagle ASMs, flying low over the Scottish coastline. Sgt Rick Brewell, RAF Public Relations

Other photographs:
British Aerospace, Bob Archer, Gordon Bartley, Derek Bower, Dave Bowers, Sgt Rick Brewell, Sgt 'Tiny' Briggs, Bill Bushell, Cpl John Cassidy, Richard Cooper, Dolphin Images, Andy Evans, Hartmut Feldmann, Jeremy Flack/Aviation Photographs International, Peter R. Foster, Fg Off Andy Glover, Werner Greppmeir, Darron Hall, Wg Cdr Mike Heath, Frank Housby, Jamie Hunter, Paul A Jackson, Sqn Ldr Mark Knight, Flt Lt Mike Lumb, Andrew March, Daniel March, Peter R. March, Pablo Mason, Sqn Ldr Stuart Osborne, Tony Paxton, Sqn Ldr Nigel Risdale, Sqn Ldr Mike Rondot, Terry Senior, Ben J Ullings, Flt Lt Nick Wilcock and Kevin Wills.

SGT JACK PRITCHARD

Contents

A fully armed 'Treble One' Tornado F3, with four AIM-9M Sidewinders underwing and four BAe SkyFlash missiles under the belly. GEOFF LEE

Introduction

An RAF Tornado GR4 of No IX Squadron formates with a VC-10 tanker of No 101 Squadron. GEOFF LEE

The Tornado was conceived as a common strike/attack aircraft for use by three of NATO's largest and most powerful members, the Tri-national programme offering advantage of commonality, interoperability and economies of scale. Its vital Cold War roles of nuclear strike and interdiction dictated that the Tornado would be one of the most sophisticated all-weather bombers ever seen, capable of hitting pinpoint targets with unerring precision and devastating power in any weather conditions, by day or night. Fortunately, the Cold War never turned 'hot' and the Tornado was never called upon to practise its deadly craft in earnest against Warsaw Pact targets.

Since the Cold War, Tornados have dropped bombs in anger on several occasions. Combat proven in the Gulf during Operation *Desert Storm*, the Tornado performed dangerous low level anti-airfield attacks with devastating effectiveness (and, contrary to popular and press opinion, with surprisingly light losses), before switching to a new and relatively untried medium-altitude PGM delivery role, in which the aircraft (with its GEC TIALD designator) also

excelled. Since then, RAF Tornados have dropped bombs on numerous occasions over Iraq, and also over the Balkans. Most recently, during Operation *Allied Force*, Tornados from all three of the original customer nations flew operational sorties over Kosovo and Serbia, which also involved all three of the major Tornado sub-variants (IDS, ECR and ADV). No single mission involved the use of all three types (or all three customers), though RAF Tornados frequently found themselves being supported by Luftwaffe Tornado ECRs operating in the SEAD role.

The Tornado has made a smooth transition from its Cold War role to new tasks undreamed of by its original designers. The aircraft continues to form the backbone of the strike/attack forces of its operators, and in Italy and Britain at least, the Tornado F3 represents the most useful and most capable interceptor available. Sometimes derided for its lack of F-16 type agility, the Tornado F3 is a very much better fighter aircraft than many of its critics would allow – with almost unmatched long range BVR (Beyond Visual Range) capability. Still untested in combat, the Tornado F3 has given

A TIALD-equipped RAF Tornado GR1B of No 617 Squadon lines up on the runway at Ali Al Salem Air Base in Kuwait during Operation Bolton. Operations in support of international peacekeeping efforts form an important part of the Tornado's post-Cold War role. CPL JOHN CASSIDY

the toughest opponents some frightening moments during exercises, and ongoing modification and upgrade programmes will maintain the type's viability until it is finally replaced by the Eurofighter after 2010.

The Tornado IDS 'bomber' will remain in service even longer, and surviving RAF and German aircraft are already undergoing ambitious upgrade programmes and are receiving new weapons and systems which will revolutionise their operational capabilities. Further upgrades and enhancements are likely before the Tornado is finally replaced by a yet-to-be-decided successor.

As well as representing a great military and technical success in service with the air arms of the three nations which created it, the Tornado has been a real industrial success. The aircraft enjoyed only modest export sales, but

was a massive programme by European standards, and did provide its manufacturers with invaluable lessons and useful experience in working together – experience which has been put to very good effect in the design and manufacture of the Eurofighter. Fifteen prototype and pre-production Tornados were followed by 977 production aircraft, taking the total production run to 992 aircraft – a tally unequalled by any European manufacturer or consortium since the days of aircraft such as the Hawker Hunter.

The Tornado has frequently been the subject of controversy and criticism, most of which has been ill-informed and often deliberately mischievous (though still damaging). To an extent, the aircraft's excellence remains overshadowed by carping criticism, and this book represents an attempt to 'put the record straight'.

© Jon Lake   November 1999

Genesis

The aircraft which eventually became the Tornado began life in the 1960s, as a number of nations came together to think about a replacement for their F-104G Starfighters, and after the successive cancellations of the RAF's three planned Canberra replacements. The TSR 2 reached flying status, but its planned successor, the RAF's F-111K never flew, and the Anglo-French AFVG never got beyond the drawing board. Each cancellation led to a life extension for the ageing Canberras. When it became known that the new project laboured under the acronym MRCA, it was small wonder that many cynics asked if the initials really stood for Multi-Role Combat Aircraft, or whether it actually meant 'Must Refurbish Canberra – Again'.

The aircraft had a tortured birth, overcoming prodigious political problems and minor political difficulties, to become a commercial, political and military success. The Tornado is still in production 24 years after the prototype's maiden flight, and just shy of 1,000 have been built. Even more remarkably, the Tornado is now giving invaluable service in a medium-level, out-of-theatre role for which it was never originally intended, and all three of the original customers are today busy refurbishing and modernising their aircraft for many years of further service.

A Joint Working Group to study a common F-104 replacement (the MRA-75, or Multi-Role Aircraft for 1975) was established following a meeting of the Belgian, Dutch, German and Italian air force chiefs of staff at Fürstenfeldbruck on 19 August 1967. Canada (another NATO F-104 operator) subsequently joined the working group. There was always a powerful dynamic in favour of adapting an existing US aircraft type to replace the F-104, although the pressure for a collaborative European solution steadily grew. The partner nations initially envisaged a relatively light, small and cheap fighter-bomber, and studied the Lockheed CL-1200, Saab Viggen, Mirage F1 and Northrop's P530 (which eventually

The first attempt to replace the RAF's Canberras resulted in the TSR 2, which was cancelled by the incoming Labour Government in 1965, with one prototype already flying and two more about to fly.

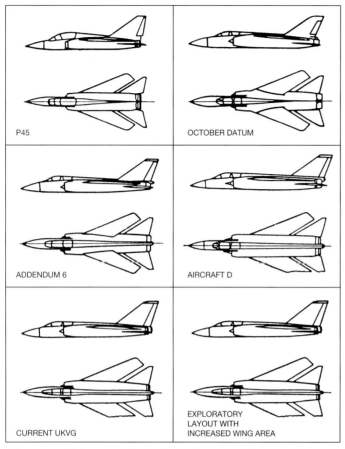

This series of drawings shows the development of the BAC MRA-75 submission from the original BAC P45. The last design ('Exploratory layout with increased wing area') eventually formed the basis of BAC's MRA-75 submission, which took the outboard wing pivot position of the NKF to become the definitive MRCA.

became the YF-17). The growing importance of the conventional attack role meant that the ability to carry multiple bombs would be as important as the ability to deliver a single nuclear device to the target, consequently driving up the weight and cost of the aircraft required.

While it might have initially seemed that the partners in the Joint Working Group required a common aircraft, each had operated its F-104Gs in slightly different roles, and saw their individual Starfighter replacements in a slightly different light. Canada wanted its F-104 replacement to be a high performance agile dogfighter with only a secondary ground attack capability, a vision shared by Belgium. The Dutch requirement was similar, with the added complication of needing a genuine recce capability. Italy needed a long-range interceptor, but placed greater emphasis on the strike/attack role, while Germany's primary requirement was for a strike/ attack aircraft, with rough/short-field capability heavily emphasised.

Britain joined the Joint Working Group (JWG) on 1 July 1968, bringing yet another different requirement to the table, though this was closer to the German vision than were the Canadian and Belgian expectations. Britain also brought a new measure of industrial experience to the group, having already designed and built a large number of successful

modern combat aircraft – an achievement shared by none of the other partners, who were already looking to collaborate with somebody outside the original grouping, whether that someone was Britain, France or USA. Britain's entry into the JWG ensured that Britain would be the beneficiary of this perceived requirement for an experienced partner. The six partner nations then signed a Memorandum of Understanding one week later, expressing a desire to pursue joint studies for an aircraft to meet the MRA-75 requirement. At this stage, the programme looked huge, with Germany claiming a requirement for 600 aircraft, Britain 385, Belgium and the Netherlands 240 each, Italy 200 and Canada 150.

Since it had been first stated, as a fairly general 'Mission Statement', the MRA-75 had gained an Operational Equipment Objective (OEO), which detailed all of the national requirements for runway length, payload/range, endurance, loiter time, and every possible performance parameter. Britain had brought to the partnership an excellent design which could meet the requirement (or at least the air-to-ground side of the requirement) better than any existing design, and this was formally submitted as a solution, together with proposals from MBB and Canadair. All of the aircraft proposed were twin-engined aircraft with variable geometry (VG) wings. None could hope to meet every point in the OEO.

The variable geometry wing had been the subject of much research by Barnes Wallis of Vickers, but its practical application was left to the Americans, in the General Dynamics F-111. The vitally important (but deeply flawed) TFX was extremely influential, and this made the VG configuration became fashionable. For the Tornado, with its wide range of performance requirements, the VG wing was ideal. When unswept, the wing possessed all the normal high-lift characteristics of a conventional high aspect ratio wing, giving good manoeuvrability, take- off performance and low-speed cruise economy. Swept, the wing gave low drag and conferred good transonic and supersonic performance, and also gave better ride (low gust response) at low level. Although Britain, Canada and Germany all proposed MRA.75 designs which featured a VG wing, there was no consensus at that time, and the benefits of the VG wing had to be demonstrated to the Dutch and other partners, who favoured a more conventional wing design.

Belgium and Canada soon dropped out of the programme, with the Belgians wanting a cheap, lightweight and simple pure fighter and with Canada's armed forces undergoing massive disruptions as they were integrated and stripped of many of their capabilities. Even without Belgium and Canada there were still conflicting (and mutually exclusive) requirements within the OEO. The landing requirement, for example, had to take account of heavy ice build-up, but also much-reduced thrust-reverser effectiveness in very hot ambient temperatures. But progress was made as a core set of requirements was identified and drawn up, with certain other requirements being relaxed, or achievable only with lower take-off weights.

On 19 December 1968, the JWG issued a Statement of Work describing the new requirement, for production by a Joint

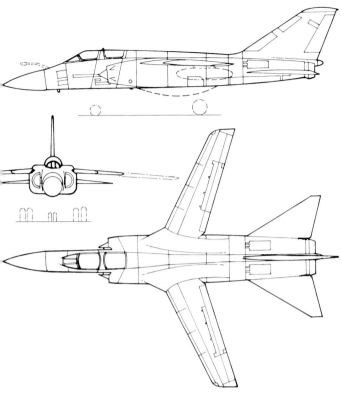

The British-led AFVG was doomed to failure by French preferences for the all-French Mirage G, and for some months, the Anglo-French programme was deliberately obstructed while Dassault quietly pressed on with the swing-wing Mirage.

Industrial Company. At this stage there were still two competing MRA-75 designs, an NKF-derived aircraft from MBB and a refined UKVG proposed by BAC, known as the ACA, and a similar design known as the FCA. The most significant differences between the configurations were that the German design used a low-set wing with pivots well outboard from the fuselage, while BAC preferred a high-set

While French Government prevarication and delay hit the AFVG hard, Dassault quietly went 'full speed ahead' on the Mirage G, so that the aircraft was ready in the wings when France pulled out of the collaborative programme, having delayed what was seen in some quarters as an 'English' competitor to the all-French Mirage.

wing whose pivots were buried within the fuselage. The Germans eventually conceded that the high wing gave superior access to the engines and other systems, and embraced it, while Britain relaxed its very long-range requirements and accepted wing pivots at the wing roots. This solution also provided large wing gloves, which enhanced manoeuvrability. But while the German pivot position was chosen, it was decided that the pivot bearing itself would be based on the British design for the AFVG, coated with Teflon. General Dynamics had lost at least one F-111 to a pivot failure, but there was a high degree of confidence in the British pivot bearing.

MBB had also favoured a conventional all-flying tail for pitch control, with spoilers and ailerons for roll control, while BAC preferred differential tailplane, spoilers and full-span flaps. The British arrangement was selected for the MRCA. Even control forces and harmonisation was subject to careful study and negotiation. Italy and Germany favoured heavier stick forces, like those of the F-104, while Britain wanted lighter controls. In the end, a compromise was reached, and as a result, the Tornado feels heavy to a pilot used to British combat aircraft, and light to a pilot used to US fighters.

Remarkably, there were areas of the MRCA which owed little to either the UKVG or the German project. One such area was the engine intakes. The German design used simple semi-circular intakes with fixed boundary layer splitter plates, rather like the intakes used by the F/A-18. The UKVG had intakes much like those of the BAC TSR 2 or the F-104, with moving conical centrebodies. The Italian requirement for Mach 2

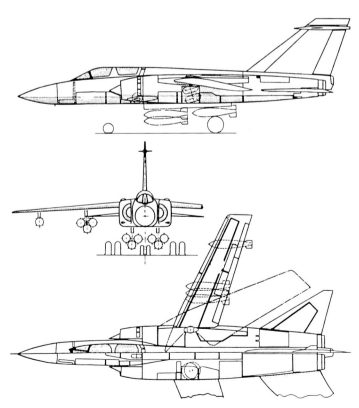

Following the French withdrawal from AFVG, BAC continued working on what became the UKVG. Following the demise of the AVS, Germany was invited to join the programme, thereby laying the foundations for the Tornado itself.

The German-American AVS (Advanced Vertical Strike) aircraft combined two main engines with four swing-out lift engines. Despite its obvious impracticality, the AVS was supported by some as a serious alternative to an Anglo-German agreement.

performance led to a new type of intake, similar to that used by the North American A-5 Vigilante or the Concorde. These incorporated variable ramps which conferred Mach 2 capability.

The relatively small size of the MRCA ruled out the provision of an internal weapons bay, and instead both MBB and BAC opted for the next best, next lowest drag solution, with a flat underfuselage on which weapons could be suspended. The wings were initially to be left clean, though after the design was finalised, the pressure for stores pylons led to the addition of underwing pylons for fuel, ECM pods and expendables (chaff and flares).

The German NKF-based design was envisaged as being powered by American Pratt and Whitney JTF-16 (TF-30) turbofans, like the F-111 and the F-14, while the British aircraft was designed around a pair of Rolls-Royce RB 199s. Both designs were subsequently offered with either type of engine. A decision on which engine would power the aircraft was not taken however.

More important arguments went Britain's way with less fanfare. Whatever its configuration, the MRCA was sized around Britain's requirement. The other partners had seen the air-to-ground role as being centred around relatively short-range close air support and battlefield air interdiction missions, whereas the RAF had decided that the Army was best supported by attacks much further behind the frontline – where enemy armour might be more heavily concentrated, more vulnerable and less heavily defended. The RAF also placed great importance on the offensive counter-air mission, attacking enemy airfields. Finally, the RAF was adamant that it required an aircraft with sophisticated avionics, for finding and attacking targets by night and in foul weather. The golden aim was to give a 'blind first pass attack' capability against interdiction-type targets.

In Italy, many believed that the country would never be able to afford to procure Tornado and Fiat continued to participate in the programme partly to gain experience and partly to give the company and the country leverage, in case it had to

licence-build an American aircraft type.

But the British were clever. The Germans and Italians would gain a larger aircraft than they had wanted, yet were 'blamed' for the aircraft's size. It was said to be Germany's insistence on fuselage fuel (with none in the wings) which sized the Tornado's fuselage, while Italian specific excess power requirements dictated the thrust required. Italy had wanted an interceptor, Germany a battlefield air superiority and close air support fighter/fighter-bomber. MRCA was a long-range all-weather interdictor strike aircraft – the Canberra replacement required by the British! The only real compromise that the British had to make was to accept an aircraft with Germany's short take-off and landing performance requirements, which imposed a minor reduction in low level combat radius, but which proved to be a blessing for out-of-area operations.

On 14 March 1969, a single configuration was finally agreed by the partners as the Baseline Configuration of what was being referred to as the MRCA (Multi-Role Combat Aircraft) at least as often as it was called the MRA-75. Until then the aircraft was still primarily a single-seater, with a minimum change two-seater to meet Britain's requirement, and to meet the need for trainer variants for other nations. In the interests

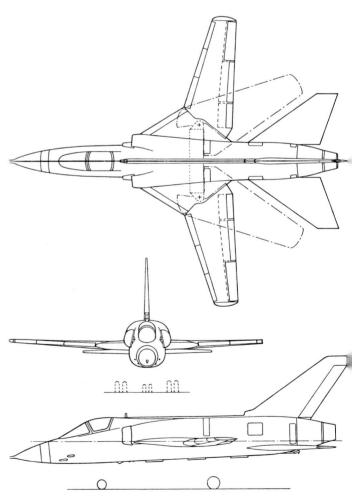

The ridiculously complex and expensive AVS was abandoned in 1967, when MBB began work on the Neue KampfFlugzeug (NKF), a single-seat variable geometry aircraft which eventually 'gifted' its wing configuration to the MRA-75.

of commonality the MRCA started to become a two-seat aircraft, with the baseline single-seat aircraft (for the Luftwaffe, and Italy) becoming the Panavia 100, and the two-seater (for the RAF and the Marineflieger) the Panavia 200. In April 1969, the aircraft was briefly named as the Panavia Panther, though the name was soon discarded. One year later, in March 1970, the Panavia 100 was quietly dropped.

The new MRCA weighed in at about 30,000 lb empty, or 60,000 lb fully laden – roughly the same as the F-4 Phantom, and about a third smaller than the F-111. Dimensionally, the aircraft was rather smaller than the F-4, and with wings swept was not very much bigger than an F-16. Twelve days later, on 26 March 1969, the Joint Industrial Company was formally constituted as Panavia GmbH, based in the offices of the defunct EWR in Munich. In September 1969, the single manufacturer was joined by a single customer, NAMMA (NATO MRCA Development and Production Management Agency) which was an umbrella organisation representing the three national government procurement machines. Everything was ready for contracts to be signed!

In July 1969, the Dutch pulled out of the programme, which had moved too far from their requirements. This lost Fokker-VFW its one-sixth share of the industrial programme. The Dutch were in some respects the unsung heroes of the Tornado project, having provided most of the research work for the low speed high lift devices fitted to the Tornado's wing.

It was then agreed that Britain and Germany would each pay 44% of the costs, and would take 42.5% of the workshare, with Italy paying 12% and securing 15% of the work. Detailed workshare provisions were finalised on 28 February 1970, with Britain allocated the nose and tail, Germany the centre fuselage, and Italy the wings. English was adopted as the programme language, and it was decided that all major decisions relating to design would have to be unanimous. This effectively gave each nation the power of veto, enforcing consensus and compromise, and meant that there was no single Chief Designer as such. Project definition was completed in April 1970, by which time the design had gained wing and fin area to compensate for a slight increase in weight.

On 4 September 1969, it was announced that the decision had finally been taken that the aircraft would be powered by the Rolls-Royce engine. This was despite the fact that the RB199-34R was a paper design, while the competing TF-30 was a mature, in-service engine, though history would later show it to have been a technological disaster, which crippled those aircraft which it powered. The ability to consider combining a new engine and a new airframe (with all the development effort and cost involved) was a benefit of the sheer size of the MRCA programme, and of the fact that risks were spread between three countries.

The RB 199 announcement came as no surprise, since a collaborative tri-national company (Turbo Union) had been formed at Filton on 1 June 1969, with 40% shares held by Rolls-Royce and MTU München GmbH, and 20% by Fiat SpA. Like the MRCA airframe, the engine would be built by a tri-national partnership. The use of a brand new engine allowed the use of the latest engine technologies, and as a

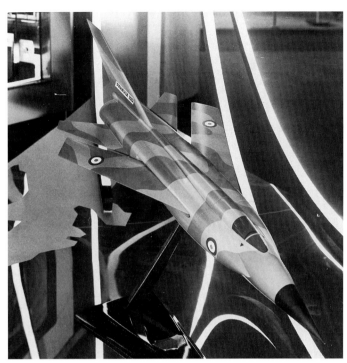

This model was the first representation of the MRCA to be shown in public (in September 1969). It showed an aircraft with undersize canopy, blended intakes and wing pivots well inboard, whereas MRCA was already planned to have its pivots further outboard. The final configuration had already been decided in March 1969, and looked very little like this!

result the RB 199 was smaller and lighter than any of its similarly rated potential competitors. The RB 199 had a thrust to weight ratio of about 7.5:1 (compared to 4.5:1 for the similarly-rated J79) and a compression ratio of 23:1 (compared to the J79's 8.3:1). Target fuel consumption was a miserly 0.63 lb/lb st/hr (compared to 0.85 lb for the J79). And on top of this, the engine was light (1,980-lb rather than the J79's 3,625 lb) and very compact. This in turn allowed the size and weight of the aircraft itself to be minimised.

Choosing a new engine for the new MRCA meant that timescales would by necessity be extremely tight, not least since engine development is normally expected to entail a longer time than airframe development. With only four years available, Turbo Union could not have the luxury of the six-year timescale usually felt to be necessary to design, build and fly a military jet engine. In order to hit the planned first flight date of December 1973, Turbo Union would have to work very hard indeed. Moreover, once the Tornado engine bay was sized for the RB 199 there was no chance of using an older engine on the initial prototypes. The engine had to be ready for a first flight to take place at all! The first RB 199 was bench run at Bristol on 27 September 1971.

Avionics development was assigned to another new tri-national company, Avionica Systems Engineering GmbH, formed in Munich on 28 August 1969, with the UK's EASAMS leading ESG of Germany and SIA of Italy. But unlike the airframe and engine companies, this was an integration and selection organisation, rather than a design and manufacturing company. The decision was taken that the

The MRCA as shown on a 1973 brochure, although a wooden mock-up (hidden in a hangar at Warton, and shown only to a select few) was closer to the final design.

Tornado's avionics would be state of the art, but would include some off the shelf systems. Britain had wanted a new radar developed by Ferranti, but Germany and Italy favoured a proven off-the-shelf radar made by Autonetics. In the end a less expensive Texas Instruments radar was selected instead, and was contracted in October 1971.

Every use of a newly developed system or equipment item of course imposed short-term risk, but this was outweighed by the greater capability and delayed onset of obsolescence. In addition to the new engine, MRCA featured a new computer assisted flight control system, a very high pressure hydraulic system, novel self-sealing fuel tanks and a brand new rapid-fire cannon.

There was no senior partner in the Panavia grouping, though Germany had ambiguous attitudes to leadership. On the one hand, Germany did not want to be seen as the leader of a major international military programme, since it was sensitive to accusations of militarism, and was aware of its lack of experience. On the other hand, many in Germany sincerely believed that the large number of aircraft required would actually be delivered, and that Germany would therefore be the largest customer for the aircraft. This, it was felt, ought to give Germany a leading role. At the same time, many in Germany were proud of the country's post war economic miracle, and were not willing to be in any way subservient to Britain in the programme. Thus it was Germany that declined a formal leadership role, while instead suggesting that workshare should be based on numbers of aircraft procured. But at the same time, German national pride demanded that the first flight should be made by a German aircraft, from a German airfield, and the decision to use a British pilot was hard for some Germans to swallow.

With the departure of the Dutch and the dropping of the single-seat version, it was apparent that the MRCA was now an all-weather attack aircraft, and not an interceptor, and this prompted the Germans and Italians to procure different aircraft (effectively off the shelf) for the air superiority role,

The Tornado programme relied on a number of testbed aircraft which flew various elements of the aircraft ahead of time, bringing them to maturity before the MRCA prototypes flew themselves. This Buccaneer was one of two (XT272 and XT285) fitted with Tornado radar and avionics, and had a radome almost identical to that fitted to the production Tornado.

Avro Vulcan XA903 was assigned to test the RB 199 engine, installed in a replica of half a Tornado fuselage, with the same intake and duct and a careful copy of the Tornado's forward fuselage contours in front of the replica starboard intake. An instrumentation pod was carried under the port wing after the first few flights.

reducing the number of MRCAs required. Germany bought 175 F-4 Phantoms, and reduced its Tornado buy from 600 to 410 (100 for the Navy), and later to 324. Four F-4 Geschwaderen replaced three of the planned Tornado wings. Italy bought 165 new F-104S Starfighters, and reduced its Tornado total from 200 to 100 aircraft. Britain's requirement remained steady at 385 aircraft.

Even before the Tornado prototypes were ready to fly, related testbed aircraft joined the programme. The Vulcan engine testbed began flying in early 1973, and the RB 199 (the fourth engine built) first ran in the air in April 1973. The ground mapping 'attack radar' flew in the USA in a Convair 240, and from November 1974 the two Buccaneers converted by Marshall of Cambridge shook down the avionics system.

Finally, with a configuration agreed, and with numbers of aircraft and workshare fixed, and with many elements of the

The Tornado's 27-mm IWKA-Mauser cannon was flown on a Lightning F2A leased back from the RAF. The weapon's fitting was not interchangeable with the 30-mm Aden, but could be accommodated in the same size bay.

weapons system already flying the programme could finally advance beyond the drawing board and beyond wooden mock-ups. But while assembly of the prototypes continued without major problems, the programme itself continued to be the subject of vituperative attacks.

In Britain there was the usual knocking campaign from a variety of sources – from those influenced by the US industry's lobbyists, who urged cancellation in favour of an (unspecified) American aircraft, from the left wing who opposed expensive defence programmes on principle, and even from Little Englanders who could not see that the days when the UK could build a combat aircraft alone had long since disappeared. The opposition to the programme was never very widespread, however, and never threatened to undermine the broadly bi-partisan political consensus which backed the programme. In Italy the story was much the same, though concerns that the air force would not be able to afford to buy the aircraft once it was developed were added to the mix. In Italy, the programme received aid from a surprising source, the Italian Communist Party, who supported (or at least did not oppose) the programme for the jobs it brought, and as a means of reducing Italian dependence on the USA.

In Germany, opposition to the programme was more intense, with the disparate opposition groups working together to produce an anti-MRCA campaign which came to threaten the programme. Some opponents of MRCA were motivated by anti-militarism, with others spurred on by a hostility to the government in power. Others wished to see closer links with the USA (on whom Germany still relied for defence) and some wanted a cheaper, simpler combat aircraft, perhaps with a more genuine German leadership.

Every tiny slippage or technical problem was seized upon as evidence of the MRCA's unsuitability or inadequacy, and the

German press began an orchestrated campaign against the aircraft. This had its effect, and by 1973, many once-supportive politicians had backed away from supporting the programme too openly. There were a variety of unflattering nicknames, from the venomous 'English Aeroplane' with its inference that Germany was being forced to buy an unsuitable aircraft optimised to meet British requirements, and a product of British industry – then seen as something of a joke in Europe. Even worse was 'die Eierlegende Wollmilchsau' (the egg-laying, woolly, milk-giving pig) which poked fun at the aircraft's claims of multi-role versatility. The US aircraft industry was more than happy to support the campaign with money, personnel and advice. The situation was serious, since the programme was being funded in relatively small 'chunks' with relatively frequent continuation checkpoints, at which any partner could withdraw from the project – probably causing its total cancellation. The key 'go, no-go' dates were 1 July 1971, 1 November 1972, 15 November 1973 and 1 May 1975. Only after that was the programme really safe from the threat of cancellation.

Fortunately, hostile press coverage and political posturing had little affect on actual progress in the factories, and the first few prototypes steadily took shape in each country. Final assembly of the first aircraft began (behind curtains) in November 1972. Finally, the first prototype was ready for its road move to the flight test centre at Manching in mid-February 1973. No-one could have anticipated that the aircraft would not fly until August 1974.

The prototype was partially dismantled and chained to a low loader, its wings fully swept, its tail unit removed. Covered by tarpaulins, the aircraft looked like a boat, and after a cheery 'Where's the figurehead, then?' from one of the British engineers a *Playboy* centrefold was taped to the front of the tarpaulins! Though topless the model wore outrageously flared trousers which were, in 1973, the height of fashion. Few would have guessed that the fashion might return in 1998, and few would have guessed that the Tornado would still be the most important military aircraft for the three partner nations. The bizarre load set off from Ottobrunn at midnight on 12 February, going through the centre of Munich (the city then had no ring road) on its 60 mile journey. A great procession of police and company officials were in the convoy, which repeatedly stopped while branches were lopped from trees adjacent to the road. A low bridge almost put paid to the whole enterprise, until the Tornado's tyres were deflated to give the final half-inch of clearance. The entire enterprise took place against the threat of a terrorist bomb attack! Fortunately, after a six-hour journey, the aircraft reached Manching safely.

After final assembly (including painting in Panavia's red and white house colours), tests and functional checks and after comprehensive engine runs and taxy trials, flight testing could at last begin. Unfortunately, the process took longer than anyone could have anticipated, and the MRCA missed its scheduled first flight date in December 1973. The Germans were waiting for the availability of flight-cleared engines which would not surge, though some suggest that the second aircraft at Warton was by then ready to fly, with Warton prepared to accept the risk of surging (which did not damage the robust RB 199) and waiting only for the German aircraft to beat their aircraft into the air – for political reasons.

The first MRCA prototype leaving Ottobrunn for Manching on 12 February 1973. A playboy centrefold was stuck to the tarpaulin covering the aircraft's nose, in lieu of a figurehead. The 60-mile road move took six hours, and necessitated lopping branches from trees, and the deflation of tyres to allow the aircraft to pass under a low bridge.

Flight Testing

As the first military aircraft programme in Europe to be developed across three separate countries, Tornado also had the first tri-national flight test programme, which, like so much of the project, had to be partially 'triplicated' for political reasons. No one partner was willing to 'go without' its own flight test centre, any more than it would relinquish having its own assembly line. But while the decision was made to have three separate Flight Test Centres, care was taken not to duplicate the work that each carried out. NAMMA and Panavia were therefore tasked with co-ordinating and allocating elements of the flight test programme to the three national manufacturers. BAC, MBB and Aeritalia selected Warton, Manching and Caselle as their respective test centres with all but the West Germans assembling their aircraft on site. MBB initially used their Ottobrunn factory near Munich for Tornado assembly, until a new plant was built at Manching.

BAC's flight test site was co-located alongside the British Tornado production and assembly line, but the German flight test organisation at Manching was 50 miles or so north of Munich and the original Ottobrunn MBB plant intended as the German assembly line. Caselle was the HQ of Aeritalia's Combat Aircraft Group, and also functioned as Turin's airport. The tri-national nature of the project necessitated a great deal of travel between centres by engineers and managers, and all three participating companies made extensive use of communications aircraft shuttling their personnel between test centres and assembly plants. This was once calculated to have accounted for 3.3 % of the total Tornado programme cost, and in 1972, long before a Tornado flew, cost the programme its first fatalities, when a Hansa Jet crashed on take off from Blackpool's Squire's Gate airport.

The infrastructure required for the programme was enormous. The early 1970s saw manufacturers in the USA introduce various modern techniques to improve flight testing, some of which originated in the space programme. One such innovation was telemetry, first used to any great extent in Europe during BAC and Aerospatiale's Concorde flight test programme. Telemetry would play an even more vital role in supporting MRCA flight trials. It gave the ability to record and down-link large numbers of flight, engine and load parameters in real-time, some of these could be assessed immediately, allowing those on the ground to clear the aircraft to go to the next test point during the same sortie. The Tornado prototypes recorded data from 460 points on each aircraft, and could simultaneously broadcast 150 parameters. Most of the parameters were simply recorded for subsequent in-depth analysis by the engineering development teams. Flight simulators also played a key role in preparing the crews who flew the early aircraft, but were also used to 'test fly' new configurations before flight, thus saving time and money.

The tri-national Memorandum of Understanding signed on 22 July 1970 made provision for nine prototypes (referred to as P.01 through P.09) plus a single static-test example (P.10), and these were to be allocated to the three manufacturers tests fleets as follows: P.01/ P.04 / P.07 to MBB, P.02/P.03/P.06/P.08 to BAC, plus P.05 and P.09 to Aeritalia. Although a number of project areas were bound to overlap (in some cases necessarily so), MRCA followed what has become the norm in test programmes with each prototype being assigned specific (and

Heading photograph: Afterburners blazing, P.02 (the first British prototype) blasts into the air at Warton for its maiden flight. The aircraft was crewed by Paul Millett, with the Italian test pilot Pietro Trevisan in the back seat, picking up tips prior to flying the first Italian prototype.

Father of them all. The first of the Tornado prototypes seen during the aircraft's formal unveiling to the press. It still lacked much equipment, including ejection seats, and the intakes were deliberately blanked off. The aircraft wore tri-national markings on the port forward fuselage with British and Italian roundels on the wings.

often unique) test functions with the overall programme leading to the validation of the aircraft as a flying machine and weapons system.

Manching employed its three aircraft for initial handling and performance work and for development of the complex fly-by-wire flight control system and the avionics suite. Warton's four aircraft also had two tasks – exploration and expansion of the flight envelope and development and testing of the dual-control trainer version. Operations at Caselle were focused primarily upon the clearance of different external stores configurations. Although Warton had only one more aircraft assigned than Manching, this did not reflect the extent to which the British Flight Test Centre was the powerhouse of the programme. Vital support aircraft like the Mauser-equipped Lightning, the Vulcan engine testbed and a pair of specially equipped Buccaneers were all based at Warton.

In March 1973, a further MoU was signed to cover production of an additional six pre-production examples (P.11 to P.16). These would be built to various standards, becoming hybrid prototype/production-standard airframes, each approaching closer to the planned production standard. Three of the pre-production aircraft were assigned to MBB (P.11, P.13 and P.16), two (P.12 and P.15) to what became British Aerospace (still BAC as the MoU was signed), with P.14 flying with Aeritalia. By this time, the production programme had itself been agreed upon as follows: Great Britain 385, Italy 100, and West Germany's Luftwaffe requiring 212 plus 112 for the Marineflieger, totalling 809. This figure included four of the pre-production aircraft, which were to be refurbished. These four aircraft joined their respective military flight test centres but none ever reached front-line service. Remarkably the MoU authorising full production was destined not to be signed for another three years.

Just as the Tornado airframe was produced by a carefully

planned and 'politically balanced' consortium, so to was the aircraft's new powerplant. Thus Turbo Union Ltd (a consortium of Rolls-Royce, Germany's MTU and Fiat) was formed to oversee development and production of the Rolls-Royce-designed RB.199 turbofan. The prototype engine reached the flight-test phase in Spring 1973, flying for the first time on 19 April 1973 in a specially constructed pod underneath the same Vulcan B1 test-bed (XA903) that had been used for Concorde's Olympus trials. The pod was designed to closely resemble a section of Tornado fuselage, with a representative intake and intake duct.

Some structural and electrical problems with the Vulcan itself reduced the aircraft's flying rate, and this slowed development of the RB.199 engine. Even when the Vulcan's problems were rectified, things did not go entirely smoothly. There were problems with the engine installation and with the engine itself, and the tests provided evidence of surge, oil starvation and blade-shedding problems. But the RB.199 was an extremely advanced engine, and there were encouraging

Meshed grids were fitted over the main and auxiliary intakes for P.01's initial taxy trials, as shown here. This smart red and white livery was applied to several of the early prototypes.

results too though clearance for the MRCA's first flight was not obtained in the timescale originally envisaged. Meanwhile, the first prototype MRCA left MBB's Ottobrunn factory by road under the cover of darkness during the night of 12/13 November 1973, for reassembly at Manching. The stripped fuselage was heavily shrouded and in some places wooden frames underlay the shrouds to deliberately distort any impression of the aircraft's overall size and shape.

Early in 1974, a modified RB.199 (the -01 version), began flight testing on the Vulcan to validate its use for MRCA flying. The hiatus in the project caused by the engine problems allowed Panavia to incorporate additional modifications and test equipment in the first MRCA prototype aircraft, so the delays were not entirely unwelcome.

Airborne

Prototype P.01, serialled D-9591 (98+04 from early 1976), was rolled out at Manching on 8 April 1974, although final approval for the first flight was still some time away, pending flight clearance of the powerplants. The multi-national flavour of the project was maintained with confirmation that Paul Millett, BAC Military Aircraft Division Chief Test Pilot and MRCA Project Pilot, would make the maiden flight, with his MBB opposite number, Nils Meister, in the rear seat.

The historic moment came on 14 August 1974, when P.01 (operating with the callsign 'Luna 23') lifted off Manching's runway into a grey overcast for a 30 minute 'general handling' flight, chased by a Luftwaffe TF-104 and a G-91T. Millett kept the wing-sweep at 26° throughout, although once a satisfactory low-speed handling exercise had been completed at 10,000 ft he retracted the gear and flaps and accelerated to 300 kt. Millett landed after a deliberate missed approach, adding 20-kts to the optimum landing speed to allow a 'first flight' margin, and to compensate for the use of only 'Take Off' flap.

Operating under the callsign 'Luna 23', P.01 was a German assembled aircraft and made its first flight, piloted by BAC's Chief Test Pilot Paul Millett, from a German airfield, with a German pilot in the backseat.

Weather delayed the second flight until 21 August 1974, during which Millett and Meister performed single-engine handling exercises, simulated isolated flight control failures, and swept the wing to 45°. Meister finally took over the front seat for the third flight on 29 August 1974, one sortie earlier than planned, and retrieved German national pride by becoming the first supersonic Tornado pilot, taking the aircraft to just over Mach 1.1, sweeping the wings to the full 68° in the process. As P.01 became increasingly unrepresentative of the full production configuration, later prototypes took over aerodynamic testing, and the aircraft was increasingly used for engine development and testing. In particular, P.01 did most of the work on thrust reverser development, leaving massive sooty deposits up the fin of what was ironically the only white tailed Tornado at Manching! The aircraft later became the first to fly with -04 engines (the first 'full-thrust' RB.199s) in March 1978, and was eventually camouflaged and re-serialled as 98+04.

Much later in its life, P.01 was re-serialled as 98+04, and was re-painted in Luftwaffe camouflage, albeit with massive patches of high-conspicuity dayglo. The aircraft is seen here with a longer test instrumentation boom on the nose, and with camera fairings in the front of the RWR and facing aft under the starboard forward fuselage.

This view of P.02 on very long, very high finals shows to advantage the square section fairings attached to the tailplane tips. These contained exciters for flutter testing, and were removed soon after this photo was taken. The trailing edge flaps are shown here in the 'take off' position.

September 1974 finally saw the MRCA lose its acronym for a real name. The name selected (after some discussion and argument) was Tornado. Understandable in all three languages, the Tornado name won out over the alliterative Panavia Panther. Panther was (apocryphally) rejected because it was the brand name of a leading toilet detergent in one of the countries, or so the story goes. On 30 October 1974, Paul

P.02 undertook the Tornado's initial AAR clearance in July 1975 refuelling from a Victor K2 of the Marham tanker wing. Unusually, the aircraft was one of those which wore the markings of No 232 OCU.

Millett flew the first British prototype (P.02, XX946) from Warton, with Aeritalia test pilot Pietro Trevisan in the rear seat picking up experience. When it first flew, P.02 carried flutter exciters in square section pods on its taileron tips, but these were soon removed. Tasked with exploring and expanding the flight envelope, P.02 went on to perform stalling and spinning trials, and explored handling characteristics at various angles of attack and speed ranges.

P.02 was fitted with RB.199-03 engines and fully variable intakes, and was the first to prove Tornado's almost unique ability to achieve and sustain 800 knots indicated air speed (IAS) at low level, equivalent to about Mach 1.3, making it one of the fastest aircraft in the world on the deck. In May 1977, the aircraft made a level high speed run at higher altitude, abandoning this as the aircraft passed Mach 1.93, still accelerating. This was fast – and contrasted with other early Tornados, whose fixed intakes and low-thrust engines limited them to Mach 1.3 and 40,000 ft.

The hard-working British prototype also validated air-to-air refuelling in a remarkably short space of time performing 'dry' and 'wet' contacts with a Victor K2 during a single sortie flown in July 1975. The Tornado proved rock-steady, though it would later emerge that at higher altitudes, the Tornado's lack of thrust could be embarrassing during inflight refuelling contacts. Quite apart from the operational implications of AAR (air-to-air refuelling), this early 'tick in the box' permitted the pace of flight testing to quicken, recovering some of the ground lost to the delays caused by early engine problems. The use of tankers in the flight test programme allowed longer sorties, and this in turn meant that more test points could be covered in a single flight. P.02 also undertook some external stores trials.

The second British prototype P.03 taking off on its maiden flight. As the first camouflaged aircraft, P.03 initially had old-style red white and blue D-type RAF roundels and fin flash.

The next Tornado to fly (on 5 August 1975) was P.03 XX947, the first dual-control aircraft. This had a fully operational radar, though this still contained no more than ballast! Crewed by Dave Eagles and Tim Ferguson, the aircraft wore RAF dark sea grey and dark green camouflage with light grey undersides instead of the red, white and black Panavia house colours applied to previous prototypes. In addition to its 'twin-stick' test work, the aircraft became the primary high Alpha test ship. It went on to undertake stall and spin recovery work alongside P.02 and unintentionally added to the data gathered by running off the runway at Warton on 4 October 1976. With Ferguson at the controls, the aircraft aquaplaned off the very wet runway onto the grass. The damage was relatively minor, but the incident resulted in the provision of enhanced nosewheel steering, a strengthened main undercarriage and revisions to the reverse thrust efflux flow to maintain maximum rudder effectiveness during the landing run. P.03 subsequently carried out maximum weight trials, taking off at 58,400 lb AUW (with -03 engines) in 1978.

The eventual end-users began to participate at the 'sharp end' of the project from an early stage. The first non-Panavia test pilot to fly the aircraft was Fritz Soos, a civilian employed by the West German Defence Ministry, who flew P.01 for a 50 minute flight on 26 November 1975. He was followed by his colleague Klaus Koglin and by RAF officers Wing Commander Clive Rustin and Squadron Leader Ron Burrows and by AMI Lieutenant Colonels Cesare Calzone and Pasquale Garriba. As these six test pilots underwent training on type, three more aircraft joined the programme. P.04 (D-9592, later 98+05) was flown by Hans-Friedrich 'Fred' Rammensee and Nils Meister from Manching on 2 September 1975. The first Italian

The first British prototype, XX946, initially flew in red and white Panavia house colours, but was soon re-painted in RAF camouflage. The aircraft is seen here during early external stores trials, with its wings in the fully swept position.

Tornado (P.05, X-586) flew from Caselle on 5 December 1975 in the hands of Pietro Trevisan, with the back seat empty. This followed a five month delay awaiting RB.199 installation. Britain's P.06 (XX948) also made its maiden flight with only one pilot aboard (Dave Eagles) on 20 December 1975.

Of the new aircraft, P.04 was perhaps the most crucial since it was the first Tornado fitted with the avionics development package. The various black boxes had already undergone months of bench-testing by Panavia's Central Design & Management Team (CDMT), and from late 1974, flight trials

P.03 was the first Tornado with dual controls, and as such was used for test pilot conversion, as well as for its specific flight test responsibilities. The aircraft is seen here with a forward looking test camera installed at the front of the RWR fairing.

of certain elements of the avionics suite were made in two Hawker Siddeley Buccaneer test-beds (XT272 and XT285) refitted with CDMT Stage 3 avionics by Marshall of Cambridge and based at Warton from November 1974. These aircraft were never capable of being fitted with the full Tornado systems package, lacking the digital fly-by-wire control system. In P.04, the key elements of the flight control system and autopilot, the attack radar (manufactured by Texas Instruments), terrain-following radar (TFR), navigation equipment and weapons interface were integrated in a single aircraft for the first time.

The aircraft had to reach certain milestones in twelve test flights conducted between late 1975 and early 1976. This clearly-defined progress was critical, since the MoU authorising full production was due for signing in the Summer of 1976. Fortunately P.04's flights from Manching proved successful. The necessary test data was produced and analysed in time for the signing of the series production MoU and Batch One production order on schedule on 29 July 1976. The Batch One order covered 23 and 17 aircraft for the RAF and Luftwaffe/ Marineflieger respectively, with no production for Italy. P.04 was later tufted for a brief aerodynamic investigation, and was eventually used for MW-1 trials and for testing of a digital autopilot, and of the ground mapping radar.

While P.04 performed its crucial tests with distinction, P.05 was less fortunate. A major set-back occurred in January 1976 when the aircraft, attempting to land at Caselle at the end of its sixth flight, pitched down onto the runway nose first, causing severe structural damage to the forward fuselage. The aircraft returned to flying in March 1978 with a new forward

From time to time there have been plans to equip frontline RAF Tornados for the buddy-tanking role, but these plans have never come to fruition. During the Gulf War, several aircraft were modified to carry Sargent Fletcher pods acquired from the German Navy, but these were not used in anger. Similarly, plans to fit Flight Refuelling Mk 20H pods have failed to result in a frontline buddy-tanking capability.

With its rear cockpit completely empty the first Italian Tornado prepares to taxy out for its first flight. Several of the Tornado prototypes made their maiden flights with a single pilot aboard. P.05 was initially painted in Panavia's striking red and white house colours.

Pre-production aircraft P.15 approaches the drogue streamed by P.03 during buddy refuelling trials. The use of buddy refuelling during the test programme allowed extended duration sorties to be mounted.

section; but in the mean time much of its development task (centred around airframe flutter and loading) was reassigned to P.02 at Warton.

The Warton-based P.06 (which first flew solo, in the hands of Dave Eagles) was the first aircraft with vortex generators on the tailfin, and was assigned to armament development. It was the first Tornado to be fitted with the new IWKA-Mauser 27mm cannon, though the first airborne firing by P.06 was not undertaken until April 1978. The weapon had already been fired during ingestion trials on the RB.199 mounted underneath the Vulcan testbed, while further trials work had

also been conducted using a bailed-back RAF Lightning F2A (XN795). The Lightning flew from Warton, though it was officially leased to IKWA-Mauser. Like P.04, P.06 was required to prove certain aspects of its task prior to signing of the production MOU. These aspects included separation and release of certain key external stores (primarily the 1,500 litre/330 gallon fuel tanks and 1,000lb bombs) which were completed successfully by the end of March 1976. P.06 was built with a redesigned fairing at the base of the rudder, this being designed in response to test pilot findings of a slight tail 'waggle' in the transonic region, caused by boundary layer separation problems. This simple aerodynamic fix successfully solved the problem, and also reduced what had been excessive base drag.

Warton's P.06 lets fly with the 27-mm Mauser cannon during early firing trials. The muzzle flash is prominent, as are the puffs of smoke streaming aft from the gun. The rear cockpit of the aircraft is filled with test equipment.

P.05 is seen here later in its life, camouflaged and liberally bedecked with camera calibration markings, and 'zapped' with the unit markings of several of the frontline units which would later receive the type. The aircraft carries test camera pods underwing, with a CASMU Skyshark dispenser weapon under the fuselage.

The seventh Tornado (P.07/98+06) took off from Manching on 30 March 1976 in the hands of Nils Meister and Fritz Eckert, joining P.04 in the avionics development role. The aircraft was fitted with an uprated autopilot, and this coupled to the revolutionary automatic terrain following system became the focus of a year-long period of trials flown by the aircraft on special test routes across West Germany. Paul Millett became the first man to fly the maiden flights of three Tornado prototypes on 15 July 1976. The aircraft (P.08/XX950) was fitted with a full set of flying controls in the rear cockpit, occupied on the maiden flight by Ray Woolett. The aircraft, together with P.03, continued the dual-control version testing and undertook weapon aiming work.

The final flying prototype made its maiden flight on the same day as the first pre-production aircraft, 5 February 1977. At Caselle P.09/X-587 was flown by Pietro Trevisan and Manilo Quarantelli while at Manching 'Fred' Rammensee and Kurt Schreiber finally took to the air in P.11/98+01 (the first West German dual-control aircraft). P.11 had almost certainly been held up deliberately, since there was believed to have been an agreement not to fly a pre-production aircraft until all the prototypes were flying, to avoid any embarrassment. Both P.11 and P.12 had been rolled out months before. P.10 had been a static test airframe.

P.09 soon deployed to Sigonella on the island of Sicily to begin external stores trials, centred around a representative standard fit based on the three basic prescribed configurations chosen by the RAF, Luftwaffe/Marineflieger and AMI. The Mediterranean summer of 1977 also provided the test team with the high temperature environment required as part of the development phase, this continuing during the live weapons trials at Decimomannu, Sardinia later the same year. Among the weapons fired by P.09 was the Kormoran anti-ship missile selected by the Marineflieger. P.11 (which featured the revised tail fillet to counteract the inherent 'snaking' of the airframe at around Mach 0.9) was initially assigned to aerodynamic

P.08 was another Warton-based twin-sticker, and was used largely for weapons aiming work. It subsequently gained the dubious distinction of becoming the first Tornado to be written off in a fatal accident.

Pre-production aircraft P.11 is seen here carrying an MW-1 test pod. The munition dispenser tubes are clearly visible, as is the modular construction of the weapon.

evaluation by the engineering teams.

The first British pre-production Tornado (P.12/XZ630) was flown from Warton by Tim Ferguson and Roy Kenward on 14 March 1977. The aircraft (regarded by some as the first 'military' Tornado) was flown by Panavia and military test pilots before being delivered by Dave Eagles to the Aeroplane & Armament Experimental Establishment at Boscombe Down on 3 February 1978. Although assigned to the A&AEE's 'A' Squadron, responsible for fast jet trials and acceptance work, a dedicated Tornado Evaluation Squadron formed at Boscombe Down under Wing Commander Clive Rustin bringing together aircrew and ground support personnel.

Maintaining the tri-national approach fostered by the three manufacturers, Boscombe Down worked alongside West Germany's Erprobungsstelle 61 (based at Manching, where MBB also established a new Tornado production assembly line) and Italy's Reparto Sperimentale di Volo located at Pratica di Mare near Rome. A&AEE work centred on aircraft handling, weapons, navigation and communications arrangements although there were overlaps between the work being carried out by the three national military test centres, and some crews moved from one to another for certain trials and tasks.

E-Stelle 61 received its first Tornado, P.11/98+01, following its aerodynamic trials work on 28 March 1979 and was soon joined by P.13/98+02, which had first flown on 10 January 1978 (in the hands of Fritz Soos and Rainer Henke). The latter

aircraft was the first with the revised production standard taileron. This featured a leading-edge kink at about two-thirds span, a new planform adopted after the discovery that in certain flight regimes with the wings at full sweep, the all-moving taileron came perilously close to the wings' trailing edge.

The next Tornado to fly was P.15/XZ631which made its maiden flight on 24 November 1978 from Warton, flown by Jerry Lee and Jim Evans. Each of the final four pre-production aircraft incorporated at least one feature of the planned production-standard airframe. P.15 had a production standard rear fuselage combined with a 'wet' fin. The so-called 'wet' fin was unique to RAF Tornado variants, and contains a fuel tank (Tank Zero) with a capacity of 551 litres/121 gallons.

Caselle-based P.14 (X-588, later delivered to the AMI as MM7001), with production-standard wings, finally flew on 8 January 1979. The crew were Manlio Quarantelli and Egidio Nappi. This machine was later converted to full production standards, though it was never issued to an AMI frontline unit. The last development aircraft to fly was the West German, Kormoran-capable P.16 (98+03), which incorporated the latest specification forward fuselage. The aircraft made its maiden flight on 26 March 1979, having been the first Tornado assembled at MBB's new Manching factory. The crew for this final 'first flight' were Armin Krauthann and Fritz Eckert. All previous German Tornados had made the awkward road journey by road from the Ottobrun plant on the outskirts of Munich, with their fins removed.

British pre-series aircraft P.12 is seen here on finals to Warton, low over the Ribble Estuary's banks. The aircraft carries six 1,000-lb bombs under the fuselage, with clean wings.

German prototypes and pre-production aircraft lined up at Manching. P.01 is second in the line up, with a long test instrumentation boom mounted on the nose, and with its white fin dirtied by extensive thrust reverser trials. The other aircraft are P.07, P.04, P.11 and P.13.

Pre-production aircraft P.13 is seen here launching an AGM-88 HARM missile. HARM compatability was a feature of German Batch 5 aircraft, and of the SEAD-dedicated Tornado ECR.

Within months of the first flight of the last pre-production aircraft, the first production aircraft began rolling off the line. The first production Tornado emerged from Warton's production facility on 5 June 1979. ZA319 was assigned the build number of BT001 (indicating that it was the first production British Trainer). All RAF Interdictor/Strike, or IDS, aircraft were designated the Tornado GR1 by the RAF, regardless of whether they were fitted with dual controls, although the designation GR1T was sometimes used unofficially. At Manching, GT001 (the first production German trainer) rolled out of the MBB plant the following day.

Six days later, on 12 June 1979, tragedy struck the Tornado programme for the first time. BAe test pilot Russ Pengelly and A&AEE navigator Sqn Ldr John Gray disappeared in P.08/XX950, whilst flying a low level test/training sortie over a fog-shrouded Irish Sea some fifty miles from Warton. No distress call was received, and it was initially assumed that the pilot had simply flown into the sea, disorientated or distracted in treacherous conditions. In fact, it later emerged that the aircraft had crashed during a simulated toss-bombing manoeuvre – most worrying for those about to take the aircraft into service in the nuclear strike role.

With the accident investigation in progress, Dave Eagles and Ray Woolett took BT001 on its 87 minute maiden flight on 10 July 1979. The aircraft was subsequently delivered to Boscombe Down on 15 November 1979 to conduct Controller (Aircraft) Release to Service trials. GT001/43+01 flew from Manching on 17 July 1979 and entered into a similar phase of manufacturer and military testing (helped enormously by the co-location of the MBB plant at E-Stelle 61). The first production Italian example (IT001/ MM55000) was the second Tornado to be built as part of Batch 2 and did not fly until 25 September 1981. In April 1980, a second prototype (P.04) was lost during an airshow rehearsal, killing both of those on board.

The Tornado prototypes and pre-production aircraft were much too non-standard to be suitable for refurbishing and frontline service, and continued in use in the development role until withdrawn for ground instructional duties as weapons loading trainers and the like.

In Service

RAF, Luftwaffe and AMI Tornados of A, B and S squadrons of the TTTE in formation over Rutland, close to their Cottesmore base. Each squadron has a small fin badge in addition to the TTTE arrowhead.

With the initial Panavia and military flight testing complete, the Tornado was ready to enter service. With three major new assembly plants 'up and running' large numbers of aircraft would be available in relatively short order, allowing a very rapid build up of the force. The timescale was so rapid, in fact, that Italy opted not to take any aircraft from the first production batch!

The first requirement was to train aircrew to fly the new aircraft, and it was decided that (in view of the commonality between the aircraft to be built for the four users) all aircrew conversion training could be conducted on a tri-national basis. This was as much a political decision as an operational one, since the 'triplication' of conversion units would have been less costly and less absurd than the triplication of flight test centres, final assembly lines, and the like. Real operational and weapons system conversion would, in any case, remain a national responsibility. But it was decided that the first Tornado unit would be unique in being genuinely tri-national, with aircraft and instructors provided by each of the customer air arms. The establishment of what was to be known as the Tri-national Tornado Training Establishment (colloquially known as the 'Triple-T E') followed on from the establishment of a Joint Operational Study Group by the three national partners in 1974. This had a remit to determine and schedule the aircraft's introduction to service.

TTTE

Studies were made of bases in Britain, West Germany and Italy, and RAF Cottesmore was selected as the TTTE's home in 1975. Cottesmore had been one of nine 'Class 1' airfields used by the V-Bomber force, and thus enjoyed extensive hangarage and support facilities coupled with a large operational readiness platform plus a 9,000 ft main runway. The station's based aircraft were re-located while preparations began for the arrival of the Tornado. The Tri-national Memorandum of Understanding, formally confirming Cottesmore as the home of the TTTE, was signed on 8 May 1979 and the following month saw the first 'Tornado people' arrive with the creation of the Tornado Aircrew Course Design Team (TACDT), whose task was to create a syllabus satisfying the requirements of all three nations.

The Tornado Ground Servicing School (since re-titled the Tornado Maintenance School) was officially opened on 31 October 1979, one week after the first course of engineering personnel had arrived. In July 1980, the Tornado Engineering and Development Investigation Team (TEDIT) was formed,

Batch 2 and Batch 3 Tornados of the TWCU at RAF Honington. The aircraft wear a sword and crossed arrow fin badge based on the Honington station badge. They subsequently gained No 45 Squadron nose markings, reflecting the unit's shadow identity adopted in January 1984.

with the Tornado In-Service Software Maintenance Team (TISMIT) setting up shop on 4 August 1980.

A cadre of pilot and navigator instructors, underwent Service Instructor Aircrew Training (SIAT) in a series of five courses managed by MBB at Manching. The first of these commenced on 5 May 1980 and the last graduated on 28 November. The majority of students only passed through the ground school element, with 15 key personnel (nine pilots and six navigators) undergoing the 13 flying hour conversion to type. The rest completed the flying element of the conversion at Cottesmore prior to the arrival of the first students.

The first TTTE Tornado arrived at Cottesmore on 1 July 1980. The aircraft, a dual-control Tornado GR1 (ZA320) crewed by British Aerospace's Paul Millett and Ollie Heath, arrived with ZA322 and were formally received by Cottesmore's station commander Group Captain M G Simmonds AFC and the Air Officer Commanding No 1 Group, Air Vice-Marshal Michael Knight. The first crews were flying by the end of the following month. From the beginning it was possible (and even routine) for two aircrew from different nations to fly together in an aircraft from the third. The first multi-national crew comprised Sqn Ldr 'Raz' Ball RAF and Major Von Sivers of the Luftwaffe. Von Sivers (with Major Jung) had delivered the first West German Tornado (43+05) to the TTTE on 2 September 1980.

British and German crews formed the first conversion course which commenced on 5 January 1981, prior to the

official opening of the TTTE on 29 January by the then current chiefs of staff: Air Chief Marshal Sir Michael Beetham (RAF), Generlleutnant Friedrich Obleser (Luftwaffe), Admiral Gunter Fromm (C-in-C Fleet, Kriegsmarine) and Generale di Squdra Lamberto Bartolucci (AMI).

As the courses progressed through, so the numbers of TTTE aircraft continued to grow. Codes were applied to all of them, with an alpha-numeric system determined by the country of origin ('B' for the RAF, 'G' for the Luftwaffe and 'I' for the AMI) followed by two digits which would easily identify operational standard aircraft (ranging between 01 to 49) and those Tornados fitted with a dual flying controls (numbered 50 and above). The first Italian Tornado IDS (MM55001) arrived on 5 April 1982, and from then on the TTTE expanded to its typical established strength of 50 aircraft (22 German, 21 British and 7 Italian). The TTTE thus took virtually all of the 43 RB 199 Mk 101-engined aircraft from production Batch 1, which consisted of 23 RAF and 17 German IDS aircraft, with 12 and 14 of these totals being twin-stickers. The remaining three aircraft were the UK's ADV prototypes.

Within the overall TTTE structure, the aircraft were allocated to the Tornado Operational Conversion Unit (TOCU). This was sub-divided into four squadrons; A Squadron (commanded by an RAF officer), B (headed by a German) and C (with an Italian CO), plus the Standards (or S) Squadron whose commanding officer rotates through the three nationalities. As its name implies, Standards Squadron s responsible for the training and standardisation of Tornado instructors. Although the instructional squadron CO's are defined by nationality, the students are assigned without regard to their country of origin. The different nationalities and air arms regularly fly together.

The conversion course lasts for 13 weeks, with flying from Week Five. Pilots perform 28 sorties (totalling almost 36 flying hours), whilst navigators fly 23 sorties (totalling 29 hours). The pilot's syllabus comprises six sorties of transition flying, three formation flying, two night flying, three instrument flying, three navigation, two attack profiles, four weapon aiming practice, plus three day and two night sorties of automatic terrain following familiarisation. The syllabus for navigators follows a similar pattern. The back-seaters fly two transition, two formation flying, two night flying, (but no instrument flying), six navigation, plus similar numbers of sorties as pilots for attack profiles, weapons aiming and automatic terrain following. 'S' Squadron provides an additional 15 hours on top of the OCU course for new flying or navigation instructors, and provides tailored courses for aircrew destined to become instrument rating examiners (IREs). The squadron also provides Senior Officer's Short Courses. These consist of a familiarisation course for personnel of station/base commander level or above who are to be closely involved with Tornado operations, but who will not be expected to become Combat Ready on the aircraft.

The first aircraft of each nationality to reach 1,000 hours were ZA361 (on 10 October 1985) with 43+05 (of the Luftwaffe) later that month, and MM55000 on 28 February 1986. The TTTE itself notched-up 100,000 flying hours during May 1991, just a few months after its tenth anniversary.

Weapons Training

With conversion and instructor training centralised, the diversity of individual national roles and national weapons fits dictated that tactical and weapons training should be undertaken nationally.

RAF Honington (another ex V-bomber base) had been the original choice of location for the TTTE and was selected as the home of the RAF's Tornado Weapons Conversion Unit. Honington received its first Tornado GR1 (ZA542) on 29 June 1981, and the TWCU officially formed on 1 August under Wing Commander Duncan Griffiths. The unit then underwent five months of syllabus ratification and instructor training before accepting its first students from the TTTE on 11 January 1982.

While the TTTE received Batch 1 aircraft, the TWCU took its aircraft from production Batch 2. The Tornados originally delivered to the TWCU thus initially lacked the chin-mounted LRMTS which equipped later GR1s, but featured a higher thrust rating. Batch 2, signed in May 1977, initially comprised 110 aircraft (55 for the UK, 15 for Italy and 40 for West Germany) although this total was later increased by three. The three extra aircraft replaced the three RAF IDS line places 'lost' when the three Air Defence Variant prototypes were added retrospectively to Batch 1.

From the start, the RAF envisaged equipping its Tornado bombers with AIM-9 Sidewinder AAMs for self defence. This No 20 Squadron aircraft is firing an AIM-9 at low level during a missile practise camp at RAF Valley. The position of the Sidewinder launch rail meant that the missile exhaust plume enveloped the tailplane, leading to nickel leading edges being fitted to Gulf War F3s, in case any aircraft had to fire multiple missiles.

With 25 aircraft on charge by the time No 1 Course commenced, the TWCU was one of the largest units in the RAF. While the TTTE taught aircrew how to fly the Tornado, the TWCU taught them how to operate it, and how to exploit its advanced weapons system. Lay-down bombing and loft attack principles, procedures and techniques were taught, together with defensive manoeuvring and use of the AIM-9 Sidewinder. Terrain following, plus tactical high- and low-level formation flying are also taught. Pilots fly 32 hours during the course with just over 29 hours being provided for navigators. Towards the end of the course, a number of sorties are flown by constituted student crews, encouraging the kind of co-operation required on a frontline squadron. The unit also has the responsibility for Qualified Weapons Instructor (QWI) training. QWIs return to their units to oversee

Above and left: The JP 233 airfield attack weapon, developed for use on the Tornado GR1, consisted of two large pods containing a mix of runway cratering munitions and minelets. All the weapons were explosively ejected downwards through ports in the bottom of each pod. The runway cratering munitions were parachute retarded, with explosive charges designed to punch them into the runway surface. The empty pods are jettisoned after use, with the rear section going first. The aircraft shown is BS007, fitted with underwing camera pods in what appear to be modified Sky Shadow ECM pods.

'postgraduate' tactical and weapons training and standardisation.

As more LRMTS-equipped Batch 3 aircraft were delivered, they replaced some of the TWCU machines on a one-for-one basis. The first Batch 3 example (ZA365) arrived at Honington on 20 September 1982. TWCU performed the RAF's first overseas Tornado deployment, despatching three GR1s to CFB Goose Bay, Canada on 10 May 1983 to conduct low-level training. These aircraft subsequently accompanied the RAF's *Red Arrows* on its tour of North America. In late 1983, the unit gained 'shadow' squadron status, meaning that during wartime TWCU instructor crews would be assigned to the front line. From 1 January 1984, No 45 Squadron became the unit's shadow identity although new unit markings had begun to appear on the aircraft during the previous month.

While the RAF established its TWCU, the Luftwaffe established its own weapons training unit in the shape of the Waffensausbildungskompenente (abbreviated to WaKo), the Weapons Training Component. This formed part of the Erding-based maintenance and overhaul unit, Luftwaffenversorgungsregiment 1 and its Tornado acceptance arm, Technischegruppe 11.

WaKo took charge its first Tornado IDS, 43+28, on 9 November 1981 and became operational on 16 February

Jagdbombergeschwader 38 was the first Luftwaffe Tornado wing to form, and functioned as the German OCU and tactical weapons training unit. The Wing initially trained both Luftwaffe and Marineflieger aircrew.

1982. The unit operated nine aircraft at that time (with a projected establishment of 16), and 31 March 1982 witnessed the arrival of Tornado serial 43+40 – the 100th example to be delivered to a service unit anywhere in NATO.

Just as the Tornado replaced the F-104G in Luftwaffe service, so the Tornado weapons training unit supplanted the Starfighter weapons school (Waffenschule 10 at Jever). This stood-down in May 1983, making way for WaKo, which moved to Jever on 1 July 1983. Oberstleutnant Hans Klaffenbach then took the unit through its transition to full fighter-bomber wing status as Jagdbombgeschwader 38, which was officially formed on 26 August 1983. With a nominal 24 aircraft on strength, all operated by a single squadron (381 Staffel), the unit accepted both Luftwaffe and Marineflieger students from the TTTE/TOCU course at Cottesmore and put them through a comprehensive tactical weapons training course (the format of which was similar to that given by the RAF's TWCU), which included 30 hours of flying. JBG 38 also trained and validated Qualified Flying Instructors and Qualified Weapons Instructors for the Luftwaffe and Marineflieger frontline squadrons.

As in Germany, the Italians earmarked the Tornado as an F-104 Starfighter replacement. The first of a number of F-104 Starfighter units to receive the Tornado was 6° Stormo. The first aircraft (MM7006) went to the wing's 154° Gruppo Caccia-Bombardieri (or fighter bomber squadron) at Brescia-Ghedi Military Airport on 27 August 1982. It was flown to the base by the 6° Stormo's new commander, Lieutenant Colonel Gabriele Ingrosso.

Having received a nucleus of instructor crews from the TTTE, 154° Gruppo was officially re-formed on 20 May 1983. The unit received the bulk of the AMI's 12 twin-stickers,

The Luftwaffe adopted a dispenser weapon for both anti-airfield and anti-armour roles similar to the RAF's JP233. The basic dispenser (ejecting munitions sideways) contained different types of sub-munition depending on the role.

though four went to the TTTE, and two each later went to 36° and 50° Stormo. The Italian Tornado force suffered from numerous difficulties, due in part to the new logistics chain but also due to lack of facilities and personnel availability. These hampered the unit's early operations and crews struggled to maintain currency. The training syllabus included delivery techniques for a range of conventional weapons (including the MBB MW-1 anti-armour/anti-airfield munitions dispenser, and also the IR version of the Hughes

In Italy, the first AMI Tornado unit was the 6° Stormo's 154° Gruppo, which decorated its aircraft with a red fin chevron, intake lips and a red devil fin badge. The unit functioned as the AMI Tornado OCU, training aircrew emerging from the tri-national TTTE at Cottesmore.

AGM-65D Maverick ASM) and for the US-owned, dual key B61 nuclear weapon. The 154° Gruppo initially concentrated on training the other Italian Tornado users, and did not itself gain operational status for some time.

Reaching the Front Line

With conversion and weapons training units in place, the build-up of the frontline Tornado force could begin in earnest. Elements for the first RAF frontline Tornado squadron started to come together towards the end of 1981, under the command of Wing Commander Peter Gooding AFC. The numberplate chosen for the RAF's first Tornado squadron was that of No 9 Squadron, then equipped with ageing Vulcans,

A No 9 Squadron Tornado emerges from its HAS at RAF Honington. The squadron's aircraft were routinely fitted with the bolt-on retractable inflight refuelling probe package, and initially lacked the undernose LRMTS.

which continued in service at RAF Waddington until 29 April 1982. The first Tornado GR1 (ZA586) for No 9 (Designate) was delivered to Honington on 6 January 1982. Today, squadrons hardly ever stand-down with one type of aircraft on one day, only for the same personnel to convert directly to a new mount the next. Some Vulcan aircrew were re-assigned to Tornado units but this was a matter of coincidence rather than planning. It was routine to have two squadrons in existence with the same 'number plate' whilst the work-up phase was underway.

Gooding's No 9 Squadron officially reformed on 1 June 1982, receiving crews from Honington's co-located TWCU for its thirteen Batch 2 aircraft then on strength. The unit became involved in a number of trials in order to smooth the Tornado's entry into service. Validation of the detachable inflight refuelling probe was just one of several 'writing the book' exercises assigned to No 9 throughout its formative months, leading to a longer than normal work-up period.

The unit was the first Tornado operator to lose an aircraft when ZA586/A crashed during a night sortie on 27 September 1983. The pilot failed to escape after ordering his navigator to eject. Total electrical failure was found to be the cause, which resulted in the entire fleet being grounded for checks, the last examples returning to service on 6 October 1983.

The second RAF Tornado squadron also took over a former Vulcan squadron 'numberplate'. Since its famous first raid on three Ruhr valley dams during May 1943, 'The Dambusters' of No 617 Squadron have a long and proud history, and are the only RAF unit to be a household name. No 617 relinquished its Vulcans at the end of 1981 and the 'new' 617 Squadron accepted its first Tornado (ZA601) at RAF Marham, Norfolk on 23 April 1982. The unit officially re-formed on 1 January 1983, under Wg Cdr Tony Harrison, headed and

The second of the RAF's frontline Tornado squadrons was No 617, the famous 'Dambusters'. This aircraft carries a BOZ chaff dispenser below the starboard wing, with a Sky Shadow ECM pod to port.

declared to NATO as being fully operational on 16 May 1983; 40 years to the day since the squadron's most famous mission.

The third UK-based Tornado squadron, No 27, was the second unit to form within the Marham Tornado wing. The new unit (then still undesignated) took its first GR1 (ZA609) at Marham on 29 June 1982. The original Vulcan-equipped unit had disbanded in March 1982, but it was a full year before

the squadron's 'Jumbo' elephant motif began to reappear. The squadron officially reformed under Wg Cdr John Grogan on 12 August 1983.

No 617 Squadron was the first Tornado unit to take part in the prestigious USAF Strategic Air Command *Giant Voice* bombing competition (codenamed *Prairie Vortex* by the RAF), in the autumn of 1984 at Ellsworth AFB, SD. Two teams from 617 Squadron, each consisting of two crews, were pitched against stiff competition from SAC's B-52 Stratofortresses and FB-111s. The RAF crews gained first and second placings for the LeMay Trophy (awarded to the best high- and low-level bombing by an individual crew) scoring 98.7% and 98.5% respectively. First and third positions were achieved in the Meyer Trophy (given for the highest damage expectancy rate from a team bombing at low-level) with scores of 90.4% and 83.1%. A 96% score gave second place in the Mathis Trophy which was awarded for the best team overall.

Following the success of their Marham neighbours the previous year, No 27 Squadron undertook the 1985 *Prairie Vortex* deployment. Having acclimatised at CFB Goose Bay since late August, the unit commenced operations at Ellsworth from 1 October and went on to reach first and second placings (out of 42 teams, drawn from SAC and the RAF) for the LeMay Trophy (with scores of 98.8% and 98.4%). Other scores achieved were first and second placings in the Meyer Trophy (with 94.97% and 90.75%) and second (at 97.2%) in the Mathis Trophy.

The second air arm to begin frontline operations with the new Tornado was the West German Navy's Marineflieger. The first Marineflieger Tornado was 43+27, which joined the Luftwaffe's test unit (Erprobungsstelle 61) at Manching during the latter part of 1981 to begin validation of maritime-specific

No 617 Squadron was joined at Marham by No 27, another former Vulcan squadron. This aircraft carries the later-style underwing fuel tanks which had two instead of four tailfins, and a practise bomb dispenser under the fuselage, containing four tiny 28-lb practise bombs.

The first frontline German Tornado unit was the Marineflieger's MFG 1 at Schleswig-Jagel. Here one of the unit's aircraft gets airborne with the aid of afterburner. It is seen carrying two BOZ pods underwing, and practise bomb dispensers under the fuselage. API BEN J.ULLINGS

weapons loads and procedures. The first squadron aircraft however was 43+43, which was delivered to the former Starfighter base of Schleswig-Jagel on 2 April 1982, to join Marinefliegergeschwader (Naval Air Wing) 1. Led by Captain Waldemar Scholz, MFG 1 personnel underwent TTTE training and by the summer of 1983 the wing had sufficient crews in place to man its established strength of 48 aircraft. Declared to NATO on 1 January 1984 by its new commander, Captain Klaus-Jurgen Wewetzer, MFG 1 conducted its first long-range overseas deployment on 20 July 1984, when two aircraft staged out of the Portuguese air base of Beja and flew the 1,000 miles to the Azores. On 24 May 1989 the wing flew its 50,000th flying hour – the first Tornado wing to do so.

Before the Luftwaffe could follow suit, the RAF continued to rapidly expand its Tornado force. Following the establishment of the three UK-based Tornado squadrons, RAF Germany then began to form the first of an eventual total of eight Tornado squadrons, to be divided equally between Brüggen and Laarbruch, replacing Jaguars and Buccaneers. Replacement of the ageing Buccaneer in the overland strike role was viewed as being of the highest priority – not least since fatigue problems had already prompted a fleet-wide grounding, and the expensive rectification of the least badly affected airframes.

The first of the RAF Germany Buccaneer units, No 15 Squadron, received its first Tornado 1 (ZA411) at Laarbruch on 5 July 1983, four days after the 'old' No 15 Squadron had ceased flying the Buccaneer S2B. Wg Cdr Barry Dove commanded No 15(Designate) Squadron from 1 July 1983 and the unit officially reformed with Tornados on 1 November 1983, declaring itself to Supreme Allied Commander Europe (SACEUR) on 1 July 1984. Although the first 11 of the RAF's 68 Batch 3 aircraft went to the TWCU at Honington, and a

A Buccaneer S2 of No 15 Squadron leads its replacement – a Tornado GR1. The Tornado lacked the Buccaneer's very long range in the overland strike role, but had considerably more survivability.

handful more went to the Marham squadrons, augmenting Batch 2 airframes the bulk of the batch (about 50 aircraft) were used to re-equip the Laarbruch wing. The RAF's Batch 3 aircraft were the first to be delivered with the undernose LRMTS fitted, and also had a new Marconi ARI 18241/2 RWR in place of the original Elettronica ARI 18241/1.

Further Batch 3 aircraft were used to re-equip the rest of the Laarbruch wing. No 16 Squadron's first Tornado (ZA458) arrived from RAF St Athan on 13 December 1983, and No 16 (Designate) Squadron formed on 1 January 1984. The Buccaneers stood-down from NATO at midnight on 29 February 1984, and were immediately replaced by the Tornado. One the squadron's pilots, Sqn Ldr Rod Sargent, subsequently became the first service pilot of any nation to

Laarbruch's two Buccaneer squadrons were the first RAF Germany Tornado units. The second to form was No 16, whose famous crossed keys, 'Saint' symbol and black and gold colours were boldly applied to the unit's Batch 3 Tornados.

reach the 1,000 Tornado flying hours milestone on 6 May 1985. Third of the Laarbruch Tornado squadrons was No 20, which operated the Jaguar until 29 June 1984. No 20 (Designate) Squadron formed in April 1984, its first Tornado GR1 (ZA461) having arrived from St Athan a couple of weeks beforehand. The first sortie with the new aircraft was flown on 2 May 1984, and the unit officially reformed with Tornado on the day of the Jaguar's demise.

The rest of the 164-aircraft Batch 3 (agreed in June 1979), included 28 AMI, 36 Luftwaffe and 32 Marineflieger Tornados. These aircraft were obviously not fitted with Ferranti's LRMTS, and so were not subject to the airspeed limitation imposed on RAF Batch 3 aircraft. This was apparently sufficient for the RAF to disable the Tornado's intake actuators, giving what effectively became a fixed intake.

The next Tornado wing to form was the first Luftwaffe frontline unit, JBG 31 at Nörvenich. After relinquishing its

F-104G's three months earlier, JBG 31 gained its first Tornado (43+93) on 27 July 1983 and transition training began six days later. Commanded by Colonel Gert Overhoff, the wing took nearly two years to become fully operational, being declared to NATO in April 1985. The unit was the first to take deliveries of the MBB MW-1 sub-munitions dispenser (in this case the Hauptzielgruppe 2 anti-armour version, the HZG-1 airfield denial variant reaching the front line some three years later).

For the RAF, the first priority had been to replace the ageing Vulcans and Buccaneers, and to build up a significant Tornado force. But once this task was underway, it became clear that to simply convert new and former Buccaneer/Jaguar/Vulcan aircrew to the Tornado and to use it in the same way as the earlier types would not full exploit the new type's potential. While squadrons would themselves eventually learn how to exploit some of the Tornado's unique capabilities, it was clear that a dedicated unit (without frontline commitments) could develop useful tactics, techniques and procedures for force-wide application. RAF Strike Command's Central Trials & Tactics Organisation therefore pushed for the establishment of a Tornado Operational Evaluation Unit. This would undertake the wide variety of trials and tactical development associated with the introduction of the new type.

Four Tornado GR1's (ZA376, ZA392, ZA393 and ZA614) were earmarked for the unit and all were delivered to Marham between September and November 1982. They were held in storage there whilst approval to form the TOEU was sought; one aircraft (ZA393) was reassigned to another unit in the interim, but was replaced by ZA457. Wg Cdr John Lumsden finally formed the TOEU at Boscombe Down on 1 September 1983. The TOEU immediately undertook trials and procedures work connected with JP233 and LGB delivery as well nuclear attack profiles, the latter in preparation for formation of the first WE177-equipped squadrons in RAF Germany. Other

JBG 31 was the Luftwaffe's first frontline Tornado wing. Named after World War One ace Oswald Boelcke, JBG 31 previously flew the Lockheed F-104G Starfighter, and was based at Nörvenich. BILL BUSHELL

The original badge of the SAOEU was based on the RAF roundel, with red-hilted white swords radiating out over a blue ring. The unit has proved to be of incalculable value in developing tactics, equipment and weapons for the RAF's Tornado force.

One of two Nightrider Harrier T4s leads two SAOEU Harrier GR5s and a pair of Tornados. The Tornado continues to provide SAOEU with the bulk of its work, though the GR1s are augmented by the Nightfox Tornado (a GR4 analogue), Harrier GR7s and Jaguars.

systems integration work (involving NVGs and ECM) was also undertaken. The importance and value of the unit soon became apparent, and Strike Command granted the TOEU a one year extension to its originally anticipated lifespan of two years before evolving it into the Strike/Attack OEU in 1987. The SAOEU carried on the Tornado OEU's functions, but also took on responsibility for the Harrier and Jaguar.

Italy had always been sanguine that it would run behind its partners in introducing the Tornado and even opted not to procure aircraft in Batch 1, and to take only sufficient aircraft from Batches 2 and 3 to equip its initial training units. One reason was that the AMI had never had any fast jet back-seaters, and so would rely on retraining pilots for the job, and to recruiting and training new officers from scratch or from the transport fleet. By necessity, therefore, the re-equipment of frontline units proceeded at a leisurely pace! Even though the German Luftwaffe also used the Tornado as a replacement for the single-seat F-104G the Germans did have a cadre of trained back-seaters from its F-4 Phantom force, and these men formed the backbone of the first Tornado squadrons.

The first frontline Aeronautica Militare Italiana Tornado squadron to form was 156° Gruppo, a subordinate unit of 36° Stormo normally based at Gioia del Colle. The unit's pilots and groundcrew were trained at the TTTE and by 154° Gruppo at Ghedi, returning to Gioia in May 1984. The unit's first aircraft (MM7043) arrived on 18 June 1984 and the unit officially re-activated, becoming operational that August under the command of Lieutenant Colonel Vitantonio Caponio. Having established initially with 18 aircraft, this number was increased to 24 by 1990 as the unit became dual-tasked with both conventional bombing and anti-shipping duties. As with German Marineflieger aircraft, the latter role employed the use of the MBB Kormoran anti-ship missile.

As German and Italian Tornados began entering service, the RAF pressed on with inducting its latest fast jet. With wings at Marham and Laarbruch, and a single squadron at Honington, the next priority was to re-equip the second wing in RAF Germany. RAF Brüggen was then home to a four-squadron strike/attack wing equipped with SEPECAT Jaguars, and the Tornado promised to extend the wing's reach and all-weather capability. The first Tornado for the Brüggen wing was GR1 ZD712, which arrived from St Athan for No 31(Designate) Squadron on 13 June 1984. Led by Wg Cdr Dick Bogg, the new No 31 Squadron did not formally come into being until 1 September 1984, and even this was two months prior to the official reformation and the standing-down of the 'old' No 31 Squadron's Jaguars. No 17 Squadron was the next Brüggen squadron to convert. The unit's ZD742 touched down at Brüggen from St Athan on 16 August 1984, and No 17 (Designate) came into being under Wg Cdr Grant McLeod on 6 January 1985. The Jaguar equipped No 17 stood down at midnight on 28 February to be replaced by the 'new' unit at one minute past midnight – officially the next day. With two

Italy's first frontline operational Tornado squadron was the 36° Stormo's 156° Gruppo, which converted to the type under the auspices of 154° Gruppo. More recently, the parent wing has gained a second squadron, operating the Tornado F3.

Tornado squadrons operational, the pace of re-equipment at Brüggen finally slowed down a little.

Brüggen's Tornados were the first of 53 RAF Batch 4 Tornado GR1s, powered by the new Mk 103 engine (subsequently retrofitted to the Laarbruch wing aircraft), and may have been the first wired for the delivery of nuclear weapons. Certainly, the first RAF Tornados with the WE177B nuclear weapons were reported to have received their weapons in 1984, when the Batch 4 aircraft entered service. The rest of Batch 4 (signed on 5 August 1981, totalling 161 aircraft) included 18 ADVs for the RAF, with 27 AMI aircraft and 64 for the Luftwaffe.

Even while the RAF's Brüggen wing continued its methodical transition to the Tornado, German and Italian wings also re-equipped with the new aircraft. Next to convert was JBG 32, its first aircraft (44+36) arriving at Lechfeld on 27 July 1984. Following work-up, the unit declared itself to NATO on 1 August 1985. Unlike other Luftwaffe Tornado units, JBG 32 was never assigned to nuclear strike duties, instead it eventually took on the SEAD role with the advent of the Tornado ECR in 1994. The ECR variant is described later in this book.

Istrana-based 155° Gruppo, part of 51° Stormo, was the third AMI unit to exchange the F-104S ASA for Tornados. Conversion began in the early autumn of 1984 (under the direction of 154° Gruppo at Ghedi), and the unit relocated to be parented by 6° Stormo at Ghedi from 1 January 1985, when the old 155° Gruppo stood down. 155° Gruppo remained as part of the 6° Stormo until 50° Stormo reformed at Piacenza on 1 December 1989. 155° Gruppo then began preparations

for transfer to the new wing and the Tornados departed during the spring months of 1990. The unit initially flew recce missions using the MBB-Aeritalia tactical reconnaissance pod, although the defence suppression task was assigned on 1 April 1994, and deliveries of AGM-88A HARMs began at the end of that year.

The sixth Tornado strike/attack squadron to form in RAF Germany was No 14, its first aircraft (ZD842) touching down at Brüggen on 11 April 1985. No 14 (Designate) formed on 1 July under Wg Cdr Joe Whitfield. The new Tornado-equipped

The first of the Tornado Squadrons assigned to the Brüggen Wing was No 31, a former Jaguar operator. These two aircraft (each laden with four 1,000-lb bombs) carry the old-style four-fin fuel tanks.

No 17 Squadron was a long-serving RAF Germany squadron, operating Canberras and Phantoms before converting to the Tornado at Brüggen. The primary role of the RAF Germany squadrons was strike/attack, using the WE177B bomb and a range of conventional weapons.

RAF Germany Tornados wore two-letter fin codes, with the first letter indicating the squadron. This aircraft, with blue diamonds across the fin and flanking a winged shield on the nose, belonged to No 14 Squadron, last of the Brüggen Wing Tornado units to re-equip from the Jaguar.

unit continued its work-up finally replacing RAFG's last strike/attack Jaguar unit on 1 November 1985. No 9 Squadron transferred from Honington to Brüggen on 1 October 1986, bringing the unit up to its full four-squadron strength. Despite having the same numerical designation as the original No 9 at Honington, the Brüggen-based No 9 was in some respects a new unit, being equipped with new Batch 4 aircraft. The first of these (ZD809), was delivered to Brüggen during early December 1985 and first flew in the unit's markings (coded 'AA') on 19 December 1985. In 1986, the Squadron became the first Tornado unit to win the Salmond Trophy, awarded annually to the best RAF Germany squadrons for combined bombing and navigation accuracy. The RAF Germany Tornado strike/attack force was virtually complete, though one more unit (No II (AC) Squadron) was destined to trade Jaguars for dual-role recce/strike/attack Tornados. The reconnaissance-dedicated Jaguar GR1As continued to operate with No II until 16 December 1988, some two years after their originally planned replacement by the recce-capable Tornado GR1A variant.

The next Luftwaffe wing to form was the Buchel-based JBG 33, another former Starfighter unit which formally accepted its first aircraft (44+86) on 2 September 1985. Led by Colonel Borchers, the unit became operational in the nuclear strike role in May 1986, gaining a conventional attack tasking in May 1988. JBG 33 was the recipient of the first Luftwaffe Batch 5 Tornados. These featured a MIL STD 1553B digital databus, a new 128 k Litef Spirit III computer, and an integrated ECM transmitter, chaff/flare dispenser and RWR. ADA software was used in the missile control unit, conferring a HARM compatibility in German and Italian aircraft, though this remained dormant except in Batch 5 IDSs delivered to the Marineflieger. The fifth Batch of 171 Tornados, ordered on 19 August 1982, contained 20 IDS and 52 ADV aircraft for the RAF, 29 aircraft for the AMI (its final order), 31 for the Luftwaffe and 39 for the Marineflieger. Following the Saudi Arabian export order in 1985 the RAF would lose 18 of the IDS variants included in this Batch, while the two survivors were completed as GR1A reconnaissance aircraft. Two West German examples were diverted on the line for the Saudi order, and were replaced by two aircraft brought forward from Batch Seven. This made a final total of 173 aircraft in Batch 5.

The German Navy completed its re-equipment with the Tornado with the conversion of Marinefliegergeschwader 2 at Eggebek. The wing received Tornados 45+12 and 45+13 on 11 September 1986, this event marking a prelude to the final demise of the F-104G in West German service. As with its sister wing, MFG 2 was to operate five dual-control and 43 'standard' IDS aircraft; 1 Staffel equipped its aircraft with the combined visual and infra-red capable tactical reconnaissance

Re-equipment of the Brüggen Wing was completed by the transfer of No 9 Squadron from RAF Honington. One of the squadron's aircraft is seen in a Brüggen HAS while being prepared for duty.

pod produced jointly by MBB and Aeritalia. Using this equipment, the unit operated daily 'Eastern Express' sorties to monitor shipping in the Baltic Sea. As with all of the aircraft that served with MFG 1, 2 Staffel/MFG 2 operates its aircraft in the conventional attack mission employing the MBB (now DASA) Kormoran anti-ship missile, free-fall iron bombs and BL755 cluster bomb units. Some of the squadron's aircraft now have the capability to fire the AGM-88A HARM, this weapon typically being used to neutralise the threat of enemy shipborne and coastal radars. Following the demise of MFG 1 in 1993, a third staffel was formed and this has taken on the responsibility of conversion training as well as trial and evaluation work. Today the wing has a complement of 52 aircraft, making it one of the largest Tornado wings in NATO. Annually it flies some 10,000 hours.

The Luftwaffe's JBG 34 at Memmingen, commanded by Oberst Stehli, received Tornado 45+61 on 23 October 1987 and was declared to NATO in July 1989. From 1 January 1996, JBG 34 formed part of the NATO Rapid Reaction Forces. JBG 34's aircraft were among those built in Batch Six. The 155 aircraft in Batch Six (signed on 5 January 1984) originally included 92 ADVs for the RAF, and 63 IDS aircraft for the Luftwaffe. The figures were again altered as a result of the Saudi order, with the RAF diverting 24 ADVs. Germany also diverted 24 of its Batch 6 aircraft, this time to the Marineflieger.

The last 'straight IDS' aircraft for the original customers were 14 RAF aircraft built as part of Batch Seven, and delivered to a variety of units. Most of the batch were delivered as GR1As, ECRs or export aircraft for Saudi Arabia, and are described separately.

The fourth and final Italian Tornado IDS squadron to form was 102° Gruppo, which replaced 155° Gruppo within 6°

Although Germany's initial Tornados wore a NATO dark green and grey camouflage similar to that applied to Italian aircraft, they were soon re-painted in a two-tone green 'Lizard' scheme, as seen on these two JBG 32 Tornados.

Stormo at Ghedi in the autumn of 1992. The new squadron accepted the first of its assigned Tornados in August 1993. The unit establishment is 19 aircraft, all of which were initially assigned to the conventional bombing role, pending their planned reassignment to a primary reconnaissance role using the podded Lockheed Martin Advanced Tactical Air Reconnaissance System (ATARS). This has failed to materialise.

Change for the 1990s

The Tornado was developed in response to British, German and Italian defence requirements during the Cold War. When the Cold War ended, few politicians were brave or honest enough to point out that the security situation had actually worsened – with greater instability, a wider range of potential threats, and less chance to rely on the balance of terror of the

The second Marineflieger Tornado wing to form was MFG 2, at Eggebeck. Within a fairly short time, Navy aircraft were being repainted in this drab but effective three-tone camouflage.

nuclear deterrent. Cynical politicians catered for public expectations of a 'peace dividend' and began to impose deep defence cuts, using the money saved to reduce taxes and increase spending on more popular social programmes. A more honest policy might have actually spent more money on conventional forces – especially those suitable for rapid deployment overseas. But such honesty was too much to expect, and in all three Tornado partner nations post Cold War defence cuts hit hard, and the Tornado force was not exempted from their effects.

Even as plans for cuts were being formulated, the RAF's Tornado force suddenly found itself at war, taking part in the international military response to Saddam Hussein's invasion of Kuwait. The Tornado played a crucial role in the military operation, as described in a subsequent chapter. Despite the distinguished record of the Tornado (and particularly the RAF Germany Tornado squadrons) in the Gulf War, the decision was taken to axe the Laarbruch Tornado wing. The three strike/attack squadrons at Laarbruch were disbanded as part of the UK Ministry of Defence's 'Options for Change' programme. The first to disappear was No 16 Squadron on 11 September 1991, followed by No 15 Squadron which officially disbanded on 31 January 1992. Recce-role No 2(AC) Squadron returned to the UK in December 1991, and the disbandment of No 20 Squadron in May 1992 marked the end of the Tornado at Laarbruch. The 'numberplates' of all three squadrons were resurrected as part of the RAF's move to keep historic squadron identities 'alive' although only as what had hitherto been known as Operational Conversion Units – second line training units. No 15 Squadron even found itself operating the Tornado again, when the TWCU at Honington

lost its TWCU title and No 45 Squadron shadow identity on 1 April 1992 to become No 15(Reserve) Squadron, although its role did not change. With the transfer of Honington to standby status, No 15(R) relocated to Lossiemouth in November 1993.

The effective halving of the RAF Germany-based Tornado strike force was followed on 31 March 1993 by the disbandment of RAF Germany itself, and its replacement as a Command HQ by a Group HQ (No 2 Gp) at JHQ Rheindahlen. No 2 Group itself disappeared on 8 March 1996, foreshadowing further reductions and the eventual British withdrawal from Germany. The four remaining Tornado squadrons in Germany transferred to the command of No 1 Group, headquartered at High Wycombe. Present plans (almost certain to be changed under the 1998 Strategic Defence Review) call for the RAF Tornado force in Germany to be further reduced to two squadrons by the end of 1998, perhaps with two squadrons returning to the UK (probably to RAF Scampton). The two remaining squadrons (probably the ALARM-equipped Nos 9 and 31 Squadrons) may then combine with a Luftwaffe ECR unit to form a joint SEAD unit.

Early plans to replace the Buccaneer in the maritime strike role had been cancelled in the early 1980s to keep two more Tornado overland strike squadrons in the frontline. With the end of the Cold War, however, these units were regarded as being surplus to requirements. Rather than disbanding the two home-based Tornado strike attack squadrons (Nos 27 and 617) the units were reassigned to the maritime strike role to replace the last two Buccaneer units. No 27 Squadron officially stood-down on 30 September 1993, although its identity had been passed to the Odiham-based No 240 Operational

Although No 15 Squadron was disbanded after the Gulf War, the squadron's numberplate was resurrected for the TWCU, which became No 15 (Reserve) Squadron. Coded 'F', this aircraft carries the 'MacRobert's Reply' crest and name.

Conversion Unit as No 27(Reserve) Squadron six days earlier. The Tornado unit itself did not disband, instead taking on the 'number plate' of No 12 Squadron from 1 October 1993, as that unit ceased Buccaneer operations at Lossiemouth. The Tornado GR1B, as the BAe Sea Eagle-capable variant was designated, was at this stage some time from frontline operations. Nevertheless, No 12 prepared to withdraw from Marham as 1993 came to an end, relocating to Lossiemouth on 7 January 1994. It was joined later that year by No 617 Squadron, which replaced the Buccaneer-equipped No 208 Squadron. This reduced the total number of RAF Tornado strike attack squadrons from nine to only four, though two Buccaneer maritime strike units did re-equip with the newer aircraft. The GR1B is described in later chapters.

In Germany, post-Cold War defence cuts led to the cancellation of plans to reform JBG37 with Tornados from the cancelled Batch 8. Other Luftwaffe units were also reduced in size, and some surplus aircraft were placed in storage, while others were assigned to a new training unit based in the USA. Only one German Tornado unit actually disappeared, however. In July 1991 the government announced that MFG 1 would be disestablished.

The need to reduce overall Luftwaffe aircraft numbers, however, led to a decision to replace Germany's recce-role RF-4Es with Tornados. MFG 1 therefore disbanded on 31 December 1993, but passed its aircraft to AKG 51 which officially reformed on 1 January 1994. A second squadron, 512 Staffel, was established on 29 August 1994. The original AKG 51 at Bremgarten had stood down in March 1993, but AKG 52 at Leck had retained its RF-4s longer, moving to Schleswing Jagel and re-designating as Aufklarungsgeschwader 51. As the Luftwaffe's sole remaining tactical reconnaissance wing AKG 51 retained the AKG 52 panther's head badge combining the traditions of the two Phantom recce wings. Preparations for the 'new' AKG 51 began on 1 July 1992 at Schleswig/Jagel, with Colonel Eckhard Sowada appointed as wing commander. The first squadron, 511 Staffel, formed on 1 April 1993 as aircraft began transfer from the co-located MFG 1. With only nine MBB/Aeritalia reconnaissance pods available initially, the unit set about procurement of further examples as a stop-gap measure pending delivery of a new dedicated reconnaissance system. This was due to enter service in 1998.

Not only did the Tornado force contract with the end of the Cold War – it also fundamentally changed its role. The low-level strike role on NATO's Central Front was diminished in importance, while medium-level PGM/LGB attacks during out of area operations were emphasised. Since the end of the Cold War, the Tornados of all three of the original customer nations have participated in international peacekeeping operations – and these are described in the following chapters. Ironically, post-Cold War defence cuts mean that the RAF, at least, could no longer carry out an operation on the scale of Operation *Desert Storm*, having lost three of the squadrons which participated in that operation. The Cold War emphasis on the strike role (strike being the term used to differentiate the use of nuclear weapons from conventional 'attack' missions) has all but disappeared, and this was reflected in

No 12 Squadron's Tornados are now mainly GR1Bs, compatible with the Sea Eagle ASM, though they retain a vital conventional attack role. For some time after the squadron formed, Sea Eagle-capable aircraft were something of a rarity.

Britain's decisions first not to replace the WE177B freefall nuclear bomb when it was withdrawn in 2005, and then to withdraw the weapon early, in 1998.

The WE177B was finally 'down-declared' (without fanfare or ceremony) on Tuesday 31 March, 1998, leaving the RAF's Tornados without a nuclear strike role. The last weapons (stored at RAF Honington and RAF Marham) were then slowly decommissioned. In something of a coup, two days before the withdrawal, the *Sunday Telegraph* ran a story about the weapon, including a colour photo of No 12 Squadron's 'FK' carrying one of the rarely seen weapons.

The Tornado's nuclear role was never detailed while WE177 was in use, but since then some details have come to light. Although developed in two forms, the WE177 was used by the Tornado only in its 'long' WE177B and WE177C forms. With an airframe built by Hunting, and a warhead produced by the Royal Ordnance Factory at Burghfield, the weapon was also prosaically known as the Bomb A/C HE 950-lb MC, a designation which successfully hid its nuclear nature! The UK-based Tornados took over their WE177Bs from the Vulcan force, with RAF Germany Tornados taking over WE177Cs from the Jaguar-equipped Nos 14, 17, 20 and 31 Squadrons).

The number of WE177s on charge is believed to have dropped from a peak of 250 to about 100, these being stored in high-security bomb-dumps, and in special vaults below certain Hardened Aircraft Shelters. Weapon loading drills (and some practice flights) were performed using accurately ballasted dummy weapons, equipped with the real bomb's four tail parachutes, compressed air reservoir and controls. The last loading of a WE177 took place at Marham on 17 December 1996 (onto No 13 Squadron's ZG726), the two GR1A recce units being the last with a nuclear commitment.

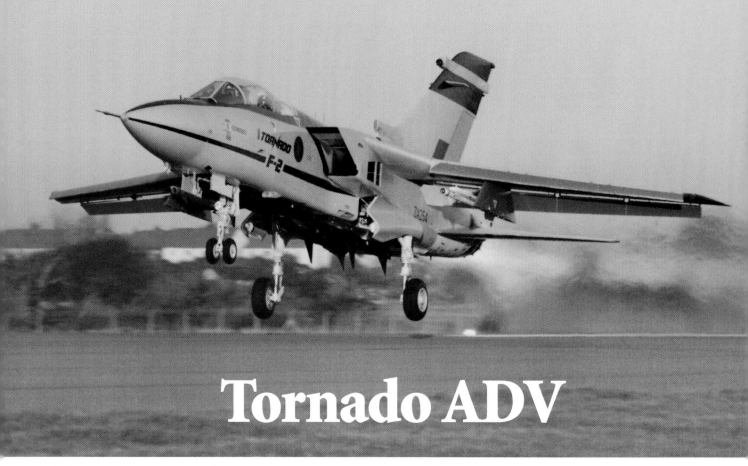

Tornado ADV

The first ADV prototype taking off from Warton on its maiden flight, resplendent in a smart grey and black colour scheme. Rolled out with a normal RWR fin fairing, a forward looking test camera was installed prior to flight testing.

The Tornado Air Defence Variant (ADV) was designed to meet a Cold War RAF requirement for a very long range fighter. This fighter was to be a bomber-destroyer, intended primarily to combat the threat posed by massive waves of Soviet long-range bombers (including Tu-95 'Bears' and Tu-26 'Backfires') attacking British targets, or transiting through British airspace. Britain's air defence region was tasked with protecting some of NATO's most vital assets. British airspace had been probed for years by Soviet aircraft, and these carefully noted the response times and intercept distances achieved by Lightning and Phantom fighters standing Quick Reaction Alert (QRA) at various airfields.

While the Soviet long range bomber fleet relied on free-fall weapons, or on limited numbers of relatively slow missiles with a relatively short stand-off range, the Lightnings and Phantoms were perceived as being able to 'cope'. Even longer-range, higher speed weapons like the AS-4 'Kitchen' held out the promise of being 'interceptable' since they were relatively ungainly, followed a fairly predictable flightpath and since every bomber could carry only one, or at most two, missiles.

But just as Western bombers began deploying longer-range, higher speed missiles which could fly more difficult low-level profiles, so too the USSR deployed the AS-6 'Kingfish', a Mach 3, 350-mile range weapon with a sea-skimming terminal approach. Intelligence sources also indicated that a new generation of smaller ALCMs would also be deployed, and that these would be carried in multiples by 'Bear', 'Backfire' and newer bombers.

Once the threat was perceived to be changing, and becoming more difficult to counter, UK Air Defence started to be accorded a higher priority by successive British governments. Development of a long-range fighter version of the Tornado formed only one element in the creation of a modern integrated air defence network, although it was arguably the most important element, and one which was able to bridge the gap between the old air defence system and the sophisticated new Integrated UK Air Defence Ground Environment (IUKADGE). The latter saw the introduction of new mobile radars, with new air-to-air and air-to-ground data links, and with a dramatic modernisation of the RAF's tanker and airborne early warning forces.

For a huge range of reasons, many of the planned capabilities of the new air defence system are only now becoming available, and when the first Tornado ADVs entered service, they operated alongside ageing Shackletons, under the direction of controllers using obsolescent radar and communications equipment. A viable AEW aircraft, in the shape of the Boeing E-3D Sentry, has taken decades to deploy, for example. The planned air defence network drawn up in the late 1960s has taken many years to perfect and the 'dreamsheet' is only just being fulfilled as the world enters the 21st Century. Against this background, the Tornado F3 seems to be a remarkable achievement, and a considerable success.

A new long-range interceptor was outlined by the UK Ministry of Defence (Air) in Air Staff Target 395 in 1971. It soon became apparent that the most cost-effective way to produce a suitable aircraft would be to produce a dedicated sub-variant of the new Panavia MRCA, and this had been in Britain's mind when the original IDS specification was drawn

The first ADV prototype is seen here later in its life, carrying test camera pods and one live SkyFlash missile. Camera calibration markings have been applied at key points along the fuselage.

up in 1968. But for a host of reasons (mostly political) the British MoD could not simply announce that it needed a fighter variant of the aircraft, and order one. Politically, having subtly shaped the 'bomber Tornado' to meet its own requirements (precipitating the departure of Belgium, Canada and the Netherlands in the process), Britain hoped to make the basic MRCA a good basis for a fighter version without revealing its hand. The British government wanted to continue to occupy the moral high ground, and for the shape, size, weight and configuration of the aircraft to appear to have been decided as a result of the other partner's requirements. Britain did not want its partners to see the aircraft as having been optimised to meet uniquely British requirements.

But it was the needs of the ADV which drove Britain's demand for Mach 2 capability, and for the very high internal fuel capacity. The ADV's origins ensured that it would never be a lightweight agile fighter in the mould of the US 'Teen-Series', and despite its compact size, the aircraft weighs more than a wartime Sunderland, or than a B-17 Flying Fortress. But this was not necessarily a bad thing, since the Tornado ADV was never intended for fighter-versus-fighter close-in manoeuvring air combat.

Instead, the Tornado 'fighter' was designed to loiter on CAP, up to 400 miles from base, using on- and off-board sensors to detect, track and engage targets at extreme range, launching its missiles at multiple high- and or low-level targets, head-on in any weather, by day or night.

In fact, the stereotypical view of the Tornado ADV as a lumbering BVR bomber-destroyer represents something of an over-simplification. Lightly laden, the Tornado ADV may not have been as agile as an F-15, but was in fact able to out-

scissors a Hunter, out-accelerate a Lightning and out-turn, out-climb and out-run a Phantom, high or low, fast or slow. On the other side of the coin, the scenario of a single Tornado engaging multiple targets simultaneously was something of a pipedream. Limited as it was to semi-active radar homing SkyFlash missiles, the Tornado could never engage more than two targets simultaneously, and the need to keep both targets illuminated throughout the missile's flight meant that both had to be within a fairly narrow quadrant from the Tornado's nose. But despite these limitations, the ADV concept was a good one, and the aircraft eventually produced from it matured into an excellent long-range fighter.

BAC took sole design authority for the Air Defence Variant (neither of the other two partner countries having expressed a need for such an aircraft), and set about turning the IDS into an interceptor. The design activity resulted in some 80% of

The second ADV prototype has enjoyed a long career, much of it spent at Boscombe Down. The aircraft is seen here with a non-standard ferry loadout, with four IDS-style small tanks.

The second ADV prototype fires a SkyFlash test round from one of the rear underfuselage stations. The Frazer-Nash launchers consist of pairs of two-stage pyrotechnic rams, which forced the missile clear of the aircraft before its motor ignited.

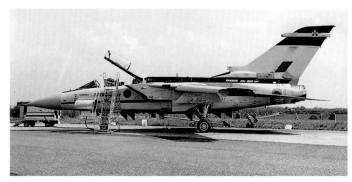

The more powerful Mk 104 engines were trialled on the second ADV prototype, seen here. The longer afterburner sections led to significant changes to the rear fuselage contours, and to the fairing below the rudder.

airframe commonality being maintained between the two variants. Basic changes eventually included an extra fuselage section forward of the wing box, which would enable the ADV to carry up to four air-to-air missiles under the fuselage. Originally, however, a higher-drag underwing missile carriage was accepted, in order to avoid a fuselage stretch to the baseline MRCA. Eventually, the lure of 10% extra fuel capacity and lower drag was sufficient to persuade the ADV's designers to stretch the aircraft. Further extra length over the IDS resulted from the longer radome covering the new AI-24 Foxhunter radar designed for the ADV by Marconi.

The Tornado ADV was not selected to fulfil AST 395 without examining other options, and the RAF was directed to look at the F-14, F-15 and F-16. The F-16 was clearly unsuitable for the RAF's role, but a two-seat version of the F-15 was viewed with some favour, especially while it appeared possible that the USAF might buy Tornado to meet its Enhanced Tactical Fighter Requirement. F-15 procurement raised its head on a number of occasions when the ADV was delayed, but the aircraft was felt to have unsatisfactory ECCM, limited radar capability and, in its standard form, a single-seat configuration. The F-14 was unaffordable in its full-standard form, with AIM-54 and AWG-9, and without the weapons system offered little improvement over the RAF's F-4s. On reliability and maintainability grounds, the original; TF 30 engined F-14 was rejected, virtually out of hand.

Of the original RAF requirement for 385 Tornados, 165 were to be ADVs. Any cancellation of the ADV would thus have had

The third ADV prototype was the first to be painted in the air superiority grey colour scheme planned for service aircraft, complete with toned-down national insignia. Here the aircraft demonstrates the staining caused by the aircraft's unique thrust reversers.

The RAF's first F2s were delivered without radar, and were used only for conversion training. No 229 OCU applied a red and yellow arrowhead to the noses of its aircraft, with a crossed torch and sword badge on the tailfin.

a major impact on the programme, reducing Britain's workshare and raising the unit cost, perhaps to a point which could threaten German commitment to the programme. Full scale development of the ADV was finally launched on 4 March 1976, and an instruction to proceed with the manufacture of two prototypes was issued on 11 March 1977.

Three ADV prototypes were eventually incorporated into the first Tornado production batch. The first of these (ZA254/AA001) flew from Warton on 27 October 1979, in the hands of David Eagles with Roy Kenward in the navigator position. Eagles took the aircraft through Mach 1 on the first flight, setting the pace for a confident flight test programme. The second ADV (ZA267/AB001), the systems and weapons development aircraft, first flew on 18 July 1980 and was followed on 18 November 1980 by ZA283/AC001. This third ADV was to be the radar development testbed, although technical problems experienced by Marconi meant that the first AI24 Foxhunter radar did not take to the air in the aircraft until 17 June 1981.

Impressive statistics were notched up by the first aircraft during the early months of the programme. Less than a year after its first flight, ZA254 demonstrated a sustainable 800 kt IAS at 2,000 ft, making the Tornado ADV one of the fastest aircraft in the world at low-level. The fuel capacity of the Tornado ADV was equally remarkable (if rather less glamorous), and was directly attributable to the need to have sufficient 'loiter capability' to be able to intercept hostile aircraft before they could launch their air-to-surface or cruise missiles. ZA254 demonstrated the type's fuel load and efficient fuel consumption by mounting a simulated combat air patrol (CAP) with a loiter time of some 2 hours 20 minutes at a range of 375 nautical miles from its point of departure. This

was achieved despite the aircraft flying with only twin 1500 litre drop tanks instead of the proposed ADV 'standard fit' of two 2250 litre tanks.

F2 to F3

Eighteen production ADV aircraft, designated Tornado F2 in RAF service, were ordered on 5 August 1981 as part of Batch 4. Despite intense work on the part of the contractors, problems with the Foxhunter radar hampered the ADV's introduction to service, and many aircraft initially flew with ballast (inevitably dubbed 'Blue Circle' in a mocking parody which used the name of a cement company because of its similarity to the code-names usually assigned to radar, such as Green Satin, Orange Putter, etc.) instead of radar. ZA283, received a Foxhunter Type B (the third set installed in the aircraft, after the initial radar set and a Type A model previously installed) during early spring 1983 and trials intensified. The problems being experienced included a substandard susceptibility to jamming as well as a track-while-scan mode performance, which fell far short of the original specification. To compound the issue, the Operational Requirements Branch were accused of moving the goalposts, 'adding a little bit here and there' to the Air Staff Target. This meant that once Marconi (working alongside Ferranti) had the solution to one problem, the standard could be changed yet again, generating new problems. Radar development should have been easy, since Foxhunter was developed from existing radars which had been flying in trials aircraft for many years, and did not represent an attempt to produce a state of the art pulse Doppler fighter radar.

The first flight of a production F2 (ZD900, fitted with dual-controls and actually the second aircraft of the 18 ordered),

The first true F3 introduced a host of improvements, but the only change which affected the variant's appearance was the installation of the new engines. Here the first production F3 taxies out at Warton.

took place from Warton on 5 March 1984. It was followed by ZD899 on 12 April 1984, and both passed to A&AEE Boscombe Down for the type's Controller (Aircraft) Release approval. The F2 proved to be very much an interim aircraft, but did allow instructors and an initial cadre of frontline crews to begin training. The majority of the F2s issued to the RAF were delivered with lead ballast in their noses until the production Foxhunter radars became available, which was by 1985 some four years behind schedule and running at nearly 60% over-budget. The F2s also lacked certain equipment which was intended to be standard in the definitive production F3, including a second inertial navigation system (necessary as the ADV's radar has no ground-mapping

The first F3s delivered to No 229 OCU wore the same markings as the F2s, as seen here. TERRY SENIOR

No 65 Squadron's distinctive markings were soon applied to the noses of the F3s, sometimes replacing the red and yellow nose chevron entirely, and sometimes displacing it to the top of the fin.

mode), the Automatic Wing Sweep/Manoeuvre Device System (AWS/MDS) which can deploy the wing lift devices as well as change the sweep profile automatically via the air data computer, a Spin Prevention and Incidence Limitation System (SPILS) to assist the pilot in keeping within the aircraft's flight envelope during hard manoeuvring, and the ability to carry four AIM-9 Sidewinder AAMs.

Other once-planned elements of the Tornado ADV had already been quietly dropped, including an electro-optical steerable Visual Augmentation System for long-range visual identification, a helmet mounted sighting system and the fire-and-forget, active radar homing SkyFlash 2 missile. The loss of these systems represented a dramatic reduction in capability, but passed virtually unnoticed.

Following the A&AEE release to service, The Tornado F2 OCU at RAF Coningsby formed under the command of Wg Cdr Rick Peacock-Edwards on 1 November 1984. It received F2s ZD901 and ZD903 (coded 'AA' and 'AB' respectively) four days later. The aircraft were flown by Dave Eagles (BAe Military Aircraft Division's Executive Director of Flight Operations) and Air Vice Marshal Ken Hayr (AOC No 11 Group) with Warton's Chief Test Pilot, Jerry Lee, and Rick Peacock-Edwards in the second aircraft. The initial cadre of instructor crews commenced their Service Instructor Aircrew Training at Warton on 4 February 1985, the last course graduating on 10 May 1985. The OCU itself officially reformed on 1 May 1985. Its staff set about training further personnel over the next 15 months prior to the first operational conversion course. The last of 16 aircraft for the OCU arrived on 21 October 1985 (ZD905, previously used for trials work with the A&AEE) and that same day the staff crews flew their Tornado F2s in the type's first air defence exercise, the three-day *Priory 85-2*.

At Warton, meanwhile, F3 development was nearing completion. The new variant was a stage nearer the full ADV specification and incorporated most of the items 'missing' from the F2 (a second INS, AMDS, four AIM-9s), as well as an upgraded 128 k Litef Spirit III main computer and more powerful and more fuel efficient RB199 Mk 104 turbofans (first trialled on ZA267/AC001 from April 1983). These had a 14-in extension to the afterburner section, and featured a Lucas Aerospace/Rolls-Royce DECU 500 Full Authority Digital Engine Control Unit. The first production aircraft, ZE154, flew on 20 November 1985 and transferred to Boscombe Down on 24 December 1985 for testing by the A&AEE.

With both the second and third production F3s held back on the production line for systems integration, the fourth aircraft (ZE157) first flew on 14 January 1986 and joined the C(A) Release programme alongside the first aircraft. The A&AEE gave their recommendations in July of that year, and ZE159 arrived at Coningsby on 28 July 1986 direct from Warton as the first F3 to enter service. Deliveries continued apace, and despite all of the F2s having Foxhunter installed by this time (although their PP standard radars still fell short of the requirement), the type started to be withdrawn for storage at RAF St.Athan from December 1986. The last F2 was withdrawn from No 229 OCU in January 1988. It was

One convincing demonstration of the Tornado F3's low-speed agility was a co-ordinated airshow routine flown by an aircraft from No 229 OCU and a Spitfire of the Battle of Britain Memorial Flight. The F3's squadron markings were redesigned so that the red chevrons (all pointing forward) appeared within a white arrowhead flanking the squadron badge, in place of the white rectangular bars. The red and yellow fin-top chevron was rarely carried.

No 229 OCU celebrated the 75th anniversary of its shadow squadron by painting up one aircraft in full No 65 Squadron markings, with enlarged nose markings and with the OCU fin badge replaced by No 65 Squadron's lion.

Arguably the most colourful Tornado flown was No 229 OCU's 1990 display aircraft, with its candy-striped fin, red intake lips, spine and canopy rail, and underfuselage chevron.

proposed that the aircraft would be upgraded to near-F3 standard as F2As (with the exception of the uprated RB199 Mk 104 engines) at a later date, but the disbandment of No 23 Squadron, the availability of the Omani aircraft and low attrition meant that they were not needed.

No 229 OCU's unit establishment of 22 aircrew instructors (plus 15 groundschool personnel) was reached during the autumn months of 1986. The first conversion course commenced on 1 December 1986 when crews for the first frontline unit, No 29 Squadron, arrived. Potential F3 crews are nominated for either the OCU's Long Course (for *ab initio* students and non-air defence experienced personnel) or a Squadron Conversion Course (SCC), designed for previous 'air defenders'. The Long Course has a duration of five months, providing nearly 65 hours of airborne time. The SCCs were originally divided into two stages, with the first lasting just over three months (giving 35 flying hours) and the second two months with 25 hours. As new squadrons formed with the aircraft, the second stage was completed as part of the unit's operational work-up phase. The OCU also provided QWI and IRE courses as well as Staff Officer Acquaint courses, the latter providing groundschool only.

To address the delays which dogged the ADV's introduction to service, the OCU was declared to NATO's SACEUR as an 'emergency air defence unit' on 1 January 1987. As a result, the unit acquired the shadow identity of No 65 Squadron, whose markings were applied to the noses of the F3s.

Following in the successful footsteps of the Tornado OEU

(later SAOEU) described in Chapter Three, Strike Command formed the Tornado F3 Operational Evaluation Unit to develop tactics, doctrine and techniques for the new aircraft. Wg Cdr Mal Gleave took charge of the F3 OEU, which formed on 1 April 1987 at Coningsby – already becoming 'Tornado Town'. Four aircraft (ZE210, ZE251, ZE252 and ZE253) were assigned, being delivered between 12 February and 25 March 1987. The unit has subsequently had a very rapid turnover of aircraft as the production standard (in particular the radar) improved. Today, the F3 OEU normally operates four aircraft at any one time, borrowing other aircraft from front-line or other trials organisations as required.

Combat Ready

Following the retirement of its McDonnell Douglas Phantom FGR2s on 30 March 1987, No 29 Squadron became the first true frontline Tornado F3 unit. 'Unofficially' formed on 1 April 1987, and commanded by Wg Cdr Lloyd Doble from 25 April 1987, the new squadron consisted of a mix of new and experienced air defence crews. The former embarked upon the OCU's Long Course (lasting six months, the second half involving just over 61 hours of flying time for pilots, with nearly 49 hours for navigators) whilst the 'older hands' undertook the Short Course of three months duration albeit with a similar number of flying hours. The first F3s for the new squadron were a mix of ex-No 229 OCU and factory-fresh machines, with ZE209 technically being 'the first' having arrived at Coningsby on 6 February 1987.

The squadron declared to NATO's SACLANT on 1

When No 56 Squadron disbanded as a Phantom air defence squadron, its numberplate passed to No 229 OCU, which became No 56 (Reserve) Squadron. Here two of the 'old' No 56's F-4Ms pose with a pair of the new (Reserve) Squadron's Tornados.

November 1987, with a maritime air defence war role. The squadron would have deployed to its FOB (RAF Brawdy in Wales) for this role. The unit was also initially the RAF's primary 'out of area deployment' fighter squadron. The squadron's first overseas deployment was the much-publicised Operation *Golden Eagle*, a round the world mission by four F3s between 21 August and 26 October 1988 to mark the Royal Air Force's 70th anniversary. The aircraft flew exercises

No.56 (Reserve) Squadron's airshow display aircraft wore a colour scheme which echoed that applied to the squadron's Lightning-equipped 'Firebirds' display team, with a red fin and spine.

Two of the four No 29 Squadron Tornado F3s deployed on Operation Golden Eagle, *a tour of the Far East, Australasia and North America undertaken during August-September 1987.*

with Thai, Malaysian and Australian air arms during their route through the Far East, before crossing the Pacific Ocean to make good will visits in the USA and Canada.

The English Electric Lightning had been at the forefront of the RAF's air defence forces for years, and two squadrons were still in operation from RAF Binbrook during the mid-1980s. Though a favourite of enthusiasts and spotters, and loved by their pilots, the short-range Lightnings were of marginal operational usefulness, and urgently needed replacing. The first of the Lightning units to convert, No 5 Squadron, assembled at Coningsby during the closing days of 1987 and officially reformed on 1 January 1988, led by Wg Cdr Euan

Black. Its first aircraft, ZE292, had arrived from BAe on 25 September 1987 and adopted the squadron's markings some two months later. ZE256 had previously worn No.5 Squadron's markings as early as June 1987. The initial aircraft on the unit, all from Batch 5, were progressively replaced in the main with Batch 6 examples from the spring of 1988 in time for the squadron's declaration to NATO on 1 May. These newer aircraft all carried Foxhunter Type Z radars, which finally met the RAF's original specification.

The RAF's last Lightning unit, No 11 (Fighter) Squadron, officially down-declared on 30 April 1988 and No 11 (Designate) Squadron formed at Coningsby under Wg Cdr

Two Tornado F3s of No 5 Squadron fly a last formation sortie with their predecessors, a pair of Lightning F6s. The squadron reformed with the Tornado on 1 January 1988. TONY PAXTON

The RAF's Tornados soon began intercepting long range Soviet reconnaissance aircraft, like this Tu-95 'Bear-D', seen with a fully-armed No 5 Squadron F3. JEREMY FLACK/API

David Hamilton on 1 April. The unit's first F3, ZE764, was delivered on 25 April. As the fourth air defence Tornado unit, the code letters to be assigned were in the 'D-' range, so Hamilton duly had this aircraft personalised with his initials as 'DH'. The unit officially reformed on 1 July 1988, also relocating that day from Coningsby to RAF Leeming, North Yorkshire which had undergone an extensive rebuilding programme in readiness for Tornado operations. The unit declared to SACLANT on 1 November 1988, and in time of war would have deployed to the civilian airport at Stornoway located in the Hebrides. Under Operation *Ovoid*, the airport had been considerably upgraded to provide the squadron with a forward operating base from which it could launch CAPs to protect allied shipping passing through the Greenland-Iceland-UK gap. It was on 23 April 1990, during its first QRA commitment at Leeming, that the unit achieved a remarkable triple 'first trade', when it intercepted two Tu-95 'Bears' and an Il-20 'Coot'.

Wg Cdr Neil Taylor headed the initially undesignated fourth F3 frontline unit. This became No 23 Squadron from 1 November 1988, following the redesignation of the Falkland Islands-based Phantom FGR2 unit as a numbered Flight. No 23's first F3, ZE809, was delivered on 5 August 1988. During its work-up, No 23 suffered the RAF's first ADV loss on 21 July

1989 when ZE833 crashed into the North Sea some 30 miles off the north-east coast. Although both crew members ejected, the pilot, Flt Lt Steve Moir, was killed. The unit was declared operational on 1 August 1989.

At its height, the Leeming wing consisted of three frontline squadrons, the third of which established on 1 July 1989, under

In recent years, No 29 Squadron's tail markings have been revised, with prominent black highlights, and with red and gold detailing. This aircraft is seen in company with a No 2 (AC) Squadron GR1A wearing temporary snow camouflage.

An incoming squadron commander reintroduced red bars flanking No 5 Squadron's fin badge, but the red nose chevron did not reappear until more recently. This No 5 Squadron Tornado was pictured during a NATO Tactical Leadership Programme exercise in Portugal during 1997. CORPORAL JOHN CASSIDY

No 5 Squadron's markings were briefly reduced to a simple green maple leaf with a superimposed yellow 'V', with no nose markings carried. Here one of the squadron's aircraft formates with a No 8 Squadron Avro Shackleton and a brand new Boeing E-3D Sentry from No 8 (Designate) Squadron – the Shackleton's replacement.

Wg Cdr Mick Martin. The unit's first aircraft, ZE858, had languished in Leeming's Aircraft Servicing Flight hangar since being delivered on 15 December 1988, before being used for the undesignated unit's work-up. During this period it acquired a large '?' symbol on its fin whilst the squadron's identity was decided upon. As the sixth F3 unit, the code range

'F-' was allocated. The mystery aircraft was subsequently coded 'FK' for 'F___ Knows!'

Because it was expected that the Wattisham and Wildenrath wings would retain their F-4s, there were no active or recently fighter squadrons whose designations could be used by the third Leeming squadron. The decision was finally made that the new unit would take over the No 25 Squadron numberplate, a unit then operating Bloodhound SAMs at RAF Wyton, Barkston Heath and Wattisham, which disbanded on 30 September 1989. Many were astonished, since Nos 32, 60, 64 and 85 were felt by many to have had more distinguished records as fighter units. But No 25 had friends (and perhaps ex-members) in high places and the squadron officially reformed on 1 October. The unit's work-up continued until the squadron was declared operational at midnight on 31 December 1989.

RAF Leuchars in Fife was for many years the RAF's northernmost fighter airfield. As such, the airfield was home to the UK's Northern Sector Quick Reaction Alert force, normally known simply as 'Northern Q', and its Lightnings and subsequently Phantoms flew regular intercept missions

Wg Cdr Hamilton's No 111 Squadron aircraft was soon decorated with a black tailfin and spine, as seen here. The aircraft is shown with full armament, and with a pair of large 'Hindenburger' external tanks.

against probing Soviet reconnaissance aircraft. Of the two based squadrons, No 43(F) ceased Phantom operations at the end of July 1989. The first Tornado F3 (ZE963) arrived from Warton on 23 August 1989 for engineering training and familiarisation. No 43's new 'boss', Wg Cdr Andy Moir, led the delivery flight of the first two aircraft when ZE961 and ZE962 flew from Coningsby to Leuchars on 23 September 1989, arriving in style during the station's annual Battle of Britain At Home Day. The unit then began its work-up, accepting the 800th production Tornado during the process, on 9 January 1990. The unit was declared operational to NATO on 1 July 1990.

The last of the eight frontline F3 Squadrons to form was No 111 Squadron, commanded by Wg Cdr Peter Walker. The unit's Phantoms flew their final operational sortie on 31 October 1989. The Northern Q commitment then passed to Leeming from that date while Leuchars transitioned to the new aircraft type. No 111 officially reformed on 1 May 1990, although its first 'new' F3, ZE969, had been delivered from Warton on 6 June 1990. The squadron began to receive a mix of new-build and older aircraft, although the majority were modified to the so-called Stage 1 standard described later. The invasion of Kuwait resulted in the squadron losing these more-capable aircraft to combat-ready units for Operation *Granby* duties. No 111 then became available to NATO from midnight on 31 December 1990, with Northern Q being taken back from Leeming at this time.

The premature retirement of the Phantom from RAF service in 1992 brought about the necessity for one final Tornado F3

unit to form, namely No 1435 Flight, based at RAF Mount Pleasant in the Falklands. With a complement of only four aircraft, the unit is manned by rotational deployments from UK-based units. The Flight's first F3s (ZE209, ZE758, ZE790 and ZE812) departed for the Falklands over 7/8 July 1992 and routed via Ascension Island. Crews for the Flight are seconded from the UK, the four week commitments normally seeing aircrew pairs detach approximately once every 18 months. 'Trade' for the unit can be quite varied, ranging from intercepting Argentinean aircraft (such as L-188 Electras or C-130 Hercules) as they probe the air defence zone as well as

The second Leeming-based Tornado unit was No 23 Squadron, now disbanded. One of the unit's Granby-*modified F3s is seen landing at RAF Akrotiri during an armament practice camp in October 1993.*

Tornado F3s from each of the Leuchars-based squadrons escort a Tupolev Tu-95MS 'Bear' en route to the 1994 International Air Tattoo at RAF Fairford.

a certain civilian Boeing 727 which transports fish between the Falklands and Chile. The pilot of the latter sometimes neglects to file a flight plan; the sight of two fully-armed Tornados pulling up alongside ought to be remarkable memory joggers, but perhaps he's an enthusiast!

Stage One and Beyond

Between October 1984 and June 1989, 142 ADVs were delivered to the RAF. All of those which were intended to remain operational (the F3s) were fitted with Type W and Type Z Foxhunter radars, and the 44 F3s originally fitted with the Type W sets had their radars upgraded to the later 'Z' standard. The radar and a number of other systems were upgraded further under the so-called Stage 1 modifications, which brought aircraft up to the same standard as the final 46 production F3s for the RAF.

ZE936 was the first new-build Stage 1 aircraft, and it arrived at Coningsby for trials with the F3 OEU during the summer of 1989. The aircraft incorporated improved radar software and installation standards as well as a new F/A-18-type stick top, giving enhanced Hands-On Throttle And Stick (HOTAS) capability for the pilot. The new stick top provided better locations for weapons selectors (gun-Sidewinder-SkyFlash) and radar command-override switches. Following OEU

examination, the first two aircraft flew with the Leeming and Coningsby wings respectively before all began to be concentrated with the two Leuchars-based units which were forming at the time. With a number of RAF F3s diverted on the production line to fulfil Saudi Arabia's Al Yamamah order,

No 25 Squadron's original squadron markings consisted of a simple black-edged silver band across the fin, with the unit's Hawk-on-gauntlet badge lower on the fin. Here one of the squadron's aircraft formates with a Jindivik drone, the normal tug for missile targets during Tornado F3 missile practice camps.

This No 111 Squadron F3 is seen dispensing IR decoy flares from its underfuselage W.Vinten Ltd Vicon 78 flare dispensers, with chaff being dispensed from Celsius Tech BOL dispensers in the underwing Common Rail Launchers.

24 replacement aircraft were ordered under Batch 7 Block 15 and these were later supplemented by eight more following the cancellation of the Omani order for Block 16 dual-control ADVs. Delivered in Stage One specification, the last of these aircraft – ZH559, the 929th production Tornado, 198th production ADV and the RAF's 404th and final Tornado – was delivered to Coningsby on 24 March 1993.

In its Stage 1 form, the Tornado F3 could finally claim to be a highly effective weapons system, though a package of further modifications followed almost immediately, prompted by the 1990 Iraqi invasion of Kuwait.

Known as Stage One Plus, the Gulf War modification package was later adopted fleet-wide. It included of a range of modifications aimed at improving the aircraft's ability to

No 25 Squadron's display Tornado F3 wore this smart colour scheme, with a unique 'low-slung' cheatline. The squadron had earlier had an anniversary aircraft with a black-edged silver spine leading into a broad band on the fin, with the squadron badge in its heraldic frame, and with the unit's battle honours in yellow scrolls on the forward fuselage.

operate in the harsh Gulf climate (with modifications to the canopy, hot weather tyres, and uprated air conditioning systems). It also included measures which improved the aircraft's survivability and combat capability. AN/ALE-40 chaff/flare dispensers were fitted below the rear fuselage, and were then replaced by W.Vinten Ltd Vicon 78 Series 210s. Provision was also made for the carriage of a Philips-MATRA Phimat chaff dispenser, while SWAM and RAM were applied to reduce Radar Cross Section. The unused Auto Wing Sweep system was finally deactivated on the Stage One Plus aircraft.

The Stage One radar was upgraded to AA standard, with enhanced software giving improved ECCM and close combat capability, and with improved cooling. The Marconi Hermes RHWR was also improved, with new software to recognise all potential in-theatre threats (and friendlies). The aircraft were fitted with *Have Quick* frequency hopping radios. The deployed Tornados were also armed with AIM-9Ms from US stocks, which offered improved performance. Engine temperature limiters were retuned to give extra thrust, with a 5% Combat Boost switch for the pilot.

But one thing that the Stage One Plus Tornados lacked was an IFF system fully compatible with that of the USAF's F-15Cs, and this led to the decision not to use the aircraft over Iraq itself, but only over friendly territory. In the years since the Gulf War, the RAF's Tornados have continued to receive modifications and improvements, although defence cuts have also reduced the force in size.

Options for Change

The Tornado air defence community remained relatively intact in the wake of the UK's defence cost cutting exercises of the early 1990s, certainly by comparison with the strike/attack force. The end of the Cold War saw a marked decline in former Soviet aircraft 'probing' the UK Air Defence Region, and the RAF's air defence fighter assets were re-organised in response, though there was no indication that the threat facing the UK had permanently disappeared. Southern QRA was disbanded from 9 January 1992, having previously been shared between Coningsby's two front-line Tornado squadrons and the Phantoms based at Wattisham. Politicians eager to provide the expected 'Peace Dividend' saw to it that the RAF's already negligible Air Defence force did suffer huge cuts, losing one of the surviving four bases, plus another in Germany. The force reductions saw the disbandment of four Phantom units (originally to have been retained until the introduction of Eurofighter) at Wattisham and at Wildenrath. From 1992 onwards, Leuchars operated as the sole UK QRA station, having previously shared the Northern Q

This Tornado F3 OEU aircraft is pictured during Towed Radar Decoy trials in the USA. The TRD was first deployed operationally by the Tornado during Operation Deny Flight.

The RAF's final frontline Tornado unit was No 1435 Flight, based on the Falkland Islands with four Tornado F3s. The unit can trace its ancestry to the Gladiator-equipped air defence flight based in Malta during the Second World War, and in recognition of this wears a Maltese cross fin badge. The unit's aircraft are even named after the Malta Gladiators – 'Faith', 'Hope', and 'Charity', with the additional aircraft being 'Desperation'. CORPORAL JOHN CASSIDY

commitment with Leeming. Since then all frontline Tornado F3 units have rotated crews to Leuchars on alert duties.

The dramatic reduction in frontline squadrons led to the re-designation of a number of training units as (Reserve) Squadrons, ostensibly maintaining the existence of a number of historic units, and certainly camouflaging the pitifully weak state of the RAF's frontline. As part of this process No 229 OCU at Coningsby (with its No 65 Squadron shadow identity) became No 56 (Reserve) Squadron on 1 July 1992. This preserved the Firebird's historic identity and 'number plate' following its disbandment as a Phantom-equipped air defence unit.

So far, the only F3 unit to disband has been No 23 Squadron, which stood down at Leeming on 28 February 1994. Many found the choice of No 23 inexplicable. The squadron certainly had a longer, more distinguished and largely unbroken history in the fighter role, while No 25 (many people's choice for disbandment) had spent many years as a Bloodhound SAM unit, and had an arguably less impressive wartime history. The reduction of the F3 force by

one squadron reflected post-Cold War defence cuts, and was made possible by a fleet rationalisation plan.

These factors coincided with a request from Italy to lease 24 F3s pending the late advent of the Quadrinational Eurofighter. Using leased Tornados to fill the gap offered some advantages to Italy and was obviously useful to the other Eurofighter partners, since it prevented Italy from acquiring an interim fighter which might have threatened Eurofighter itself. The agreement for the package, covering aircraft, technical and logistics support as well as personnel training, was signed on 17 November 1993 with a Memorandum of Understanding being signed on 18 March 1994. This covered a five-year no-cost lease, with provision for a five-year extension. The Italian aircraft, drawn from Batches 5, 6 and 7, and modified to Stage One Plus standards at Italian expense, with full 25FI life extension modifications, remain RAF property and one clause of the MoU allows for the aircraft to be recalled to the UK should the need arise. It has been suggested that the Italian Tornado F3s have Italian RWR and ECM equipment, but this cannot be confirmed. Although theoretically compatible with

This Stage Two radar-equipped F3 of the F3 OEU was pictured en route to the USA for JTIDS trials mounted from NAS Oceana. The aircraft wears the current OEU markings, with a triple-winged sword superimposed on a red chevron. The SAOEU sometimes uses an identical badge on a blue chevron. PETER R FOSTER

the Italian Alenia Aspide missile, there are no plans to integrate this weapon, and the AMI acquired 96 SkyFlash rounds for its aircraft.

The first aircraft for the AMI, MM7202 (formerly ZE832), was handed over at RAF Coningsby in July 1995. The first 12 aircraft equipped 36° Stormo's 12° Gruppo at Gioia del Colle, and the rest went to 53° Stormo's 21° Gruppo at Cameri, with the last aircraft being delivered in June 1997. 12° Gruppo was declared combat ready in February 1995, and immediately began flying CAP missions in support of the UN's Operation *Deny Flight* over the former Yugoslavia. With no air defence backseaters, the AMI F3s are flown by two pilots, with the backseaters staying in flying practise using MB339s provided for the purpose. The initial backseaters will transition to the front seat after three years, with a level of WSO/weapons management experience which will make them particularly well suited for the Eurofighter, when it finally enters service.

JTIDS Revolution

Operational experience since the Second World War has demonstrated the value of giving fighter pilots the fullest-possible idea of the 'big picture' of the overall air battle. With advances in technology, it became apparent that all friendly assets (AWACS, GCI radar, surface ships and fighters) could usefully be linked to contribute to and share a 'big picture' to which all could contribute. This would allow a fighter to gain a useful appreciation of the tactical situation far beyond the range of its own sensors. Thus while the Tornado ADV was still little more than a gleam in the eyes of its designers, it was assumed that the RAF's new fighter would incorporate an 'on-line, netted-data, ECM-resistant datalink system'. With a NATO-wide requirement for a common datalink system,

there was little point in the RAF 'going it alone', but an inability among NATO members to agree a common standard led to prolonged delays.

The Joint Tactical Information Distribution System (JTIDS) was developed by US industry as NATO's common tactical datalink, in response to a military requirement for fast and secure data communications between friendly assets on land, sea and air. BAe selected the second production Tornado F3 (ZE155) to act as the Link 16 JTIDS development aircraft and held the aircraft back on the line until a terminal was installed during 1985/6. The aircraft finally flew from Warton on 16 October 1986. During September 1987, it left Boscombe Down for Marine Corps Air Station Yuma, Arizona becoming the first ADV to fly across the Atlantic. Upon successful completion of JTIDS integration trials, ZE155 then made history by performing the first unrefuelled Atlantic crossing by a British fighter. Having positioned to CFB Goose Bay in Canada, on 24 September 1987 the aircraft flew direct to Warton, covering the distance of just under 2,200 nautical miles in 4 hours 45 minutes. The aircraft, flown by Peter Gordon-Johnson and Les Hurst, was fitted with two 2,250 litre and two 1,500 litre fuel tanks.

BAe then joined forces with the A&AEE at Boscombe Down to continue JTIDS trials. Subsequently the F3 OEU at Coningsby also became involved in the JTIDS project, drawing up operational guidelines for the equipment, and conducting a variety of tests both at home and overseas. These included a successful data transfer between two F3 OEU Tornados and four E-3 Sentries (two British and two French) on 27 October 1993. Frontline F3 units began to receive JTIDS in 1994, when Coningsby-based Nos 5 and 29 Squadrons took delivery of their first JTIDS-equipped aircraft. The first aircraft with JTIDS provision (which were originally from Batch 7

Blocks 15 and 16) was delivered on 14 August 1991 when ZG751 arrived for No 5 Squadron, with the necessary equipment being added in-house at a later date. Only a relatively small number of JTIDS Class II terminals have been supplied for use by the F3 fleet although most aircraft are now equipped to carry the equipment. The Leeming wing currently employs the bulk of the available JTIDS sets in support of its NATO Reaction Force (Air) role.

As well as JTIDs the RAF's Tornados have received a diverse range of improvements. Since 1994, Tornado F3s have been able to carry the GEC-Marconi Aerial towed radar decoy (TRD). Housed in a modified BOZ chaff-dispenser pod, Aerial is towed at least 200 metres (660 ft) behind the aircraft, and is jettisoned after use (preferably over the home airfield, to be recovered and re-used). Tornado F3s carrying Aerial are fitted with IDS-type outboard underwing pylons, and carry Phimat or BOZ pods outboard under the starboard wing to counterbalance the TRD to port. There are two separate types of Aerial TRD available, one fully autonomous, and one repeating signals transmitted by the towing aircraft's EW systems, and it is unclear which version is used by RAF Tornados. Frontline aircraft can now also carry a Common Rail Launcher (CRL), incorporating a Celsius-Tech BOL chaff dispenser and an integral cooling gas generator. The CRL replaces standard LAU-7 Sidewinder launch rails and can be used with the AIM-9 Sidewinder or with the new ASRAAM missile. Use of the CRL allows the Tornado to fly without a Phimat chaff dispenser, while retaining a Sidewinder station. Some expect the older missile to be adopted early if the AIM-9 is finally withdrawn from use by the RAF. The replacement of the Sidewinder would represent a spend-to-save measure, since the weapon is becoming increasingly expensive to support.

While previous radar upgrades (Stage One and Stage One Plus) have been undertaken alongside packages of other modifications, the latest Stage Two (AB) radar upgrade has been more of a stand-alone programme, although the 'Stage Two' name has been erroneously applied to the current tranche of largely unrelated and separate improvements to the RAF's F3s. The Stage Two improvements centred around the provision of a new processor, allowing automatic target acquisition and tracking, and discrimination between head-on targets through analysis of their first and second-stage compressor disc characteristics. The aircraft's main computer is also being improved, allowing the introduction of new clearer display symbology and display formats. Auto Wing Sweep may finally be re-activated in the 'Stage Two' aircraft.

Despite a shortage of fast jet units to meet existing peacetime commitments, the new Labour government's Strategic Defence Review saw a reduction in the RAF's Tornado F3 force, with the disbandment of No 29 Squadron at Coningsby on 30 October 1998. The choice of No 29 was no more surprising than the earlier disbandments of the Phantom-equipped Nos 19, 23, 56, 74 and 92 Squadrons, the RAF having seemingly decided to get rid of the most historic and famous of its Battle of Britain fighter units, rather than those whose wartime histories are arguably less distinguished. The reason may simply have been to 'make space' at Coningsby, which is destined to be the RAF's first Eurofighter base, and which already had three resident flying units, while Leeming and Leuchars each housed only two Tornado F3 squadrons.

But as with the RAF's Tornado GR1/1A/1B force, it is debateable as to whether the Tornado F3 fleet should be reduced at all. While the RAF's present overseas peacekeeping and UN commitments primarily involve ground attack and reconnaissance aircraft, Tornado F3s continue to play a vital

Nose markings (like No 43 Squadron's traditional black and white checkerboards) are gradually disappearing from the RAF's Tornado F3s. This No 43 Squadron machine has a reduced-size fin badge located higher on the tail, alongside the re-located fin code, where they can more easily be over-painted for operations or prior to reallocation to another unit.

One of the RAF aircraft 'leased' to the Italian air force, prior to delivery. It wears 36° Stormo tail markings, with 12° Gruppo markings on the intake, and is seen in company with a No 56 (Reserve) Squadron Tornado F3, on which the Italian aircrew received their conversion training.
CORPORAL JOHN CASSIDY

role over Bosnia, and the type could easily be called upon to fulfil other commitments. Even one extra commitment would cause a degree of overstretch to the F3 force at its present strength. Despite this, the force is maintained ready for action, and aircraft are presently being repainted to allow more rapid deployment, with squadron markings reduced in size and reloacted to the fin cap, where they can be more easily removed or over-painted.

The piecemeal application of Stage One, Stage One Plus, and Stage Two modifications have led to the threat of a 'mini-fleet' and fleet-within-fleet problem developing. An ongoing Tornado Capability Sustainment Programme (CSP) launched in 1996 as a Mid-Life Update aims to bring all remaining in-service F3s to a common ergonomic and equipment standard, with all the various Gulf War and subsequent modifications productionised and applied fleet-wide. When the MLU was announced on 5 March 1996, the stated aim was to extend the service life of 100 F3s until 2010. This is to be achieved via a surprisingly modest package of improvements, centred on adding AMRAAM and ASRAAM missile capability to the most advanced in-service F3 configuration, and then bringing all 100 long-term aircraft to this standard.

Integrating AMRAAM requires the provision of a MIL STD 1553B digital databus, together with a changed main computer processor, a new missile management system (using ADA software) and improved display graphics. Remarkably, new AMRAAM and ASRAAM missiles are not being procured for the Tornado F3, and CSP modified aircraft will borrow AMRAAMs from RN Sea Harrier AIM-120 stocks, and will use AMRAAMs originally ordered for the RAF Harrier GR7.

Moreover, not all CSP aircraft will actually be fitted with AMRAAM missile launchers, since only a limited number of these are being acquired, and these will be temporarily fitted to aircraft on an as-required basis.

Three long-term test aircraft at Warton were used in support of the CSP programme. F2 ZD899 was used as a radar target, F3 ZG797 flew with software for ther new displays, and ZE155 performed missile carriage trials before being modified to virtually full CSP standards. At the time of writing, it was expected that BAE Systems working parties would modify the first 24 CSP aircraft at RAF St Athan, with RAF personnel producing the next 76 aircraft using BAe-supplied kits. The last aircraft will be returned to service by 2001. Any reduction in the Tornado F3 force imposed as a result of the Strategic Defence Review may of course have an affect on the number of aircraft cycled through the CSP.

Separately from the CSP, the F3s are receiving Elmer SRT-651N V/UHF dual 'Have Quick' frequency hopping radios, and are likely to receive new LCD display screens, further improving their ability to operate as a fully-integrated part of the modern air defence environment.

Probably the most advanced Tornado fighter flying will never see squadron service. This is F2A ZD902, now flying as the TIARA Tornado (Tornado Integrated Avionics Research Aircraft). A dedicated research aircraft, TIARA has explored advanced sensor fusion concepts, and has a state-of-the-art LCD cockpit and provision for a FIRSTSIGHT IRST, Blue Vixen radar, and a range of other sensors and systems. But the work undertaken will be applied to Eurofighter and other advanced fighters, and probably not to Tornado derivatives.

Reconnaissance

The RAF's Tornado GR1As operate from the snowfields of northern Norway to the deserts of the Near East. This No 13 Squadron aircraft is flying over Turkey during Exercise Distant Thunder *in April 1994.* SQN LDR MARK KNIGHT

All of the MRCA partners had a requirement for a new tactical reconnaissance aircraft, Germany and Italy to replace recce-roled Starfighters, the RAF to replace ageing Canberras and the interim Phantoms and Jaguars. With this in mind, it is perhaps surprising that only one Tornado operator (the UK) actually produced a dedicated reconnaissance version of the aircraft, though all have deployed podded reconnaissance systems on the Tornado.

The Panavia consortium did originally look at providing a podded optical reconnaissance system for all of the Tornado's customers, and unsurprisingly, W.Vinten Ltd (European and probably world leaders in optical recce technology then, as now) won the competition to supply the sensors for the new pod. The new pod was to have incorporated twin Type 900 panoramic cameras, with the complete unit being known as the FX142. This was designed specifically to allow for the very high V/H ratios encountered at low level. The pod also incorporated an F144 (Type 690) with an 18-in lens and a rotating nose cone assembly forward for oblique and stand-off photography. This was the same basic type of camera that is now carried in W.Vinten's GP(1) pod. Some sources suggest that the new sensors were flown in a converted F-4 Phantom-type reconnaissance pod, and (in the case of the Type 690) by a Fairey Surveys (later Clyde Surveys) DC-3 test platform (G-ALWC). The pod was remarkably similar in size, fit and capability to the GP(1) pod now proving so useful to the Tornado force, and to the recce pod actually used by German and Italian aircraft.

But in the end, the pod fell victim to arguments about workshare, and an inability of the three partner nations to reach agreement on what the pod would actually contain. Germany wanted a larger pod, with more sensors, and also favoured giving work to Zeiss, Germany's 'home team'. The Vinten sensors were flown in a modified F-4 Phantom pod, which confirmed their superb performance. But in the face of German intransigence, the individual nations went their own way. In Britain it was felt that an internal or conformal/semi-conformal reconnaissance fit would offer considerable advantages over any podded system, giving lower drag and allowing the carriage of more fuel and weapons and BAe began design of the Tornado GR1A as we know it today.

Even after the original pod was abandoned, attempts were made to find a common solution. For some time, a very low drag, semi-conformal 'slipper' was the favoured option, since it marked a compromise between internal carriage and a conventional bulky pod. But the RAF had by then decided that it wanted internal sensors, while on the other hand, the proposed slipper could not accommodate the existing sensors which the Italians wanted their recce Tornados to carry.

When the MRCA was originally mooted, Britain hoped that it would be able to replace all of the RAF's reconnaissance assets, in both tactical and strategic roles. But it soon became clear that the Tornado's range, altitude and stability characteristics mitigated against the aircraft's use at high altitude, while the lack of available volume was also a problem. Thus from an early stage, the MoD decided that the

The first reconnaissance tasked Tornados in service belonged to the Marineflieger's MFG 2, using a reconnaissance pod designed and developed by MBB/Aeritalia. The pod is usually carried on the aircraft's centreline. HARTMUT FELDMANN

reconnaissance Tornado would have to be capable of all-weather, day/night penetration (a classic Cold War Central European scenario) and this automatically ruled out the use of daylight cameras.

In Germany, the Luftwaffe could not afford a dedicated reconnaissance Tornado with an internal IR/EO sensor fit, nor could it wait for such a version to be developed. Instead the two wings of RF-104Gs were replaced by a similar number of RF-4E Phantoms. The Marineflieger and Italian AMI did not really operate dedicated single-role tactical reconnaissance aircraft, and instead procured relatively simple and straightforward reconnaissance pods to give their strike/attack Tornados a measure of reconnaissance capability. A relatively

The MBB/Aeritalia recce pod contains a Texas Instruments IRLS and two Zeiss optical cameras. The pod was originally delivered to the Marineflieger and AMI, and later to the Luftwaffe. JEREMY FLACK/API

simple 380-kg (840-lb) reconnaissance pod was designed for use on the Marineflieger and AMI Tornados, with a Texas Instruments RS-710 IRLS and a pair of Zeiss optical cameras. The pod is carried on an adaptor on the centreline station. Some 26 pods were originally acquired by the Marineflieger, and more were delivered to Italy. In German Navy service, the recce role was assigned to MFG 2's first Staffel, while in Italy the recce pod originally tended to be regarded as 'just another store' and was likely to be used by any unit, as requirements dictated. More recently, a degree of specialisation has crept in and 154° Gruppo have tended to be the AMI's recce specialists. The 6° Stormo maintains a photographic interpretation unit and parents the stock of recce pods, though these remain available to other units when required. When fully re-equipped with Tornado ECRs, 155° Gruppo may take on a greater recce commitment.

In Britain, the decision to design an internal EO/IR-based reconnaissance fit necessarily meant a rather longer development time, and the RAF lagged behind Italy and the Marineflieger in deploying reconnaissance roled Tornados. Once the decision had been made to develop an internal reconnaissance fit, BAe had to decide where the new reconnaissance equipment could be accommodated. From the start the intention was to build some recce aircraft from scratch, but to produce others through the conversion of existing 'bomber' airframes. One option would have been to add a completely new recce nose, like that fitted to reconnaissance versions of the Phantom or F-5, but this would have entailed major structural changes (limiting the potential for retrofit of the recce system to existing airframes). It would also have meant the loss of the aircraft's Terrain Following Radar, which was felt to be essential for the low-level recce role.

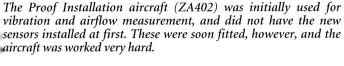

The Proof Installation aircraft (ZA402) was initially used for vibration and airflow measurement, and did not have the new sensors installed at first. These were soon fitted, however, and the aircraft was worked very hard.

Even by removing the Tornado's guns very little internal volume could be created, and this limited the extent of equipment which could be fitted, ruling out a full multi-spectral reconnaissance system. But it was decided that the former gun and ammunition bays would be used for the new variant's reconnaissance equipment, with a fairing under the nose housing a downward/panoramic sensor, and with sideways looking sensors 'looking' through IR-transparent windows in the lower sides of the forward fuselage. These sensors would each incorporate cameras, which would record onto conventional wet film.

It was at this stage that the decision was taken that the Tornado's reconnaissance sensors would operate in the IR spectrum, for optimum night/all-weather performance. IR sensors also allow extra information to be gleaned from imagery. During an airfield recce for example IR sensors may show cold fuel in an aircraft's tanks, or recently run-up engines. Cool shadows below a recently departed aircraft may even be detected. IR sensors do have disadvantages too, of

The prototype GR1A (more accurately a Proof Installation aircraft) had previously served with No 20 Squadron, and continued to wear No 20 Squadron's markings during its time at Warton.

course, with lower resolution than optical cameras or visual spectrum electro-optical sensors, with some problems in very humid and moist conditions and with problems when the heat signature of the target matches the heat signature of the background.

But the proposed system, using IR sensors recording onto film was no faster than conventional cameras in getting useable imagery to those who want to exploit or interpret it. In fact, any system using conventional wet film processing (even with the latest high-speed processing equipment) imposed a delay in getting imagery to the end-user. Moreover, with the increased capacity of modern film magazines and the tendency to use multiple camera installations, the production of useable imagery was no quicker in the early 1970s than it had been at the dawn of aerial reconnaissance. In fact, some

ZA369 of No 2 (AC) Squadron was not one of the six GR1As deployed to the Gulf during Operation Granby, but is seen here carrying fuel tanks, BOZ pod and Sky Shadow pod. ANDY EVANS

A No 2 (AC) Squadron Tornado GR1A (en route to Cyprus in 1993) wearing the squadron's standard markings. Sky Shadow ECM and BOZ pods are virtually permanent fixtures on the RAF's Tornados, even on the rare occasions when external fuel tanks are not carried.

While No 2 (AC) Squadron re-equipped with Tornado GR1As to fulfill RAF Germany's reconnaissance requirements, No 13 became the UK-based Tornado recce squadron.

reconnaissance crews in the First World War actually dropped glass negatives directly to their HQ or artillery batteries, together with hand-drawn sketch maps and notes!

There was strong desire to increase the speed of image delivery, and this led to a drive to go to video-based sensors. Video tape could be reviewed and even edited by the backseater in flight, and was useable as soon as the aircraft landed, without an intermediate processing stage. Because video-based IR imagery requires no processing, and is immediately available for interpretation and exploitation, there is even the theoretical possibility of real-time data-linking from reconnaissance platform to ground station. This was very much a theoretical capability, however, since up-linking or down-linking from very low level was fraught with technical difficulties and promised to be prohibitively expensive. But even without any form of data-linking, video was clearly the way to go.

The sensors, ground stations and other elements of the recce

package were selected competitively, with BAe Hatfield providing SLIRs based on the MoD's TICM (Thermal Imaging Common Module) used in tanks and on board warships, with a new panoramic IRLS jointly developed by BAe and RAE Malvern. These sensor originally recorded onto film, but within three months of the contract having been let, the decision was taken to switch to tape, for speed and ease of data handling and for more rapid exploitation of the imagery.

At one time it was felt that the Tornado GR1A should have an optional interchangeable EO sensor, which could be used to replace the all-IR sensor fit according to mission and role requirements. Vinten's Type 8002 sensor was designed and built to meet the requirement. This had three optically abutted 70° FoV (Field of View) Linear CCD sensor arrays, giving a

The Tornado is a considerably smaller aircraft than the RF-4E Phantom, as this photo shows. Two of No 13 Squadron's aircraft are seen in company with a pair of Spanish Air Force 'Photo Phantoms' during a squadron exchange. SQN LDR MARK KNIGHT

The Marham Wing reconnaissance Tornados have made frequent deployments to Norway, during which they have usually worn temporary snow camouflage. This aircraft has white painted mainly over the green parts of its usual camouflage. The aircraft has toned down pastel fin flashes and a single roundel above the port wing. CPL JOHN CASSIDY

combined FoV of 210°, reduced to 142° after roll stabilisation. Each sensor had 1,728 pixels, giving a very high resolution image. The sensor proved extremely impressive, offering much the same resolution as an IR linescan even in its prototype form, and promising a potential for about five times the resolution. It had excellent performance in daylight, and at dawn and dusk, with some night and weather/haze penetration capability, and with much better medium level performance, and range. Moreover, the EO sensor could function without cooling, at ambient temperatures, and produced a 'natural' visual spectrum image. The Type 8002 was the world's first low altitude EO sensor, and was flown in a converted Phantom pod between 1976 and 1981, occupying much the same space as the original AN/AAS-18 Linescan. The only problem (if it could be described as a problem) was that the sensor's very high data rate meant that recorder tapes were filled up extremely rapidly. Cost and installation constraints led to the eventual adoption of an IR-only kit for the Tornado GR1A, and the Type 8001 was dropped. This was a controversial decision which provoked much criticism and opposition, although because the sensor remained classified until 1989, the story was not picked up by the press.

The Type 8002 started Vinten on a track which led to a new generation of EO sensors, and these are being deployed in an EO version of the GP(1) pod for the Jaguar force, as a direct replacement for optical sensors – such is their clarity and resolution. The Tornado GR1A could have had a similar level of capability for more than ten years, had different decisions been made.

The IR-based system actually selected for the new Tornado variant was developed by BAe (who took responsibility for integration and structural modifications to the aircraft), and Vinten, with CDC providing the reconnaissance management system. The sensors themselves consisted of a BAe/Vinten

The effectiveness of the Tornado's temporary snow camouflage can be gauged by this No 13 squadron aircraft over Norway.

No 13 squadron celebrated its 80th anniversary in 1995, decorating one of its aircraft to mark the occasion. JEREMY FLACK/API

Linescan 4000 IRLS, scanning from horizon-to-horizon through the panoramic window in the bottom of the underfuselage fairing, with two BAe SLIRs (Sideways Looking Infra Red), each with a 10° FoV (from the horizon to 10° depression) giving augmented coverage of the 'edges' of the main IRLS's field of view. The SLIRs can be locked to give a constant view in relation to the aircraft, or can be roll-stabilised, continuing to point at the horizon as the aircraft rolls and banks. A recent modification allows the sensors to look up to 4° above the horizon, or up to 14° below it, but

The transfer of Nos 2 (AC) and 13 Squadrons to Marham from Laarbruch and Honington in December 1991 and February 1994 concentrated the RAF's main reconnaissance units at this Norfolk base, alongside No 39 Squadron, which moved in from RAF Wyton. This formation was photographed in August 1995. SQN LDR MARK KNIGHT

these angles must be pre-set on the ground before take off. The sensors were heavily influenced by the UK's TICMS (Thermal Imaging Common Module System) using Signal Processing In The Element (SPRITE) technology with Stirling Cycle cryogenic cooling. Together, the IRLS and SLIRs were known as TIRRS (Tornado Infra Red Reconnaissance System). The recce package was completed by six video recorders. These use standard VHS format E-180 tapes, but run them at three times the usual speed for improved definition, and thus give 60 minutes of recording time.

The 'prototype' for the Tornado GR1A was ZA402, a Batch 3 aircraft previously assigned to No 20 Squadron, which confusingly retained its squadron insignia after conversion by BAe at Warton. ZA402 had been delivered to Warton for development work unconnected with the recce programme in June 1984, and was then selected to serve as the GR1A Trial Installation. It made its first flight in its new configuration on 11 July 1985, though the reconnaissance equipment was not fitted initially, and the aircraft was used for the measurement of vibration levels, pressures and airflow in and around the new equipment bays, windows and undernose fairing, all of which were 'in place'. Trials of the sensor package itself began in the late summer of 1985.

Thirteen more GR1s (ZA369-373, 394, 395, 397, 398, 400, 401, 404, and 405), all from Batch 3, were selected for conversion to GR1A and from 3 April 1987 these aircraft were redelivered from Warton, without TIRRS, and with no side windows, along with the first two new-build GR1As (ZD996 and ZE116). The latter aircraft were the only RAF aircraft in Batch 5, the other aircraft intended for the RAF being diverted to the Saudis. One more of the GR1As remained with BAe for trials and the remaining 14 aircraft went to 'holding' units in the UK (primarily the TTTE) and RAF Germany, being used by the units as 'gunless bombers' pending the formation of the first Tornado reconnaissance squadron.

RAF Germany's reconnaissance-dedicated Jaguar GR1As continued to operate with No 2 (Army Co-operation) Squadron from Laarbruch until 16 December 1988, some two years after their originally planned replacement by the Tornado GR1A. Problems in the development of the GR1A's state of the art Tornado Infra Red Reconnaissance System was the main cause of this delay.

Wg Cdr Alan Threadgould, who led the 'new' squadron, undertook the unit's first Tornado sortie on 30 September 1988. The squadron standard was handed-over from the Jaguar unit on 20 December 1988, although only three Tornados were on strength by that time. These were a single dual control GR1 and two GR1As (ZA370 and ZA395), though the latter still lacked their TIRRS equipment. It was decided that since the programme delays were likely to continue for some time, No 2 (AC) would work-up in its intended secondary role of strike/attack. This aside, Threadgould was keen for his crews to become 'recce converts' from the outset and the unit flew many 'dry runs' against typical recce targets, with crews becoming expert in making accurate and concise visual reports. During February 1989 the squadron's navigators were issued with hand-held 35mm cameras; the first trials proved unsuccessful, although the discovery that the cameras needed to be loaded with film dramatically improved subsequent results!

The first production TIRRS was fitted into ZA373 at Laarbruch in June 1989, and the aircraft first flew as a 'proper' GR1A the following month. Side windows began to appear on several aircraft in October 1989, indicating that recce equipment had finally been fitted. The process was a slow one,

Like the rest of the RAF's Tornado IDS fleet, the GR1As are slowly adopting an all-grey colour scheme, similar to that applied to the RAF's Harrier GR7s and Jaguars. KEVIN WILLS

ZA370 was one of the six aircraft used in the Gulf War, and even as late as February 1997 still carried its wartime mission tally, with each operational sortie represented by a palm tree. KEVIN WILLS

A November 1997 deployment to Norway by No 2 (AC) Squadron marked the first time that the Vicon GP (1) pod and the Tornado GR1A's internal TIRRS were used simultaneously. The use of the Vicon pod (procured primarily as theatre assets for UN peacekeeping and monitoring operations) gives the Tornado a medium-level capability it has always lacked. SQN LDR MARK KNIGHT

A No 2 (AC) Squadron GR1A manoeuvres hard over the Lake District during a low-level training sortie. The aircraft carries a practice bomb dispenser under the belly. SGT RICK BREWELL

however, and by January 1990, only six aircraft of the eleven GR1As on strength had received their equipment, giving the RAF eight role-equipped aircraft of 20 extant GR1As, two being in use with No 13 Squadron and at Warton.

Despite the fact that the unit could muster only six mission-capable aircraft, and despite the fact that it had yet to be declared operational, No 2 (AC) Squadron was told to prepare for service in the Gulf. The six recce-equipped aircraft (ZA370, 371, 372, 373, 397 and 400) received the *Granby* modifications applied to the Tornado bombers deployed to the Middle East, together with *Granby 2* modifications, a package of changes to the recce software devised by Computing Devices Co. which improved reliability. The modification package was trialled at Laarbruch between Christmas 1990 and New Year 1991, and five crews from No 2, with four from No 13 (which had only formed in January 1990) deployed to Dhahran on 14 January. The air war began on 17 January.

During the Gulf War, the reconnaissance aircraft operated only by night, and only at low level, making extensive use of the Tornado's terrain following radar. The aircraft often operated without AAR support, often with big ADV-type 'Hindenburger' tanks underwing and small tanks under the fuselage. This represented a doubling of the GR1A's internal fuel capacity. NVGs were issued, but crews generally had not trained with them, and they were little used. The detachment

flew 128 sorties during the war, with some success, although imagery was not entirely satisfactory, and placed great demands on the interpreters.

Following the Gulf War, No 2 (AC) Squadron was finally able to consolidate its operations, down-declaring from its limited attack capability on 20 November 1991 and finally declaring combat-ready to NATO in the reconnaissance role on 3 February 1992. The squadron then became operational in its secondary strike attack role on 1 May. During this period of intensive training and assessment, No 2 (AC) Squadron left Laarbruch on 3 December 1991, re-locating to Marham, this move being part of the UK's 'Options for Change' defence restructuring, which saw the disbandment of Laarbruch's Tornado wing.

The second of the RAF's two reconnaissance units was No 13 Squadron, initially based at RAF Honington. Twin-sticker GR1 ZA357 was the unit's first aircraft, arriving on 2 October 1989 although No 13's CO, Wg Cdr Glenn Torpy, suffered the inconvenience of a stuck canopy on arrival! The unit accepted its first Batch 7 Tornado GR1A (ZG705) on 13 October 1989, and it flew to Laarbruch on 15 December 1989 for a five day long TIRRS installation by No 431 Maintenance Unit. The unit officially reformed on 1 January 1990, and had flown 1,000 hours by 29 June; the figure increased rapidly as operational low flying training commenced due to the Middle

This ex-Marineflieger Tornado, wearing the original grey and white colour scheme, was one of those transferred to AKG 51 for reconnaissance operations. Though the wing received some 40 Tornados, it initially had only 9 recce pods – not much of a ratio. HARTMUT FELDMANN

East situation. Although four crews were sent to the Gulf alongside five crews from No 2 (AC) Squadron, others were involved in the frantic activity to ready the TIALD pod for combat use. Further details can be found in Chapter 8.

Upon return from Gulf War operations, No 13 settled down to complete its proper work-up phase and it was the unit's new CO, Wg Cdr Steve Dalton, who declared it combat ready to NATO on 1 October 1992. The squadron re-located to Marham on 1 February 1994, as part of the centralisation of the RAF's reconnaissance assets. Now that they are fully settled into reconnaissance operations, the two Tornado GR1A squadrons have an 80% reconnaissance tasking, but continue to spend 20% of their time in the attack role. The nuclear strike role was finally relinquished on Tuesday 31 March 1998, with the retirement of the WE 177 freefall nuclear bomb.

Reconnaissance Tornados have been extensively used during peace-keeping and monitoring operations over Iraq, flying from Incirlik (Operation *Warden*) and from Dhahran and more recently Al Kharj (Operation *Jural*). But with the main threat to low-flying recce aircraft coming from disgruntled Iraqi soldiers armed with AK 47s or rifles, or at worst a shoulder-launched SAM-7, low level has been the riskiest place to be, rather than the safest. Moreover, the task has generally been to provide area coverage, rather than to do detailed target reconnaissance. Together these factors have tended to dictate flying missions at medium altitude, where the GR1A's internal reconnaissance fit is less effective and less well optimised.

In order to provide the imagery required, Tornados on *Warden* and *Jural* therefore carry a W.Vinten Ltd Vicon 18 Series 601 GP(1) reconnaissance pod on the centreline. Previously deployed on Jaguar GR1As and Harrier GR7s, the RAF procured a total of 12 pods, primarily as 'theatre assets' to be carried by whatever aircraft type was fulfilling the commitments in Turkey, Saudi Arabia and Italy (the latter based at Gioia del Colle for operations over Bosnia).

The GP (1) pod is compact and relatively light, imposing little drag penalty, and yet it represents an extraordinarily versatile and high quality reconnaissance tool, being capable of LOROP (Long Range Oblique Photography), tactical stand-

off or vertical photography, at low-level or medium-level. The small pod is only 90.55-in long, with a diameter of 18-in and contains a Type 690 (F144) Framing Camera with a superb high-resolution 450-mm lens and a Type 900 (F152) Panoramic camera with a 3-in lens. The Type 690 camera incorporates a rotating nose cone assembly allowing it to be aimed at various angles of depression. These sensors are conventional film-based optical cameras, and thus rely on the usual paraphenalia of wet film processing support, which is costly, time consuming, and which is becoming increasingly perceived as being old-fashioned, environmentally unfriendly (because of the use of chemicals) and unfashionable. W.Vinten Ltd have produced an electro-optical version of the pod (generally regarded as the best EO recce pod in its class) and this will be deployed by the Jaguar force from about 1999, but on Tornado, GP(1) will be replaced by the larger RAPTOR pod. Perhaps the supreme irony is that GR1As deployed on *Warden* and *Jural* actually tend to have their internal TIRRS removed and replaced with ballast, and thus rely entirely on the GP(1) pod, like the 'ordinary' GR1Bs and GR1s using the Vicon pod.

Just as the RAF's attack Tornados are being upgraded to GR4 standards, so the reconnaissance aircraft will become GR4As in the same programme. They will retain their TIRRS equipment, but will increasingly come to rely on the new generation RAPTOR reconnaissance pod, described in greater detail in the GR4/4A chapter of this book.

Post-Cold War defence cuts left the German armed forces with a surplus of almost new, relatively low-houred Tornados, while ageing RF-4E Phantoms remained in service. These aircraft were well-equipped, but were becoming increasingly obsolescent and Panavia was asked to draw up five options for converting surplus Tornados to the reconnaissance role as Phantom replacements. The options were of varying cost and complexity, ranging from an aircraft like the RAF's GR1A with the addition of Zeiss optical sensors, and to aircraft fitted with internal or podded IRLS equipment, with the BAe/Vinten 400 and Honeywell systems being shortlisted. Some proposed configurations had a modified and strengthened nose, while others used podded sensors – one proposal even suggested

The wing's Panther's head badge is carried very small on the tailfin of this AKG 51 Tornado, which wears the final Marineflieger colour scheme, and carries an MBB/Aeritalia reconnaissance pod on the centreline. HARTMUT FELDMAN

This AKG 51 Tornado is seen in the latest Luftwaffe grey colour scheme, and carries a recce pod on the centreline. The Luftwaffe's next generation reconnaissance pod is now in flight test, and should soon be deployed. HARTMUT FELDMAN

retrofit of Eurofighter EJ200 engines.

In the end, a very modest solution was found, involving the transfer of ex-Marineflieger Tornados to re-equip AKG 51, with the transferred aircraft receiving the necessary re-wiring and control panels required to carry and operate the basic MBB/Aeritalia reconnaissance pod, six of which were transferred from the AMI, and three from the Marineflieger, before further pods were transferred. The unit is now believed to have some 10 Marineflieger pods 'on loan' with more transferred from the AMI.

The reconnaissance capabilities offered by the Tornado ECR persuaded the German MoD that the two wings of RF-4Es could usefully be replaced by a single 40-aircraft wing of recce-roled Tornados. The original AKG 51 at Bremgarten disbanded in March 1993, after ceasing flying in December 1992. AKG 52 at Leck stood down later that year, moving to Schleswig Jagel to re-equip with Tornados. It re-numbered as Aufklärungsgeschwader 51 'Immelmann' but retained its own Panther's head insignia. It effectively formed on 21 September 1993, taking over the aircraft of the disbanding MFG 1, which deactivated on 1 January 1994. From August 1995 the unit contributed six aircraft to Einsatzgeschwader 1 at Piacenza, flying operations over Bosnia as part of Operation *Deliberate Force*. During operations over Bosnia, the pods usually contain cameras fitted with 150-mm lenses (for vertical photography) and with a 610-mm lens for stand-off LOROP reconnaissance.

The Luftwaffe regard the basic MBB/Aeritalia pod as purely interim equipment, and a new family of pods is being procured for AKG 51's Tornados. Daimler-Benz Aerospace

were awarded a contract to develop a reconnaissance system for the Tornado, and as part of this contract designed, built and qualified a new modular reconnaissance pod. This contains Zeiss optical cameras and a Honeywell Regelsysteme GmbH linescanner, with off the shelf Ampex Digital Tape Recorders, CCD Recce Control Panel, Honeywell Power Supply unit and a Lockheed Martin/Honeywell Scanner Receiver Unit. Some 37 pods are to be procured (with six sets of spares). There are two basic configurations of pod planned, the first being the basic 'GAF Recce Pod' with provision for a forward oblique camera, 20 of which are being procured. The second is the 'Telelens pod', containing a new daylight LOROP camera and an upgraded linescan, useable at higher altitudes (up to 8,000 ft rather than the original 2,000 ft) and longer stand-off range. The potential exists for the IRLS to be useable at altitudes of up to 15,000 ft.and the longer-range IRLS. The last 17 pods will be delivered in Telelens configuration, with a prototype that first flew in June 1998.

Flight tests of the basic GAF Recce Pod began in September 1997, and have now been completed successfully. Elint and SAR versions of the modular pod have been under consideration. The Elint pod seems to have stalled, with the manufacturer waiting for the Luftwaffe to rejustify its military requirement before it can be funded, but with an RFP for the SAR expected later in 1998. The basic GAF Recce Pod and Telelens Pod may attract an order from the Marineflieger, who are reportedly examining the system with aview to placing an order.

Some Saudi Arabian aircraft were delivered in recce configuration, and these are described in the appropriate chapter later in the book.

Scruffy in its heavily-worn Marineflieger camouflage with large areas of primer, the prototype ECR (converted from P.16) is pictured during an early test flight. PAUL A JACKSON

SEAD

When the MRCA was originally conceived, it was widely believed that speed and ultra-low level penetration would generally be sufficient to protect aircraft against enemy radars and SAMs. But from a relatively early stage, it was realised that there were occasions when enemy defences would need to be suppressed, with aircraft attacking enemy radars using dedicated anti-radar weapons. This was the SEAD (Suppression of Enemy Air Defences) role, carried out by aircraft that were often known as 'Wild Weasels'.

Anti-radar missiles have long been a traditional weapon for anti-ship use, since they allow a relatively small weapon to destroy a warship's antenna arrays, and thus its ability to communicate and to fight. They may also be an effective way of knocking out radar pickets prior to an attack on a capital ship or task force. The same job can be achieved by using the electro-magnetic pulse caused by a nuclear weapon, although an atomic bomb may also kill the vessel's complement and may even sink the ship. To sink a warship by conventional means is a very much more difficult task, requiring heavy weapons and a great deal of luck!

But it was the maritime possibilities of the anti-radar missile that led to its first application to Tornado. Batch 5 Tornados were thus designed to be compatible with the US AGM-88 HARM missile, and aircraft delivered to the Marineflieger's MFG 2 exploited this capability. Even before the Batch 5 aircraft were built, Germany ordered 23 HARMs for evaluation, and followed this with an initial order for 866 operational missiles.

But despite being armed with an anti-radar missile, the Batch 5 aircraft of MFG 2's second Staffel (and Italian HARM-armed aircraft of 155° Gruppo) were far from being fully-functioning dedicated SEAD aircraft in the same way that the USAF's F-4G was. However, a dedicated defence suppression Tornado variant was under development.

The Tornado ECR (Electronic Combat and Reconnaissance) was developed to meet a German requirement for a dedicated reconnaissance aircraft to replace the RF-104G and RF-4E, though it was soon decided that the new aircraft should also operate in the SEAD role. As the programme (known in Germany as the EKA or Elektronische Kampfführung und Aufklarüng) progressed, less and less emphasis was placed on reconnaissance, while SEAD capabilities became the main design driver.

Plans originally included the provision of a centreline reconnaissance pod, and a podded version of the AN/ALQ-99 jammer, as used by the EF-111A Raven and EA-6B Prowler. These systems were not procured for the ECR, whose mission systems are all internal. The heart of the ECR is the Emitter Locator System, which uses six digital processors, a surface wave channeliser and a cued analysis receiver to determine signal characteristics, bearing and range. The system is served by antennas in the wing glove and forward fuselage, and thus gives coverage only in the forward hemisphere, unlike the F-4G which has full 360° coverage. The use of two aircraft flying in a simple racetrack pattern obviates this minor shortcoming. The system uses a comprehensive but entirely

The second ECR prototype wore high conspicuity orange lightning flashes on its lizard camouflage, these running up the fin on each side and spanwise across the top of each wing. The aircraft carries a test pod which appears to have been converted from an MBB/Aeritalia recce pod airframe. PAUL A JACKSON

An initial defence suppression capability was added to Marineflieger and AMI Batch 5 Tornados in the shape of the HARM missile. The aircraft had no specific emitter location system, so could only use the AGM-88 missile in its most basic modes, but it was a start.

pre-programmed threat library (new threats cannot be programmed in the air, or even on the line). Threat information is displayed to the WSO on the TV tabs, and can be superimposed on IRLS imagery to produce a real-world threat map. The pilot can view threat information on his combined map display.

Data gathered using the ELS can be transmitted to suitably equipped aircraft or ground stations using the ODIN (Operational Data Interface) data link, giving a real-time electronic reconnaissance capability. Enemy air defence radar locations and status could also be transmitted to friendly strike/attack aircraft. The ODIN data link can also be used to transmit IRLS imagery to other aircraft and to ground stations.

The ECR's imaging systems include a steerable Carl Zeiss FLIR, originally intended to allow covert penetration at night. FLIR imagery may be displayed in the pilot's HUD, or on the new combined map display, or on the WSO's TV tabs. The HUD picture may be overlaid with flight data and steering commands, to allow 'heads up' operation. Below the fuselage, in a fairing reminiscent of that fitted to the RAF's Tornado

GR1A is a Honeywell/Sondertechnik IRLS, known officially as an Imaging Infra-red System or IIS. Packaged in the former gun bay, the sensor is broadly equivalent to the BAe/Vinten IRLS 4000.

Panavia made a formal proposal to the German MoD in January 1985, outlining 40 dedicated ECR aircraft at an estimated cost of DM3700m. The 35 production ECRs ordered in June 1986 formed the German part of Batch 7, begining with 46+23 (GS256), which made its maiden flight on 26 October 1989. None were fitted with dual controls. The production ECR aircraft was similar to the Batch 6 IDS in many respects, with a MIL STD 1553B digital databus, MIL STD 1760 weapon interfaces and a 128K mission computer. The ECR introduced the RB.199 Mk 105 engine (first flown in May 1987). This featured a new Type 62B fan LP compressor, giving an increased pressure ratio, with single crystal blades in the intermediate and HP turbines. These improvements gave a 10% increase in thrust.

Long before any production ECR could fly, two 'ordinary' IDS aircraft were converted to serve as prototypes. The first of these was the former P.16 (98+03), in Marineflieger colours, which had ECR (rather than the German EKA acronym) crudely stencilled on its fin. The aircraft first flew on 18 August 1988, with IRLS and a test version of the ELS installed, but initially without FLIR. The aircraft carried test instrumentation in what was obviously a converted MBB/Aeritalia reconnaissance pod. The second prototype (GS217, formerly 45+75, wearing the new code 98+79) was smarter, in lizard camouflage with bold orange lightning flashes up the fin and along the wings. This aircraft flew in its new guise on 30 November 1988, soon gaining a smart red and white test instrumentation pod. The new FLIR began flight trials (on 98+03) in mid-June 1989.

The first frontline unit to receive the ECR was 382 Staffel, the second squadron of JBG 38 Friesland. ECRs bgan arriving at Jever in January 1990. These aircraft were not fully

Seen from the rear cockpit of another Tornado, this ECR was one of those assigned to the first unit to operate the type, JBG 38. The wing's second Staffel later passed its ECRs on to JBG 32 and reverted to the standard IDS. The Tornado ECR has tended to carry a pair of AGM-88s under the fuselage, with fuel tanks underwing.

The second Tornado ECR unit was JBG 32. This aircraft wears the standard lizard-type camouflage, but its refuelling probe and underwing stores have clearly been taken from a grey-painted aircraft. HARTMUT FELDMANN

An overall single-tone light grey colour scheme was adopted in 1995 on aircraft deploying to Piacenza for operations over Bosnia. This colour scheme proved to be very short-lived on the Tornado ECR however. HARTMUT FELDMANN

equipped or fully operational due several development setbacks. These mainly affected the Texas Instruments' Emitter Locator System, or ELS, pre-production examples of which did not reach Manching until February 1993. Five aircraft then flew trials with ELS test equipment, and the first production equipment did not reach the Luftwaffe until that summer. The frontline ECRs were thus delivered without the crucial ELS, relying on RHAWS and the missiles themselves to locate targets. The aircraft did have FLIR, IIS and the ODIN data link, and this allowed them to conduct reconnaissance training and limited SEAD role training.

One of the JBG 32's squadrons (321 Staffel) at Lechfeld, was

the next unit to transfer out its 'standard' IDS aircraft in exchange for the specialised version and the unit became operational with the ECR on 1 July 1994, after having received its ECRs between June 1991 and 28 January 1992. 322 Staffel converted to the ECR with the transfer of the remaining aircraft from JBG 38 during July-October1994. JBG 38 then reverted to standard IDS aircraft, while JBG 32 consolidated as the Luftwaffe's dedicated SEAD wing. Since then German ECRs have flown operational missions over Bosnia as part of Einsatzgeschwader 1 at Piacenza. These aircraft received unspecified new equipment, and a new overall light grey colour scheme.

A Tornado ECR of JBG 32 wearing the later grey camouflage adopted for operations over Bosnia. The unit badge of Einsatzgeschwader 1 is carried on the intake. HARTMUT FELDMANN

Not camouflage, but a toned-down version of the Tiger stripes so often applied to aircraft participating in NATO 'Tiger Meets'. Despite the non-operational colour scheme, the aircraft carries AGM-88 HARM missiles under the fuselage. HARTMUT FELDMANN

Operational experience has shown that simultaneous operation in the SEAD and reconnaissance roles is not practical, and the ECR's Honeywell/Sondertechnik Imaging Infra-red System may be removed and re-packaged within the GAF's new reconnaissance pods. The new pods may receive a new IRLS, however, since the existing equipment is used to help provide the ECR's threat map display.

The Tornado was the obvious choice as an Italian SEAD platform, and an interim, limited capability was obtained by providing HARM capability on 20 Batch 5 aircraft, converted by the AMI's 1° Reparto Manuntenzione Veliivoli at Cameri, and by Alenia at Turin. But these aircraft were not dedicated SEAD platforms, and were generally similar to the HARM-equipped aircraft operated by Germany's Marineflieger. The first two aircraft were handed over to 155° Gruppo in February 1992, when the decision was taken to provide

The Italian Tornado ECR prototype wore the same orange lightning flashes as the second German prototype. The aircraft made its maiden flight in July 1992.

The prototype IT-ECR in flight with a full load-out of four AGM-88 HARM missiles. Externally, the Italian and German ECRs are identical, though some internal equipment differs.

Wearing the overall desert camouflage originally applied for participation in Operation Locusta, this 50° Stormo Tornado carries a pair of HARMs under the fuselage. HARTMUT FELDMANN

HARM capability fleet-wide, and to procure full-spec ECR Tornados as dedicated SEAD platforms.

The Italian ECR programme has been extremely protracted. Economic considerations dictated that the AMI's 16 SEAD-dedicated Tornados should be converted from existing airframes, rather than being newly built, but the conversion should have been relatively straightforward, since the IT-ECR differs little from its German counterpart. As a conversion from existing aircraft, the Italian ECR retains the original RB 199 Mk 103 engine, rather than the uprated Mk 105 used by Batch 7 ECRs delivered to the Luftwaffe. The Italian ECRs have a higher indigenous avionics content than the German ECRs, and also have a different RHAWS, produced by Elettronica. The Italian ECRs were to have featured the same Panoramic Honeywell/Sondertechnik Imaging Infra Red System (IIS) as the German ECRs, but recording onto video rather than dry silver film, with a new tape recorder formatter unit. When delivered, however, they had no distinctive undernose fairing, and clearly lack the equipment altogether.

The IT-ECR prototype (MM7079) made its maiden flight in its new guise on 20 July 1992, and subsequently went to 311° Gruppo of the RSV at Pratica di Mare, but the type did not start entering service with 155° Gruppo until February 1998, crews having started undergoing ECR conversion at Caselle during early 1997. The unit will in turn operate up to 16 Tornado ECR variants (all of which are being converted from standard IDS examples).

The Royal Air Force originally saw SEAD as being a capability which should be enjoyed by all of its Tornado Strike/Attack aircraft, with all aircraft able to carry anti-radar missiles in the same way that they might carry AIM-9 Sidewinders for self defence. The formal Air Staff Target 1228 outlined a missile which could be carried 'in multiple' by tactical aircraft in addition to their normal interdiction payload. The service did not originally see a need for the SEAD role to be undertaken by dedicated aircraft or units, and saw the successful AST 1228 weapon as being a missile that would be carried by Jaguars and Harriers, as well as by Tornados. The weapon was envisaged as being small, light and relatively cheap, closer in some ways to the AIM-9 based AGM-122 Sidearm than to the massive AGM-78 Standard ARM. The weapon was seen as being a 'fire and forget' missile, requiring no input from the launch aircraft except for connections to turn on the missile's battery and seeker, and to fire it.

The BAe ALARM (Air Launched Anti Radiation Missile) was selected to meet AST 1228 in April 1983, after evaluation of a number of competing systems, including the US AGM-88 HARM. BAe were unable to package the weapon to 'fit' inside a SkyFlash airframe (which was the original intention) but did produce a weapon that was smaller and lighter than HARM.

The ALARM missile was designed around a sophisticated seeker designed by Marconi. This featured four spiral helix broad band receiver antennas, which fed signals received to a digital processor which could be pre-programmed to assign target prioritisation. The missile was designed to be fired towards a target area following a pre-briefed flight plan – flying a certain distance in a certain direction, and then 'looking' for certain types of radar. The missile can also use a loiter mode, climbing to altitude (40,000-70,000 ft plus) to descend below a parachute, waiting for specific types of emitter to 'come up'. Once a target is detected, the missile then ignites the second

With test cameras fore and aft under the fuselage (the forward camera facing back from the modified LRMTS fairing), ZA354 is seen carrying nine ALARM test rounds.

An ALARM missile on the outboard stub of a Tornado's inboard underwing pylon. Intended to be light enough to be carried alongside a normal load, the ALARM was once intended to use a Sky Flash airframe. JEREMT FLACK/API

attack aircraft penetrate airspace or while they attack their target. If a target radar comes back on line, a 'hard kill' is virtually guaranteed.

The 'universal carriage' concept was abandoned during development of the RAF's new generation ALARM missile, with the recognition that cost and training constraints would make it desirable to form dedicated 'Pathfinder' units who would specialise in the SEAD role, clearing and maintaining corridors through enemy air defences, suppressing target defences or escorting bomber formations. In the Tornado application, the navigator was given the ability to update launch parameters, threat priorities or target co-ordinates at any time up to firing.

BAe was awarded a fixed price development and production contract for 750 missiles, against an eventual requirement for about 2,000 rounds. Carriage trials of inert rounds began on 13 February 1985, using ZA354 to carry up to nine missiles in triples under the fuselage and inner wing stations. Captive carry trials of live weapons began in January 1986.

The ALARM programme was subject to some delays, most notably due to problems with the missile's single-chamber/dual grain Royal Ordnance Nuthatch rocket motor. In 1987 this was finally replaced by a simpler dual chamber rocket supplied by Bayern Chemie. This delayed firing trials until November 1988. Firing trials were carried out by ZD708 at MCAS Yuma, Arizona, under the auspices of No 32 JTU. The trials were completed in October 1988, with a single firing against a single live radar target. Acceptance trials then began.

stage of its rocket motor, burns off the chute, and homes onto the emitter (or, if it turns off, its last known position). The aim is for the missile to impact at great speed, providing a kinetic kill even in the event of a fuse or warhead failure. But if enemy radars refuse to transmit, knowing an ALARM is in the air, or even knowing only that an ALARM carrying aircraft is in the area, then the Tornado/ALARM combination can obtain a 'soft kill', shutting down the enemy radar while the friendly

This No 9 Squadron Tornado GR1 has a Gulf War mission tally on the nose, and carries three ALARM missiles under the fuselage. No 9 Squadron was the first unit to be declared operational with ALARM, after No 20 Squadron's deployment used the weapon in the Gulf.

Two No 31 Squadron Tornados demonstrating the maximum ALARM load carried in service. Nine missiles could theoretically be carried, but only by sacrificing the AIM-9s on the inboard stub pylons. SGT RICK BREWELL

This No 31 Squadron Tornado GR1 wears the new reduced-size squadron markings adopted by the Brüggen wing from 1997. These are reportedly designed to allow rapid over-painting or removal during overseas operational deployments. HARTMUT FELDMANN

ALARM was very far from being a mature system when Saddam Hussein invaded Kuwait in 1990. The missile had never demonstrated its ability to differentiate between multiple radar targets, let alone to attack a priority target, and more test firings were planned. But since a proportion of No 9 Squadron's aircraft had already been modified to carry ALARM, it was decided to take the missile to war in the Gulf, before the issue of a formal release to service, and before No 9 Squadron could be declared operational.

Although No 9 Squadron had been planned to be the first ALARM unit, it was actually No 20 Squadron which took the weapon to war. Eight of the 12 crews deployed familiarised themselves with the weapon and its associated techniques and tactics, before flying to Tabuk with nine of No 9 Squadron's ALARM-capable aircraft (ZD719, 746, 747, 748, 789, 810, 850, 851, and 893). Initially the aircraft operated with two missiles underwing, but soon switched to carrying three under the fuselage

ALARM was usually fired from very low level, often streaking upwards past allied bomber formations, necessitating the use of a code-word to reassure friendly aircraft that they were not coming under attack. Tornado missions in the Gulf exhausted the supply of available missiles, even though BAe's Longstock factory worked around the clock to build more. From 26 January 1991, aircraft reverted to carrying only two missiles, and operations ceased on 13 February. 121 missiles were expended in 24 missions (52 individual sorties, four of which were aborted after take-off). ZD893 was lost due to a control restriction, but the other eight aircraft were returned to No 9 Squadron, who continued to work up to a full operational capability, with a number of additional aircraft converted to be ALARM capable, including ZD709, 739, 741, 745, 809, and 890, and ZA457. No 9 Squadron was declared to NATO with ALARM on 1 January 1993.

No 9 Squadron has been joined in the SEAD role by No 31, which received the RAF's Batch 7 Tornados (apart from one aircraft retained by BAe for GR4 development, and excluding the GR1As). These aircraft were built to be ALARM compatible and comprised ZG754, 756, 771, 775, 777, 779, 791, 792 and 794. The first peacetime ALARM firing took place in August 1994, and since then, tactics and techniques have been refined and honed. The two ALARM-capable squadrons in RAF Germany have practised integrated operations with German Tornado ECRs, and there have been some suggestions that a combined wing may form, though this now seems unlikely.

Today, despite the formation of dedicated ALARM units, there are reports that it is still planned that all RAF Tornados will eventually have the ability to carry a pair of the missiles to augment their normal mission payload. This will certainly be relatively easy to achieve when the GR4, with its MIL STD 1553B databus and MIL STD 1760 weapons capability, finally enters service.

Perhaps the most capable SEAD version of the Tornado was the unbuilt Tornado FOWW (Follow On Wild Weasel), proposed to meet the USAF's requirement for an F-4G replacement. This requirement envisaged the procurement of 150 new *Wild Weasels*, which would be cheap to operate, and which would be based on an existing, in-production two-seater. Panavia teamed with Rockwell North American aircraft on 16 December 1988 proposing a Tornado version equipped with the AN/ALQ-99 emitter locator system, and with all round coverage for its RHAWS and emitter locators. The aircraft was primarily intended for deployment with the 52nd TFW at Spangdahlem, where inter-operability with Luftwaffe assets would be an advantage. In the end, the USAF decided not to directly replace its F-4Gs, procuring a less capable variant of the F-16 with a simple HARM targeting system.

Export

Two of Saudi Arabia's initial four Tornados are seen here at low level off the Saudi coast. The two aircraft (subsequently re-serialled 751 and 754) served with No 7 Squadron at Dhahran.

Even though it dropped out of the MRA Joint Working Group in 1968, Canada continued to follow the aircraft's progress with great interest, and even as late as 1978 there was a reasonable expectation that Canada might order the aircraft. Canada needed a ground attack/interdictor aircraft to replace its European-based Starfighters, while Canada's 'Home Sovereignty' role was similar to the RAF's own ADV requirement. A detailed offer was made to Canada, including the offer of considerable industrial participation (with Canadian airframe and engine assembly lines) and CAF pilots evaluated the aircraft in 1978. But in the end, the Canadian DND decided that it needed an aircraft more closely optimised for air superiority duties. Another early potential customer for Tornado was Australia, with BAC hoping to sell Jaguars as an interim Mirage III replacement in the ground attack role in the 1970s. This would allow the Mirages to be run on in the air defence role, with Tornados being delivered during the 1980s.

One of the first nations to express an interest in the Tornado was Iraq, which evaluated the aircraft in 1982 in anticipation of placing an order for 100 aircraft. Sanctions applied as a result of the Iran-Iraq war effectively prevented any deal from being finalised.

Panavia was able to announce that Oman had actually ordered Tornados on 14 August 1985, even before the successful Saudi order. The Kingdom ordered eight F2s, at a time when only 14 aircraft had been delivered to the RAF. The total value of the contract was said to have been in excess of £250m, but it was subsequently cancelled, together with options on a further eight aircraft, which could have been IDS-based.

After Jordan's attempt to acquire ADVs from Saudi Arabia failed, the country's interest turned to the IDS. A contract for eight aircraft was signed in September 1988 and eight line positions were reserved. The order was cancelled in March 1989, due to Jordan's parlous financial state.

Malaysia reached preliminary agreement on the supply of a package of defence equipment in September 1988, including 12 Tornados, four of which were to be dedicated SEAD aircraft, broadly equivalent to the RAF's GR1A but armed with ALARM and equipped with a new Marconi emitter loaction system. The package was susbequently altered, without the Tornados.

Similar SEAD aircraft (and German-built ECRs) were offered to South Korea, which required 50 Tornados, and to Thailand, which needed four SEAD platforms within a 16-aircraft order. Neither nation signed a contract for Tornado, and their interest switched to alternative types. Other customers that never were included Greece, Spain and Turkey, with a Turkish order for 40 aircraft falling through when Britain's Export Credit Guarantee department refused to underwrite the deal.

Arguably the most significant missed opportunity for Panavia was Japan, where the Tornado was a strong contender to replace the indigenous F-1. The initial requirement was for 24 aircraft, with options on 76 more, to meet an eventual requirement for 132 aircraft. Japan's long-range, maritime attack requirement prompted the development of a number of air-to-ground/anti-ship derivatives based on the ADV airframe, including the Tornado J, the Tornado International, and the Super Tornado. The third ADV prototype had its outboard underwing pylons activated for promotional photography, but development of a further version was not felt to be justified by the limited market opportunity.

Al-Yamamah

The signing of a Memorandum of Understanding between the British and Saudi Arabian governments on 26 September 1985 heralded the start of the UK's largest ever defence export sale. Termed Project Al-Yamamah ('The Dove'), the Saudi deal formed the centrepiece of the modernisation of the Royal Saudi Air Force for the next twenty years. Apart from the supply of aircraft, spares, weapons and other hardware, the Al-Yamamah contracts included the provision of training and infrastructure for the air force and navy.

This pre-delivery photo of the last of the original batch of Saudi aircraft shows off the type's desert camouflage scheme to advantage. The RSAF followed US practise, in positioning national insignia above the port and below the starboard wings, with the RSAF legend opposite.

Two Saudi Tornados cruise over the desert at what looks like a fairly comfortable height. Low flying over featureless desert can be disorientating, and the TFR can sometimes fail to 'see' sand dunes, but only the underlying rock. The Saudi aircrews make light of these difficulties, however, and proved their abilities during Desert Storm.

Al-Yamamah produced the one and only successful Panavia export sale to date, with an eventual total of 120 Tornados being supplied. In previous years, BAe and its predecessors had successfully courted the Royal Saudi Air Force (RSAF), selling the desert kingdom BAC Strikemasters and Lightnings in 1966. This was itself a remarkable achievement, since Saudi Arabia had hitherto relied on heavily subsidised US aircraft and defence equipment. The then-BAC became more and more involved as the years went by, taking on responsibility for aircraft maintenance and training and support tasks from 1973. These strong links made the RSAF a priority target for BAe sales teams from the early 1980s.

Gulf Tensions

The Middle East is one of the world's most volatile areas, destabilised by Arab resistance to what they have often seen as the imposed state of Israel. But Israel is not the only de-stabilising factor, and Saudi security has been threatened by Pan-Arab nationalism, by revolutionary regimes in neighbouring countries and by the age-old conflict between Sunni and Shia Muslims. And Saudi Arabia has always been a potentially desirable target for aggressors – for its oil, for its status as guardian of Islam's holiest places, for its strategic location or even for those wishing to see an end to what has sometimes (largely erroneously) been seen as a corrupt despotism. Shockwaves were caused by the long-running war between Iran and Iraq, and by Israel's continuing foreign policy adventurism and the continuing suppression of its Arab population. The instability of the 1980s led many Gulf nations to review their defences, and many countries in the region embarked on re-equipment programmes. The market potential for military aircraft grew rapidly, with attendant benefits for those providing the equipment. The UK Government saw the provision of arms to Saudi Arabia as being in the national interest, and not just in the commercial interests of the defence contractors involved. Conservative,

Saudi Arabia's first four Tornados in a neat formation, shortly after their arrival in the country. The first squadron, No 7, acted as an OCU and tactics and weapons training unit.

stable Saudi Arabia was seen as a bulwark against Israel, and against the forces of extremism.

Saudi Arabia's most significant military aircraft order since the BAC package of the late 1960s was for 60 McDonnell Douglas F-15 Eagles, delivered from January 1981. The F-15s were intended purely for air defence duties, replacing the Lightnings, and the RSAF continued to rely on four squadrons of Northrop F-5s to fulfil the ground attack role. One of the most impressive and frightening aspects of the Iran-Iraq War had been the land battle, with massive casualties failing to dent the suicidal tactics of the Iranian Islamic Revolutionary Guards and the Iraqi Republican Guard. It became clear that both Iran and Iraq could field armies of such size (and of such ideological conviction) that conventional defences on the ground would be inadequate. There was a clear need for a ground attack aircraft to replace the F-5Es, and to provide the air force with a long-range interdiction capability which it had previously lacked, but which Israeli rearmament was making increasingly vital.

The Dove Flies

Foreign Military Sales by the US Department of Defense are always subject to congressional approval, especially those to countries in the Middle East. A strong Jewish lobby in Congress and in the House has always ensured that Israel has not been put in danger by arms deliveries to potentially hostile Arab states. Weapons packages have been overwhelmingly defensive in character, and have usually been more than balanced by aid to Israel. The 'Peace Sun' program under which the Saudis received their initial batch of F-15 Eagles in the early 1980s was thus subject to a mandatory limit of 60 aircraft by the United States Congress, and the delivery only went ahead with the agreement that the aircraft could only be used solely for air defence. This policy remained in place, as it turned out, until after the 1991 Gulf War.

Even had the policy not been formally stated, the experience of other customers for US defence equipment had a salutory effect on the Saudis. A complete reliance on US aircraft types

The first Saudi reconnaissance aircraft (6628) seen before delivery, laden with ADV-type 495-gal tanks. Six such aircraft were delivered as part of the second Saudi Tornado batch.

threatened to impose too much vulnerability to shifts in US foreign policy, and to the danger of arms embargoes. The USA's political position left the stage wide open for its overseas competitors, infuriating some of those in the US aviation industry. The geographic size, economic wealth and oil reserves of Saudi Arabia made it the largest potential customer (and the most valuable ally) in the region, with other Gulf states operating aircraft in much smaller numbers due to their relative size and economic power.

British Aerospace's Military Aircraft Division at Warton still had a large number of personnel in the Kingdom supporting the remaining elements of the original BAC defence package. It was thus in a superb position for marketing its Tornado to

the Saudis. The only other serious contender for providing the Saudis with a new attack aircraft was France, whose links with the Kingdom were weaker, and were somewhat dated. But the Saudi Tornado order was far from being a foregone conclusion. Despite the disadvantages of 'buying American', the Saudis had a huge support network for US aircraft and systems, and the aircraft already in service had themselves built up a formidable reputation. The F-15 in particular had proved very popular, and attracted vociferous support within the RSAF. The new Strike Eagle was thus a strong contender to meet the Saudi requirement, although the aircraft was immature and far from proven (relying on Pave Tack rather than the later LANTIRN) and there was a real danger that the USA would refuse to supply the essential long-range conformal fuel tanks (CFTs) and the MERs necessary to carry the maximum bombload. But the aircraft was a very real competitor to the Tornado, and it was not until Saudi aircrew evaluated the aircraft at Honington in 1984 that the decision started to swing in favour of the Tornado.

The UK MoD's Defence Export Sales Organisation acts as a management agency for UK contractors wishing to approach overseas governments. DESO is a political structure, with many layers and many obstacles to be overcome before sales of military equipment can be approved. The process was particularly convoluted when discussing sales of such enormity. The new Labour Government made great play of wishing to institute an ethical defence sales policy, though in truth, the UK has always been one of the more scrupulous suppliers of military equipment, generally refusing to supply aggressive, oppressive or even vaguely distasteful regimes, as Chile's General Pinochet might ruefully confirm! But civil servants, politicians and even Heads of State all played a part

Seen wearing a mix of RAF and Saudi markings, ready for their delivery flights to Saudi Arabia, are a recce-configured Batch 7 Tornado and one of the RSAF's Hawk T65As.

This aircraft, a recce-configured Tornado IDS wearing the markings of No 66 Squadron, appears to have had its SLIR window painted out.
JEREMY FLACK/API

in the process of selling Tornados to Saudi Arabia. Nevertheless Britain's traditionally strong ties with the Kingdom made the approval of Al-Yamamah a comparatively easy process.

The nucleus of Al-Yamamah was the package of military aircraft supplied to the Saudis. These included 30 BAe-assembled Pilatus PC-9s delivered as basic trainers and a similar number of BAe Hawks for advanced flying training. The revitalised training machine would provide the crews who would man the 48 IDS and 24 ADV Tornados also on order. The Tornados for Saudi Arabia were very similar to those delivered to the RAF, and indeed many began life on the Warton line intended for the RAF. The Tornados included 14 IDS trainers, and six twin-stick ADVs. Six of the IDS aircraft were delivered in a reconnaissance configuration, very similar to the RAF's GR1A.

Although Al-Yamamah included an extensive aircrew training package, contractual arrangements provided for early delivery of the first Tornados, which were diverted from British orders. The first four Saudi crews arrived at Cottesmore in October 1985 where they formed the Royal Saudi Training Flight of the TTTE's No 73 Course. Further students passed through the TTTE over the next year, prior to training being transferred to Saudi Arabia. The Saudi training machine placed great emphasis on training backseaters, since the air force had hitherto had only single-seat frontline fast jets. The training operation therefore included two BAe Jetstream aircraft configured as flying classrooms for navigator/weapons system operator training.

Sir Colin Chandler, head of the DESO, and Prince Sultan bin Abdul Aziz, the Saudi Minister of Defence and Aviation,

This ALARM-wielding unpainted Saudi recce IDS was photographed en route to Boscombe Down for Saudi Batch 7 EMC trials. The unusual fit does not indicate that Saudi recce aircraft will carry ALARM operationally. DEREK BOWER

signed the definitive Al-Yamamah contract in February 1986. The first Saudi aircraft, Tornado IDS 701/CS001 (originally to have become ZD997, an RAF GR1) made its first flight on 7 February 1986. This was the first of eighteen Batch 5 examples diverted from the RAF, all of which had been assigned UK military serials and BS/BT build numbers. Saudi IDS build numbers were prefixed by 'CS' for standard and 'CT' for dual control trainer versions. With Tornados 702, 703 and 704 (the first 'twin-sticker') taking to the air over the following weeks, these initial four aircraft left for Dhahran via Akrotiri on 26 March 1986. The first digit of their serials indicated their assignment to No 7 Squadron, based at Dhahran's King Abdul Aziz Air Base. The squadron received two further dual-control

Later Saudi Tornados wore a mix of Saudi and British serials and national insignia for test flying, but the British roundels and fin flashes were then removed for the ferry flight, leaving only the serial, as seen here. These aircraft left Warton on 3 October 1996.

aircraft, 705 and 706, on 29 April 1986 and spent the following months developing procedures for flying, operational conversion training and engineering in the extremely harsh Saudi climate. During this time the Tornados were re-serialled as 751-756.

The desert conditions caused a number of difficulties for the aircraft, similar to those which were later to be experienced by RAF Tornados during their deployment at the start of Operation *Granby*. One problem was caused by sand ingestion by the RB 199 engines, this causing a glass-like build up on the fan blades. Most of the problems were overcome, and deliveries continued in February 1987. In addition to the 18 aircraft taken from the line, two other aircraft (768 and 769) were added to the batch to make up the required 20 for 'fast track' delivery. With the twentieth Tornado (770) arriving at Dhahran on 8 October 1987, the unit then consolidated its operations and received four more dual-control variants between May and September 1989. The unit never reached its full complement of 24 aircraft, with Tornado 756 crashing on approach to Dhahran on 28 August 1989.

Saudi ADV

With Saudi IDS Tornados in squadron service, the Saudis turned their attentions to introducing and integrating the fighter version, which was closely comparable to the RAF's F3. The ADVs actually supplied to the RSAF were all diverted

from the RAF's order in Batch 6, being to Block 13 standard. The RAF again provided conversion training for the Saudi aircrew, with ten crews passing through No 229 OCU at Coningsby from mid-1988. Jordanian pilots evaluated the Tornado F3, and Jordan requested that Saudi Arabia should order ten extra aircraft for transfer to the Royal Jordanian Air Force. Saudi Arabia was happy to fund the aircraft, but the Panavia partners refused to contemplate such an indirect deal.

The first aircraft to fly, 2905 (build number DS001), lifted off from Warton's runway on 1 December 1988 and was soon joined by 2901(build number DT001), 2902 and 2906. The build number prefixes of 'DS' and 'DT' differentiated between the standard and dual-control versions. The four aircraft were accepted by General Ahmed bin Ibrahim Al Behery, Commander of the RSAF, in a ceremony at Warton on 9 February 1989. All were delivered to Dhahran-based No 29 Squadron on 20 March 1989. Deliveries to the unit continued up to its twelfth ADV on 19 September 1989, at which point the second unit (No 34 Squadron) began to form. Also based at Dhahran, the squadron accepted its first aircraft (3451) on 15 November 1989. The final Saudi ADV, 3462, left Warton on 8 October 1990 in time to join in the defence of its home country under Operation *Desert Shield*. This second unit, despite having reached its complement of twelve aircraft, was by no means near operational status and its limited crews joined with those of No 29 Squadron to fly combat air patrols. Eventually, the decision was made to abandon the

This Saudi ADV was photographed before delivery, carrying a full load-out of AIM-9Ls and Sky Flash AAMs. The Sidewinders have camera calibration markings, for test firing.

establishment of No 34 Squadron, and its aircraft and crews augmented those of No 29 from mid-1993.

More Deliveries, More Orders

The second IDS unit, No 66 Squadron, formed at Khamis Mushayt's King Khalid Air Base in the summer of 1990. Its first aircraft (6601) departed Warton on 31 July 1990 in company with 6602. One further aircraft was delivered the following month, although the Iraqi invasion of Kuwait on 2

One of the original Saudi ADVs seen taxying at Warton. The aircraft were delivered in full Saudi markings (including squadron insignia) and never wore British markings or serials for ferrying or test flying.
TERRY SENIOR

August 1990 focused the RSAF's attention (and that of BAe!) on other matters.

From quite soon after the end of Operation *Desert Storm*, the Arab perception of the war changed, and today, many see it as a most regrettable episode, best forgotten and certainly not to be glorified. Moreover, Saudi traditions discourage the celebration of individual achievement, or the achievement of specific units, so the part played by the Saudi Tornados in *Desert Storm* can only be told in the most general terms. When war broke out, the RSAF had 31 Tornado IDS aircraft on charge, and these were concentrated at Khamis Mushayt, where the based No 66 Squadron aircraft and crews were effectively absorbed by No 7 Squadron, which moved in from Dhahran.

The Saudi Tornados joined the fray on 17 January 1991, attacking an Iraqi airfield (though to have been H-3) with USAF F-15s providing cover, and US Navy EA-6Bs giving ECM support. The defences had already been woken up by an attack by six F-111Es, but the Tornados escaped unscathed. Throughout the war the Saudis relied heavily on their own inflight refuelling assets – Lockheed KC-130 tankers whose slow speed and limited operating altitudes made things more difficult, and which made it difficult to combine the Saudi Tornados into integrated packages, since they were more subject to delays. The aircraft tended to carry JP233 airfield attack weapons, or up to eight 1,000-lb bombs, either 'slick'

The first batch of Saudi ADVs, with squadron badges applied at Warton, were ferried to Saudi Arabia with RAF tanker support. The aircraft wore the standard RAF air superiority grey colour scheme, with standard RSAF national insignia.

for toss bombing (or later for medium level delivery) or with Mk 117 retard tails for low level laydown delivery. One Saudi Tornado was lost (fortunately without its crew) on 19 January. By the end of the war, No 7 squadron had flown 590 interdiction and 75 Offensive Counter-Air sorties, while the Saudi ADVs flew 451 sorties.

Deliveries of aircraft to No 66 Squadron re-commenced, somewhat slowly, in 1991 and the unit gradually built up to its initial strength of 24 Tornados. In the process, the squadron received six reconnaissance variants (6615 to 6620) during November 1991. Although unconfirmed, it is quite likely that the crews for these particular aircraft were trained by RAF personnel due to the complex nature and relative immaturity of the TIRRS system employed by this variant.

Weapons fits for the Saudi aircraft have never been officially confirmed by either the manufacturer of the operator. It is likely that the majority of the RAF's standard Tornado weapons were offered to the Saudis, with the exception (of course) of the nuclear capability. Saudi aircraft have been seen test-flying from Warton with ALARM missiles, and the JP233 airfield denial weapon system was used by Saudi Tornado IDSs during the Gulf War. It is understood that the Sea Eagle ASM has also been supplied, though it is not known whether Saudi aircraft have the same stores management system and adaptors as the British GR1Bs, which would allow the missiles to be fired in their computed launch mode. The Saudis are also understood to have taken delivery of a number of Sargent Fletcher 28-300 inflight refuelling 'buddy' pods.

Sightings of a Saudi recce aircraft carrying ALARM led to some speculation that some Saudi recce sub-variants might carry an emitter locator system, giving them some form of enhanced SEAD capability. In fact, the aircraft spotted was merely transporting an ALARM to Warton for EMC tests, and the Saudi recce aircraft will not actually be ALARM capable.

July 1988 saw the signing by British and Saudi defence ministers of the MoU covering Al-Yamamah II, which was to include an additional 12 IDSs and 36 ADVs. Various wranglings, mainly on the political level, ensued and the order was terminated in July 1990. Following further negotiations by both industry and politicians alike, the deal was re-struck in July 1993 – only this time, all 48 Tornados procured were IDS versions, comprising 32 standard, six reconnaissance and ten dual-control examples. The first of these, build number CT015, first flew in August 1996 with the UK serial ZH905. It finally left Warton, wearing its RSAF identity 7501, on 3 October 1996. The aircraft entered service with No 75 Squadron which had formed at Dhahran. Deliveries to the unit were interspersed with the six additional reconnaissance aircraft, all of which augmented augmented those already in service with No 66 Squadron from May 1997. The final Saudi Tornado unit, No 83 Squadron, received the first of its aircraft (8301) at Khamis Mushayt in November 1996. Nos 75 and 83 Squadrons received their final aircraft in 1998, the airframes concerned being the final Tornados to be built.

There remains the strong possibility that the Saudi aircraft may undergo a similar upgrade to that being applied to the RAF's GR4s, and the country is a target for the manufacturers of the RAPTOR reconnaissance pod.

Tornado at war

One of the first Tornados deployed to the Gulf as part of Operation Granby *seen emerging from its HAS at RAF Brüggen for the long flight to Muharraq. These aircraft did not embody the full package of* Granby *modifications, and were subsequently replaced in-theatre.*

Operation *Granby*

The 1991 UN operation to free Kuwait from the invading Iraqi army, generally known as the Gulf War, was divided into a preparatory phase (labelled by the US DoD as Operation *Desert Shield*) and combat operations (Operation *Desert Storm*). To the UK Ministry of Defence (MoD), the entire period from August 1990 to March 1991 was Operation *Granby*. By whatever name, the operation to force an Iraqi withdrawal from Kuwait provided the Tornado with its first opportunity for active service, and to actually drop bombs 'in anger'.

It was perhaps ironic that an aircraft so carefully and exhaustively tailored for the conditions on the NATO European Central Front, and for operations against the best the Warsaw Pact could field, should actually find itself going to war many hundreds of miles away from its central European 'playground', in a hot desert environment, facing a developing nation as its enemy. The air campaign over occupied Kuwait and Iraq was certainly very different to any European scenario.

'Different' was never going to mean 'easier'. Although Iraq's potentially potent air threat failed to materialise, Allied aircraft had to face SAM and AAA defences every bit as deadly as those they might have expected over the Central Front, had the Cold War ever turned hot. Moreover, there was less opportunity for the use of terrain masking, navigation was more difficult over the often featureless and always unfamiliar terrain, and many of the targets were more difficult to knock out. Iraqi airfields, for example, were huge and sprawling affairs (many were bigger than London's Heathrow) with multiple runways, reserve take off strips and taxiways, and were provided with the latest hardened aircraft shelters (HAS) and with an array of highly effective anti-aircraft defences.

Three nations – the UK, Italy and Saudi Arabia – used their Tornados in the conflict with Iraq. Immediately after the Iraqi invasion of Kuwait, it was clear that any military eviction of Saddam Hussein's forces would involve a massive deployment of personnel and equipment on the part of the coalition of nations which aligned against the aggression. The Allies, operating under the leadership of the largest participant, inevitably the USA, were quick to recognise the potential threat that Iraq's forces in Kuwait posed to neighbouring Saudi Arabia. There was an obvious need to recover Kuwait's oilfields, and to prevent any move by Saddam Hussein to occupy Saudi oil fields. Operation *Desert Shield*, was launched

The Stage One Plus F3s sent to the Gulf to replace the original aircraft from Nos 5 and 29 Squadrons wore no unit insignia, but had No 11 Squadron codes. They often carried GR1-type 330-gal underwing tanks, donating their own 495-gal tanks to the bombers. VIA ANDY EVANS

to rapidly reinforce Saudi Arabia, and to provide a show of force which might prompt Saddam into some kind of negotiated withdrawal from Kuwait.

Air Defenders

The initial priorities for the coalition were to deploy forces which could counter any further Iraqi aggression, and especially any Iraqi armoured thrust against Saudi oil production areas and facilities, and to deploy an integrated air defence structure. Britain's initial deployment was thus of

A No 5 Squadron Tornado F3 on patrol with an F/A-18C of VFA-81 during Operation Desert Shield. DOLPHIN IMAGES

Jaguar fighter bombers, which left their base at Coltishall on 11 August 1990. The Jaguar's somewhat limited payload/range capability and limited night/all-weather and precision attack capabilities were more than offset by the Jaguar force's much practised ability to deploy virtually without warning. For air defence the British government elected to divert a squadron of Tornado F3s from Cyprus to Dhahran in Saudi Arabia. The unit was made up from aircraft and personnel from two squadrons, Nos 5 and 29(F), both of which were at RAF Akrotiri, Cyprus at the respective beginning and end of their annual Armament Practice Camps. A flash signal was issued from HQ Strike Command at 1930 hr on 7 August 1990, ordering No 29(F) to remain in Cyprus with No 5. This was followed by a Warning Order on 10 August 1990 which instructed twelve Tornados (drawn from both units) to 'Move to Dhahran, Saudi Arabia'.

The next day, the aircraft flew direct to King Abdul Aziz Air Base at Dhahran, led by No 5 Squadron's OC, Wg Cdr Euan Black. Operating alongside the based RSAF Tornado ADVs and the newly-detached F-15C Eagles of the USAF's 1st Tactical Fighter Wing, the composite unit flew its first four-hour combat air patrol (CAP) mission on 12 August 1990. The RAF detachment, consisting of 22 crews plus around 200 support personnel, was headed by Gp Capt Rick Peacock-Edwards.

As it became apparent that Saddam Hussein's troops were intending to remain in Kuwait indefinitely, the Allies began to consolidate their forces and begin preparations for a military

By the time Desert Storm *began, No 11 Squadron's two-digit codes had given way to single-letter fin codes on the Dhahran-based Tornado F3s. Here one of those aircraft prepares to taxy out for a CAP.* RAF DETACHMENT DHAHRAN

resolution to the crisis – an offensive military operation to forcibly evict the Iraqis. With an ongoing programme of improvements being applied to the Tornado F3, it was inevitable that some squadrons had more fully-equipped and more operationally capable aircraft than others. It was recognised that replacing the original No 5 and No 29(F) Squadron Tornado F3s with the latest standard aircraft would be advantageous, but that the original aircraft could 'hold the line' during the build-up, while the definitive aircraft received the necessary modifications to improve their ability to operate in the harsh climate, and to ensure that they had the best possible 'war fit'.

Rather than simply swap over aircraft it was decided to rotate home the scratch detachment from Nos 5 and 29(F) Squadrons and replace it with a new composite unit especially equipped and manned for the task. Wg Cdr David Hamilton, as OC No 11(F) Squadron, was appointed to command the replacement unit, which was effectively an enhanced squadron of 18 aircraft, mainly drawn from the Leuchars wing, manned by Leeming aircrew. The unit was colloquially designated as No 11(Composite) Squadron in deference to its commanding officer, although it was officially referred to as 'Tornado F3 Detachment - Dhahran' when in-theatre. A total of 24 Combat Ready crews, were drawn from Nos XI(F), 23 and 25 Squadrons. Non Combat Ready, Limited Combat Ready and

Before Operation Desert Storm, *Tornado F3s were seldom seen with a full operational load, but this became routine in the Gulf. Lack of USAF-compatible IFF kept the Tornados south of the border, with little opportunity to engage the enemy.* RAF DETACHMENT DHAHRAN

QRA-only, qualified personnel were temporarily reassigned to the latter two units, which continued (as far as was possible) 'normal duties' in the UK.

The first three Tornados for the unit (ZE936, ZE942 and ZE961) arrived at Leeming from No 43 Squadron on 11 August 1990 – the day on which the Cyprus-based aircraft arrived in Saudi Arabia. Other F3s followed from Leuchars and Coningsby, and even, in one case (ZE982), direct from the

Wings swept, and still carrying its full load of four SkyFlash and four Sidewinders, a Tornado F3 taxies in after a fruitless CAP mission.
RAF DETACHMENT DHAHRAN

factory at Warton. The modifications they carried came under the so-called Stage 1+ standard, which took the Stage 1 improvements and added theatre-specific and war-fit modifications.

Apart from airframe and engine modifications required for desert operations (which had largely been developed for the aircraft exported to Saudi Arabia), the F3s received the new Type AA Foxhunter software upgrade (with enhanced close-in combat and electronic counter-counter measures) plus an improved cooling system. They also had provision for Raytheon AIM-9M Sidewinder AAMs (with better target discrimination and improved performance by comparison with the older 'Nine Lima'), and were fitted with twin Tracor AN/ALE-40(V) chaff/flare dispensers under the rear fuselage (these were replaced in theatre by twin Vinten Vicon 78/Series 210 dispensers). A single underwing Philips-MATRA Phimat

chaff pod was added to most aircraft after arrival at Dhahran, normally carried on the starboard 'shoulder' pylon.

The engines were retuned, with a 20ºC rise in stator temperature limits, giving a 5% 'combat boost' facility. The aircraft had a Night Vision Goggle (NVG) compatible cockpit, and were fitted with Have Quick frequency hopping radios, plus an improved GEC-Marconi Hermes Radar Homing and Warning Receiver (RHWR). SWAM (surface wave absorbent material) was applied to the leading edges of the fin, wings, tailplanes, and pylons, while solid RAM tiles were applied to the engine intakes to reduce the F3's radar cross section. SWAM is a dense paint-like substance so heavy that it takes two men to lift a five litre tin! Nickel-chrome tailplane leading edges were fitted to prevent damage by the Sidewinder's launch plume. One by one, modified 'war fit' F3s emerged from Leeming's Aircraft Servicing Flight wearing fin codes in No 11(F)'s 'DA-DZ' range.

The first six aircraft left Leeming for Dhahran on 29 August 1990, night-stopping at RAF Akrotiri en route. Six more flew out on 16/17 and 22/23 September 1990, and within one month the unit had flown 1,100 hours in 453 sorties. Wg Cdr Andy Moir of No 43(F) Squadron led crews from his own unit and No 29(F) plus one crew from No 25(F), out to the Gulf from late November 1990, to replace Hamilton's unit. Upon its return to the UK, No 11(F) Squadron took up the status of the 'Rapid Reinforcement Squadron', which would have been used had Iraq chosen to launch further and overwhelming aggression. The F3s left in Saudi Arabia had a fairly quiet war, and like the US Navy's F-14s were prevented from ranging over Iraq itself because they lacked the necessary compatibility with the USAF F-15's IFF. They were not held back (as has often been intimated) out of fears for their safety or due to any lack of faith in their ability to cope with the perceived threat.

The Pipe Major at RAF Leuchars (Sgt Ian Hughes) deployed with the detachment from No 43 Squadron, and was on hand to pipe the aircraft away from Dhahran on their return home at the end of the war. RAF DETACHMENT DHAHRAN

In the build up to Operation Desert Storm, *the Tornados practised their low level attack capabilities in the belief that the Iraqi Air Force would make medium level missions impractical. Few could have predicted that the Iraqis barely put any aircraft into their air, making the upper airspace almost completely safe. After a return to Germany, modification, re-coding (as FN) and redeployment, this aircraft (ZA392) was shot down (or flew into the ground) on the first night of the war, while running out after a successful JP233 attack.* SQN LDR STUART OSBORNE

RAF Bombers

Having deployed a squadron of Jaguars to Oman at the same time as the first F3s, it soon became clear that an offensive air campaign might be required in order to evict the Iraqis from Kuwait, with coalition aircraft attacking semi-strategic targets around the clock. The Jaguar was limited to the Offensive Air Support (OAS) role, and longer range, more capable interdictors would clearly also be needed. On 23 August 1990 the RAF accordingly announced that a squadron of Tornado GR1s was to deploy to Bahrain. While it would have been possible to deploy RAF Tornados to the Gulf with no modifications, it was apparent that certain minor improvements would bring a worthwhile improvement in survivability and capability. Virtually all of the GR1s deployed to the Gulf were drawn from RAF Germany units (re-engined Batch 3s from Laarbruch and Batch 4s from Brüggen) as these were already equipped with the more powerful Mk 103 engine, and featured enhanced RHAWS. A pool of airframes was formed by the Brüggen ASF, and they were each resprayed into an overall 'desert pink' temporary camouflage.

Ten Tornados, led by OC No 14 Squadron, Wg Cdr Vaughan Morris, left RAF Brüggen on 27 August 1990 for Akrotiri and arrived at Muharraq Air Base the next day. Gp Capt Richard 'Rocky' Goodall was appointed as the overall detachment commander. The desert conditions played havoc with the aircraft, especially during low-level flying when sand ingestion caused engine difficulties. One other hazard associated with those early low-level missions was a tendency for the Tornado's terrain following radar to react to rocky terrain, but not always to the sand dunes surmounting it. Using the technical support of its own engineers, as well as the British Aerospace personnel responsible for overcoming similar problems with the Saudi export Tornados, the aircraft were rotated back to their home bases in Germany for modification during late September 1990.

A second squadron of 'bomber' Tornados received notice to deploy on 14 September 1990. They were again drawn from RAF Germany units, and all received additional modifications to the aircraft previously deployed. A range of modifications were made to the Tornados deployed to the Gulf, drawn from 23 planned mods and 19 new STFs (Special Trials Fits). It seems that no one aircraft had all the modifications and STFs embodied, but that most received the same basic core of modifications among the average figure of 18 planned mods and 13 STFs per aircraft. All aircraft were repainted in an overall ARTF (Alkali Removable Temporary Finish) desert pink colour scheme, and all were fitted with the 'bolt on' in-flight refuelling probe (rarely fitted to RAF Germany Tornados). The standard 'core' enhancements included the application of SWAM to all leading edges and engine intake areas to reduce the aircraft's radar signature. All aircraft also had a number of communications upgrades, to allow inter-operability with the USAF. Thus RAF Tornados in theatre had a Mk XII Mode 4 IFF set and Have Quick frequency hopping radios (effectively, but not technically, secure voice). Some aircraft also had navigational upgrades including hand-held GPS receivers, and others had NVG compatible cockpits.

Simple metal stops were fitted to wing sweep controllers to limit sweep to 63.5°, this allowing carriage of the 2,250 litre

The view from the back seat. Wg Cdr Mike Heath calmly snapped this evocative photo as his pilot banked the aircraft along a narrow, twisting canyon during Operation **Desert Shield.** WG CDR MIKE HEATH

'Hindenburger' drop-tanks normally used by the Tornado F3. On the F3 wing sweep is automatically limited when the big tanks are fitted. Wg Cdr Bob Iveson, OC No 617 Squadron, led the composite unit to Muharraq in two waves on 19 and 26 September 1990. The squadron soon switched to Tabuk in Saudi Arabia, officially transferring to King Faisal AB on 8 October 1990 under the overall charge of Gp Capt Ron Elder.

Ready for War

During the last quarter of 1990, the Allied forces set about preparing for war as Iraq showed no signs of giving up its annexation of Kuwait. On 29 November 1990, the United Nations Security Council passed Resolution 678 which authorised the Allies to use all necessary means to remove Hussein's forces from Kuwait, had it not done so by 0500hr UTC on 15 January 1991. Military planners calculated that an overwhelming superiority of 3:1 would be needed to liberate Kuwait, with an acceptable level of casualties, and the already formidable Allied military presence began its transformation from a defensive to an offensive posture.

Most of the crews who had deployed to the region during

Already heavily weathered, this Muharraq-based Tornado was photographed during a pre-war training sortie. Weapons were almost inevitably carried below the fuselage, and initially consisted of a pair of JP233s or four 1,000-lb bombs. SQN LDR MIKE RONDOT

August and September 1990 were systematically replaced by new personnel who began to work-up for the impending conflict. The RAF composite units, although remaining at their assigned locations, received new commanding officers and it was during this period that the units ceased to be referred to according to the 'allegiance' of the CO. The composite squadrons became officially referred to as, for example, 'Tornado Detachment - Tabuk' and this nomenclature continued for the remainder of Operation *Granby*.

A third Tornado GR1 squadron was prepared for deployment from late November 1990, although the Warning Order to deploy was not issued until 31 December 1990. Wg Cdr Jerry Witts, then OC No 31 Squadron, headed the deployment of the first six aircraft on 2/3 January 1991. When up to full strength the unit included crews from Nos 2, 9, 13, 14, 17 and 31). The Tornados joined their air defence counterparts at Dhahran, which were by then crewed by Nos 29(F) and 43 Squadrons, the latter's CO (Wg Cdr Andy Moir) having taken charge on 1 December 1990. Now leading the other deployed Tornado squadrons were Wg Cdr John Broadbent of No 15 Squadron at Muharraq (with crews from Nos 9, 15, 17, 27, 31 and 617 Squadrons) and Wg Cdr Ian Travers-Smith of No 16 Squadron at Tabuk (with crews from Nos 2, 9, 13, 14, 16 and 617 Squadrons). Grp Capts Cliff Spink, David Henderson and Bill Hedges had all assumed command of the respective RAF base groups by the beginning of the war, whilst Air Vice-Marshal Bill Wratten was appointed Air Commander and Deputy Commander British Forces Middle East.

In addition to the Tornados actually deployed to the Gulf, the Brüggen and Marham Tornado Wings each took turns in maintaining four aircraft and four crews on standby to deploy as attrition replacements, with each base taking one week on and one week off the commitment.

As well as the 'bog-standard' bombers deployed to the Gulf, the RAF also deployed a number of specialised Tornado sub-variants, some of which were still in development as the crisis broke, and which had to be rushed into operational service before trials were complete.

Two months after the invasion of Kuwait, British Aerospace completed manufacturer's trials of its Air Launched Anti-Radiation Missile (ALARM) at NAWC China Lake, in California's Mojave Desert. The testbed aircraft (ZD708), then moved on to the second phase of joint BAe/RAF testing under the auspices of No 32 Joint Trials Unit. The international situation demanded an acceleration to the trials, since the RAF wanted to achieve some form of operational capability in order to field the weapon in the Gulf.

No 9 Squadron at RAF Brüggen had been earmarked as the first ALARM unit, although the disruption caused by Operation *Granby* resulted in a hasty revision to plans. Laarbruch-based No 20 Squadron, led by Wg Cdr Mike Heath, was therefore selected to provide the nucleus of crews who would take ALARM to war, and began an intense period of training. Like the other RAF Germany Tornado squadrons, the unit's crews had to undergo refresher training in the art of air-to-air refuelling. Flying ALARM-configured aircraft

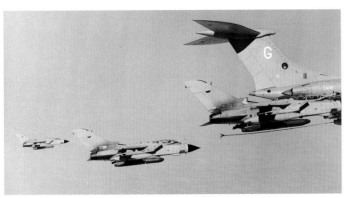

A gaggle of JP233-armed Tornados refuel from one of No 101 Squadron's VC-10 tankers. The Tornado's war began with a brief but intense anti-airfield campaign, during which JP233 was the primary weapon. FLT LT MIKE LUMB

Tornado ZA467/FF was lost in action on 22 January 1991, along with its crew – Sqn Ldr Gary Lennox and Sqn Ldr Kevin Weeks. The aircraft was taking part in a toss-bombing attack against Ar Rutbah radar station. FLT LT NICK WILCOCK

nominally assigned to No 9 Squadron, the unit deployed to Tabuk AB. Flying direct from Laarbruch on 23 October 1990 were ZD746, ZD850 and ZD851. Three more aircraft (ZD748, ZD810 and ZD893) routed via Akrotiri, arriving on 25 October 1990.

Teething problems with the Tornado GR1A's TIRRS (Tornado Infra-Red Reconnaissance System) prevented an early deployment to the Gulf, despite such a deployment having been ordered on 8 August 1990. Still very new, the GR1A was a recent addition to the force. In January 1990, for

example, only eight of the aircraft assigned to Nos 2 and 13 Squadrons even had reconnaissance equipment installed. With both RAF and civilian contract personnel working at full stretch, a so-called *Granby Two* modification devised by Computing Devices Co was incorporated into six TIRRS equipped GR1A aircraft. This improved sensor reliability and the first of the modified aircraft reached the theatre on 14 January 1991. The nine crews, drawn from both Nos 2 and 13 Squadrons, were led by the former's commanding officer, Wg Cdr Al Threadgould. Although the aircraft formed part of the

The Tornado/JP233 combination played a vital part in the opening stages of the air war. It was the only weapon capable of closing enemy airfields, allowing enemy aircraft to be picked-off at leisure using LGBs. FG OFF ANDY GLOVER

This aircraft (ZD744), seen during pre-war training with the Muharraq detachment, was later named 'Buddha', flying at least 35 operational missions with the Tabuk detachment, though ironically, as far as can be ascertained, none used the JP233. FG OFF ANDY GLOVER

GR1 Detachment at Dhahran, they were tasked directly by the Allied Combined Air Operations Centre in Riyadh. The US commanders in particular were keen to use the GR1A's infra-red capability, which proved extremely valuable. The GR1As role encompassed searching for normal military and infrastructure targets, pre- and post-strike recce and also intelligence gathering in support of special operations.

While ALARM and recce-jets arrived in the Gulf prior to hostilities, a vital handful of Tornados modified to carry TIALD did not arrive until well into the air campaign, as will be described.

The lull before the storm

With no sign that the Iraqi Army were preparing to leave Kuwait, coalition war plans proceeded. The majority of combat work-up flying by the Allied air forces ceased on 13 January 1991, this hiatus allowing crew duties to be rescheduled for operational missions as well as giving support personnel the opportunity to perform final maintenance activities and suchlike. The deadline set by the UN came and went. Saddam Hussein remained in defiance of international pressure mounted on him.

During the early evening of 16 January 1991, at bases throughout the Gulf, allied crews were summoned for briefing on Operation *Desert Storm*. The crews were given their assigned targets taken from the classified Air Tasking Order, a document of over 1,000 pages which detailed the entire Allied air operation on a daily basis. The Tornado was going to war.

One of the main priorities for the allied air forces was to prevent Iraq's air force from playing any part in the conflict – the classic counter-air mission. In order to achieve this, the first priority was to deny the enemy the use of his airfields, after which aircraft could be picked off in their hardened shelters or in their dispersals. Airfield attacks were assigned to

a number of coalition aircraft types, but RAF Tornados shouldered the main burden of the anti-airfield campaign.

The air campaign begins

One of the primary weapons used against Iraq's massive airfields was the Hunting JP233 airfield denial weapon. Carried in pairs below the aircraft's belly, each JP233 dispensed sixty SG357 runway-cratering munitions together with 430 HB876 area-denial mines designed to hamper repair operations. These were ejected downwards from the pods (which were then jettisoned) from a straight and level, low-level (150 ft AGL), circa 500 kt pass, cutting a swathe across runways, or strategic taxiways (eg those connecting shelter areas to the rest of the airfield). The delivery profile obviously imposed a degree of vulnerability on the aircraft during their attacks, and the JP233 missions were to prove to be some of the most dangerous of the war. Despite this the loss rate remained relatively low, and certainly lower than the RAF had expected. The popular press, however, made much of the losses that did occur, and erroneously inferred that the later switch to medium-level operations was forced on the RAF by the 'heavy attrition'.

With an individual take off weight of just under 31 tonnes, four RAF aircraft from the Dhahran detachment and eight from Muharraq were the first RAF Tornados to launch on 17 January, each carrying two tanks and two JP233s each. The flights were led by their respective unit commanders (Wg Cdrs Witts and Broadbent) and launched just before 0100hr local time, all bound for a co-ordinated attack on Tallil AB. Airborne at 0210hr, four Tabuk Tornados, led by Wg Cdr Travers-Smith, headed for Al Asad AB, accompanied by a pair of ALARM-carrying aircraft. A second wave from Tabuk attacked Al Taqaddum. Meanwhile Muharraq's second wave had their take off delayed, and as a result found themselves toss-bombing Shaibah (actually Ar Rumaylah Southwest) in daylight. ZD791 crashed during the egress, its pilot and navigator (Flt Lts John Peters and 'Adrian' Nicholl) ejecting to become Iraqi PoWs. Officially explained as being caused by one of the aircraft's Sidewinders exploding after a lucky AAA hit, some believe that ZD791 was downed by one of its own bombs, jettisoned live on the run out after the crew failed to release them during the attack!

The standard procedure for these early raids was to rendezvous with a RAF tanker (either a Victor K2 or VC-10 K2/3) over northern Saudi Arabia, before heading north into Iraqi airspace at low-level. The crews selected the 'hard' ride on the aircraft's autopilot/terrain following radar coupling, giving the best possible terrain masking from enemy radars. The four aircraft in the cell would fly in 'Card 4' formation, each being laterally separated by some two to three nautical miles. Individual crews were responsible for their own navigation, and the flights were conducted in strict radio silence and without navigation lights.

On the final run-in to the target, maximum afterburner was selected to increase airspeed to 600 kt before being cancelled before reaching the target. This was intended to provide enough inertia for the Tornado to pass through the high threat area without using reheat in the short-range SAM engagement zone. Fixed-position and shoulder-launched SAMs were augmented by heavy anti-aircraft artillery (AAA) which would rake the sky in a fearsome display of tracer fire. One or two aircraft within the four-ship strike packages were usually armed with 1,000 lb bombs for 'diversionary' loft or lay-down attacks against these emplacements and other parts of the base infrastructure. The tactic proved successful in the most part, drawing some fire away from the JP233 aircraft as they released their munitions on runways and taxiways. In the cockpit, the sound of the dispensing bomblets is alarming, and has been described as being akin to machine gun fire, or to driving at speed over a cattle grid. The whole process lasts just under six seconds, before the empty canisters are jettisoned automatically, causing a noticeable jolt throughout the airframe.

Two more waves of JP233 attacks were made on the opening day. Tabuk sent four aircraft to attack the airfield at Al Taqaddum, striking their target just before dawn. Aircraft from Dhahran and Muharraq attacked Ar Rumaylah AB at much the same time. That evening Tabuk despatched an eight aircraft raid (callsigns *Dundee 21-28*) on Al Asad, although two aircraft had to return to base prematurely. Post-strike reconnaissance of targets revealed near-perfect results from all of the attacks, the JP233 munitions cutting considerable swathes across runways and taxiways thus preventing enemy aircraft from getting airborne. Those Iraqi aircraft which did take off were either shot down by the Allies or fled, some running for the comparatively safe haven afforded by neighbouring Iran. Muharraq sent four aircraft to Ubaydah bin al Jarrah, one returning safely after a severe birdstrike. The detachment sent four more aircraft against Shaibah, with ZA392 crashing (with the loss of its pilot, Wg Cdr Nigel Elsdon, OC No 27 Squadron and the navigator, Flt Lt Max

Paveway II laser-guided bombs were usually carried in threes below the Tornado's broad, flat belly, as seen here. This left the underwing pylons free for fuel, Sky Shadow ECM pod and a Phimat chaff dispenser.

A Muharraq-based Tornado returns from a successful LGB sortie, accompanied by its designator – a Pave Spike-equipped Buccaneer. The latter has an AN/ALQ-101 ECM pod under the starboard wing, with an AIM-9 and the Pave Spike pod below the other. Later in the war, the Buccaneers carried one LGB as well. PABLO MASON

Collier) shortly after successful completion of the attack. The loss was officially blamed on a catastrophic hit from a short-range SAM, possibly a Euromissile Roland. Elsdon was the highest ranking Allied officer to be lost during the campaign.

Of all the JP233 missions mounted by the RAF, only one failed to reach its target. In the early hours of 18 January 1991, a Tabuk-based four ship (*Lincoln 01/04*) was assigned to the massive H-3 airfield in western Iraq. One aircraft suffered technical problems, and played no further part. The three bombers pressed on but on nearing the target, the enemy defences were very active having been attacked by other Allied aircraft only a few hours beforehand. The formation leader, having had his JP233 capability reduced by one aircraft, took the decision not to risk an ineffective attack on such a prepared target.

Tabuk flew its final JP233 mission on 18/19 January 1991, against H-2 airfield, whilst Dhahran and Muharraq flew JP233 airfield-denial sorties for a further twenty-four hours. One of those final missions on the night of 19/20 January 1991 was an eight-ship attack on Tallil AB, carried out by the Muharraq Detachment. The first four aircraft each carried four airburst-fused 1,000 lb bombs for use against various airfield targets,

This aircraft (ZD744/BD of No 14 Squadron) was one of several of the Tabuk-based aircraft decorated with a ferocious-looking sharksmouth. It also wore the name 'Buddha' with an appropriate piece of nose-art.

to 'soften' the approach for the four JP233 aircraft coming in one minute behind. Tornado ZA396, flown by Flt Lts David Waddington and Robert Stuart, was one of the first four aircraft and suffered a hit from a Euromissile Roland SAM. Both ejected safely and were captured.

Despite these losses, morale continued to be surprisingly high amongst the RAF personnel. The generally upbeat atmosphere was reflected in the application of nose art and individual names to the aircraft. Applied by budding artists (mainly groundcrew with more enthusiasm than artistic talent) many of the Tornados received artwork and inscriptions. With most individual nose art applied to the aircraft's port side, the Muharraq Detachment's flights adopted the legends Snoopy Airways and Triffid Airways to starboard. Tabuk applied 'sharksmouth' markings on a number of its aircraft.

An estimated total of 96 JP233s were delivered by RAF

Tornados during the war, with Muharraq making most of the attacks and expending 50. Next came the Tabuk Detachment, which dropped 32, whilst Dhahran released only 14.

The first SEADs

The Tabuk Detachment's initial JP233 raid on Al Asad AB on 17 January 1991 had seen the first RAF suppression of enemy air defence (SEAD) mission of the war. Flying ALARM-equipped aircraft, Flt Lts Roche and Bellamy (ZD810), and Flt Lts Williams and Goddard (ZD850), left Tabuk one hour after the main strike force. The aircraft flew direct to the target area without the need for aerial refuelling thanks to their light load of three ALARMs. At 0350hr local time, five minutes ahead of the air strike, two ALARMs were fired by each Tornado. The missiles went straight into their programmed 'loiter' mode to await activation of any of the search and fire control radars protecting Al Asad.

The second ALARM mission, during the evening of 17 January 1991 saw four Tornados (Stamford 51-54) support a co-ordinated Allied raid on the H-3 airfield. As with the first sorties, ALARMs were fired into 'loiter' mode ahead of the bomber force and this became the normal *modus operandi* throughout the conflict. Iraqi radar operators quickly learned that extended use of radar left them extremely vulnerable to SEAD attacks. Their fire control radars would therefore transmit only up to missile launch, and thereafter the SAM was left to fly without updated guidance information.

Unlike its contemporary anti-radar missiles, ALARM could be pre-programmed before and during a mission to prioritise threats. Each individual missile could therefore search for a specific set of targets, 'preferring' the more threatening weapons. The rushed deployment of ALARM meant that this

This Tabuk-based Tornado wore an unfinished sharksmouth, with white teeth but no red and black inside the 'mouth'. The extent of the bomb tally and the three underfuselage LGBs show that the photo was taken fairly late in the war.

By early January 1991, the ALARM-equipped Tornados were flying with missile launch rails fitted to the outboard underfuselage pylons, allowing the re-location of the underwing tanks to the inboard underwing stations. SQN LDR MIKE RONDOT

capability had not been validated, and indeed before *Desert Storm* the missile had only ever been fired once against a live radar (on the China Lake ranges in California).

One ALARM-capable Tornado was lost on 20 January 1991, although not during a SEAD sortie, nor even under combat conditions. Crewed by Sqn Ldr Peter Battson and Wg Cdr Mike Heath, ZD893 (Stamford 11, carrying 1,000lb bombs) was designated as the lead aircraft of an eight-ship attack on Al Taqaddum AB. Immediately after take off from Tabuk, control problems were experienced and the crew struggled for 80 minutes to resolve the problem. After two failed landing attempts, navigator Heath elected to abandon the aircraft and both crew members ejected, suffering minor injuries.

Despite this loss of an ALARM aircraft, the effect on the force was minimal. From 21 January 1991, revised procedures were introduced which reduced the normal strike package ALARM support aircraft from four to two. This was due not only to the effective neutralisation of Iraqi radars, but also over concern about the dwindling stocks of the new missile. The availability problem was eased by fitting only two missiles (normally on the inner wing pylons) to the carrier aircraft. The final four-ship ALARM mission was flown on 21 January 1991, supporting USAF F-15E Strike Eagles of the 4th Tactical Fighter Wing (Provisional) in a raid on a 'Scud' depot at Al Quaim.

Three additional ALARM-capable Tornados arrived on 24 January 1991, including the attrition replacement for the one lost four days earlier. This brought the number available to eight, and the use of these aircraft to cover normal bombing missions became commonplace. The final ALARM mission of the war took place on 13 February 1991, when ZD851 and ZD748 (Dundee 21/22) supported a medium-level attack on HAS complexes at Al Taqaddum AB. One further mission was

When initially deployed, the RAF's ALARM-capable Tornados could only carry a pair of missiles underwing, with the fuel tanks displaced below the fuselage. Nine aircraft were deployed (from No 9 Squadron) but were operated by hastily trained crews from No 20 Squadron. FLT LT NICK WILCOCK

This No 9 Squadron jet was the aircraft which had to be abandoned by Sqn Ldr Peter Batson and Wing Commander Mike Heath after suffering control restrictions after take off. WG CDR MIKE HEATH

This ALARM-equipped aircraft shows the standard loadout used during Operation Desert Storm. Gulf War operations entirely exhausted the RAF's stock of ALARMs, despite BAe's Lostock factory working overtime to produce the weapons.

The final ALARM load-out used in the Gulf has rarely been seen in published photographs, although it was the standard wartime loadout. Here one of the nine aircraft deployed shows off the three ALARM fit, with one missile on each of the underfuselage stations. WG CDR MIKE HEATH

planned for the morning of 26 February 1991, but bad weather forced all of the aircraft involved to return to Tabuk.

In all, 48 ALARM sorties (in 24 missions) were mounted during the conflict. Four others were aborted whilst en route to the target. A total of 121 ALARMs were fired, although it is difficult to assess exactly how many actually 'killed' targets.

'Scudhunters'

One major thorn in the side of *Desert Storm* war planners was the threat posed by Iraq's mobile 'Scud' missile launchers. Although ineffective as a surface-to-surface missile in comparison with modern weapons, the 'Scud' could provide a means by which Saddam Hussein could unleash chemical and biological attacks on the Allies and their host nations. Perhaps more importantly Iraqi threats to attack Israel promised to draw the Jewish state into the war against Iraq, which would have seriously undermined the unity of the anti-Iraqi coalition. The 'Scuds' were thus placed high on the target priority list. But finding them was never going to be easy.

The sheer expanse and featureless terrain of western Iraq's deserts was ideal for concealing 'Scud' launchers and launch sites. Despite frantic efforts by special forces and other intelligence assets to locate them, the convoys containing the missile launchers could set up, fire and then disperse in a very short time. Fortunately one aircraft in the Allied inventory was well suited to the task of finding them – the Tornado GR1A, and 'Scudhunting' became the detachment's most high profile task.

The Dhahran-based reconnaissance Tornados flew their first combat sortie during the night of 17/18 January 1991. Three aircraft, led by Wg Cdr Threadgould and Flt Lt Tim Robinson in ZA397, were tasked with their first 'Scudhunt' over western Iraq. Threadgould's aircraft experienced fuel starvation on approach to the search area, and he was forced to divert to King Khalid Military City in northern Saudi Arabia. The remaining aircraft, ZA400, crewed by Sqn Ldrs Dick Garwood and Jon Hill from No 2 Squadron, and ZA371, with Flt Lts

Brian Robinson and Gordon Walker of No 13 Squadron aboard, went on to successfully locate a mobile 'Scud' site. Worsening weather in the target area however precluded an Allied air strike, the missile battery relocating within a short time of being spotted.

The mission dramatically illustrated the GR1A's capability, and the type continued to enjoy great success during the war. 'Scudhunting' missions aside, the aircraft were tasked to reconnoitre Iraqi troop concentrations, searching for tell-tale infrared signatures of key targets within them, as well as with providing surveillance when conventional optical systems were restricted by the weather. The special forces support role, primarily for elements of the British Army's Special Air Service, saw the aircraft gather fresh information on 'areas of interest'. Depending on the intelligence subsequently gathered, the targets could be moved onto the daily target lists for aerial bombardment. In some cases, the special forces troops provided laser designation of key points to ensure maximum damage by the ensuing air strikes.

Preparations for the ground phase of the Allied offensive also provided tasks for GR1A. General Norman Schwarzkopf, Supreme Commander of the coalition forces and C-in-C US Central Command, planned to breach the Iraqi line in what he termed as a 'Hail Mary' manoeuvre. The armoured divisions under his command would enter into Iraq from Saudi Arabia, much further west than the Iraqis anticipated. This was helped by an elaborate deception plan, which saw Allied amphibious forces move up to just off the Kuwaiti coast as well as 'false' radio traffic (simulating tank formations) being broadcast all along the Saudi/Kuwaiti border for the Iraqis to eavesdrop. The infrared reconnaissance undertaken by the Tornados gave ground commanders confirmation of minefield positions and other key obstacles which might otherwise have hindered their progress.

From their first mission on the night of 17-18 January 1991, the GR1As were active every night until the end of the war. They flew missions only at night, usually landing before dawn. When tankers were unavailable the aircraft sometimes flew with four tanks, two ADV-type 'Hindenburgers' underwing,

The RAF's recce Tornados were singularly anonymous looking, with only one of the aircraft deployed even bearing a name, and none having nose art. Operating only at night, the aircraft were rarely photographed. During operational sorties the aircraft usually carried the big 'Hindenburgers' underwing, sometimes with smaller tanks under the fuselage. VIA ANDY EVANS

Thick cloud and frequent sandstorms caused many LGB sorties to be aborted, though the Tornados often seemed able to find gaps through which to bomb, on days when other allied types simply had to take their weapons home.

A Change in Tactics

Once the runways and taxiways of Iraq's main airfields had been cut, there was little need for further costly attacks using the JP233. The last attacks using the weapon were made on 18 January 1991, when the three RAF Tornado Detachments switched almost exclusively to delivering 1,000 lb bombs against infrastructure targets at military sites. Despite the 'blinding' of Iraqi radars, the ferocity of defences close-in to these targets continued to be a problem. The Tabuk Detachment mounted an eight-ship low-level 'loft attack' against the Ar Rutbah air defence operations centre on 22 January 1991 and, despite three aircraft aborting whilst en route, the mission continued. The lead aircraft, ZA467 callsign *Stamford 01*, was crewed by Sqn Ldrs Gary Lennox and Paul Weeks of No 16 Squadron. It was brought down by AAA over the target area, with the loss of its crew. The next day, the Dhahran detachment suffered its only loss, ZA403 falling after one of its bombs exploded prematurely. The crew, Fg Off Simon Burgess and Sqn Ldr Bob Ankerson of No 17 Squadron, ejected and were captured. This was, ironically, the first Tornado loss at medium-level, demonstrating that

with smaller tanks under the belly. The last GR1A mission landed back at Dhahran in the early hours of 28 February 1991, completing the recce flight's 137th operational sortie. Of these, 33 had been aborted en route to target areas.

medium-level tactics were not a complete panacea.

This brought Tornado attrition to five aircraft lost in action (excluding Mike Heath's aircraft) – 26% of the coalition's air losses to date. The Tornado force accounted for only 4% of the total number of aircraft. To the press, this highlighted the need to switch to medium-level bombing, to give crews a greater safety margin against certain SAMs and most AAA. In fact the

Tabuk Tornados taxy out for a mission, with pairs of bombers being trailed by single TIALD-equipped 'Spikers'. While the Dhahran and Muharraq-based Tornados tended to use Buccaneers as laser designators, the Tabuk aircraft relied on the five TIALD-equipped Tornados. SQN LDR NIGEL RISDALE

loss rate merely reflected the intensity of Tornado operations, and the dangerous nature of the missions assigned. But the non-appearance of the Iraqi Air Force did make medium-level a relatively safe and benign place to be, and the changing nature of targets did allow a switch to medium-level operations. This did not invalidate the RAF's reliance on low-level tactics however. The absence of Iraqi fighters, the effectiveness of SEAD in closing down the SAM threat and the nature of the targets assigned, all made *Granby* a unique and non-standard operation.

Flying at altitudes in the region of 15,000 ft brought about its own set of problems however. The Tornado, its weapons system and the weapons it carried were all optimised for low-level attacks, while crews had been trained to operate 'down in the weeds'. The move to higher levels necessitated software changes to the aircraft's targeting computer to allow for greater variances in attack geometry. Re-programming of the radar homing and warning receiver (RHWR) and the wing-mounted Skyshadow ECM pod was also required, in order to take into account new threats. SAMs such as the SA-2 Guideline can be ineffective against low-flying targets but become of much greater concern to aircraft operating at higher altitudes.

Tabuk's first medium-level sortie was flown on 22 January 1991, when eight Tornados (*Dundee 01-08*, although *02* became unserviceable) were allocated to attack the ammunition dump

Already wearing their sanitised war-suits (stripped of unit badges and insignia) and g-suits, aircrew from No 31 Squadron brief for a mission from Dhahran. Most aircrew opted to wear desert-coloured flying suits on operations, but some wore the standard issue dark green flying clothing. RAF DETACHMENT DHAHRAN

at Qubaysah with 1,000 lb bombs. Two ALARM aircraft acted in support. Muharraq followed suit, flying a straight and level radar bombing attack on Mudaysis AB with a similar number of aircraft on the night of 23-24 January 1991. On the same night, Dhahran Tornados flew an eight-ship mission against Ar Rumaylah AB. This was the mission marred by the loss of

The reflection of a Dhahran-based Tornado shimmers in a massive puddle on the flightline – a very rare sight in Saudi Arabia, even in January. The aircraft carries a pair of LGBs underfuselage, each inscribed with slogans by the groundcrew and armourers.

By the end of January, the Tornado's desert pink paintwork was looking decidedly well-worn. For most of the air campaign, the Tornados flew as bomb trucks, flying Paveway II LGBs to their targets at medium level, supported by a handful of specialised aircraft operating as dedicated 'spikers'. RAF DETACHMENT DHAHRAN

Bad weather over the target often forced Tornados to bring back their weapons. Here a Dhahran-based aircraft deploys its thrust reversers after a long and fruitless operational sortie. The crew logs another mission, but someone will have to return to the same target again the next day. RAF DETACHMENT DHAHRAN

ZA403. Another Tornado (ZD843 of the Muharraq detachment) was very nearly shot down on 24 January. The severely damaged aircraft was nursed back for an emergency landing at Dhahran by its shaken crew, following a very near miss by a SAM.

Optimised as it was for low-level missions, the Tornado was sluggish and lacking in 'grunt' at medium-level, especially when heavily laden. ("The Tornado took to medium-level missions like a duck to accountancy" wrote Paul Jackson at the time). Further refinements to tactics were clearly needed in order to offset the aircraft's deficiencies.

Weapon loads were cut from eight to five 1,000 lb bombs per Tornado in an attempt to increase aircraft performance at the higher altitudes. Accuracy was also still a problem despite attack computer adjustments. One method employed to improve aiming was dive bombing, first used on 11 February 1991 by four Muharraq Tornados attacking the barracks at Al

At Muharraq, the Tornados rested between sorties beneath massive open-sided shelters, to keep them out of the harsh sun, and to keep the cockpits as cool as was possible. Concrete blast walls were hastily erected between each pair of aircraft. SQN LDR MIKE RONDOT

Jarrah, situated west of Kuwait City. In the medium-level role, airfields (and especially HAS complexes) continued to be a major focus for Tornado missions, but POL (Petrol, Oil and Lubricants) facilities, petro-chemical plants, oil production sites, barracks, ammunition storage sites and radar facilities all came under attack. In a typical dive attack the pilot would roll the aircraft inverted at 24,000 ft, pulling down through the horizon into a 30° dive to acquire the target in his HUD. The aim was to maintain positive g loads on the heavy aircraft throughout the procedure, and the pilot rolled the aircraft erect when established in the dive. Pulling out at around 16,000 ft (still above the envelope of AAA and the SA-8), the navigator left weapons release to the on-board computer for optimum effect. The real answer to the problem of accuracy at medium-level, however, was the use of precision guided weapons and targeting systems.

At the time, only No 20 Squadron had experience of using such systems, although the Paveway II laser-guided bomb was rapidly being integrated as a major Tornado force weapon. The RAF's Paveway II consisted of a standard British 1,000lb bomb fitted with the Texas Instruments CPU-123B Paveway II laser head and tail. No 20 Squadron had practised LGB delivery with the Buccaneer S2Bs of No 237 Operational Conversion Unit in early 1990. Buccaneers operating in the laser designator role used the AN/AVQ-23E Pave Spike laser designator, and the OCU had a war role of providing designation for Tornados carrying Paveway II. In the much longer term, GEC was busy developing its TIALD (Thermal Imaging Airborne Laser Designator) pod for use by the Tornado itself, aiming to allow the aircraft to co-operatively and autonomously self-designate for LGBs.

With the switch to medium-level operations, there was clearly an immediate need for the Tornados in the Gulf to use the Paveway II, and this in turn inferred an urgent need for airborne designation capability. On 23 January 1991 a flash signal was therefore sent to RAF Lossiemouth requesting that six Buccaneers be made ready to deploy. The first of these arrived at Muharraq late on 26 January 1991, and work-up began the next day.

Pictured at the end of the war are some of the Tornado detachment commanders. Left to right are Wing Commanders Al Threadgould (OC No II (AC) Squadron, commanding the recce detachment at Dhahran, Jerry Witts (OC No 31, commanding the bombers at Dhahran), Bill Cope (the Buccaneer CO), Bob Iveson (OC No 617 and commanding the TIALD aircraft), John Broadbent (OC No XV and commanding the Muharraq bombers), Mike Heath (OC No 20 and in command of the ALARM aircraft), Ivor Evans (OC No IX Squadron) and Ian Travers-Smith (OC No 16, and in charge of the Tabuk-based bomber aircraft). WG CDR MIKE HEATH

Flying with four Muharraq-based Tornados each carrying three LGBs, a pair of Buccaneers flew their first sortie on 2 February 1991. The target for *Belfast 31* formation was a road bridge, which crossed the Euphrates River north of the city of As Samawah. Each Buccaneer designated for two Tornados, the method being for the bombers to drop their weapons and turn away from the target whilst the Buccaneer entered a gentle turn to keep the target in view of the Pave Spike. The Buccaneer navigator would keep the desired point of impact illuminated for the duration of the LGB's flight, which lasted just under 40 seconds. Of the 12 bombs dropped on this first mission, nine scored direct hits (although one failed to explode); the damage being sufficient enough, however, to destroy the bridge's central span.

Muharraq then concentrated on daylight LGB attacks, with Dhahran following suit from 5 February 1991, as the Buccaneer Detachment at Muharraq received a further six aircraft between 2-8 February 1991. Bridges continued to be the main targets until 13 February 1991, the final mission being made against the road bridge at Fallujah. At the end of this phase, some 24 bridges had been destroyed by Buccaneer/Tornado strikes, using 169 LGBs. HASs next fell victim to the RAF raids, as part of the move to destroy as much of the Iraqi Air Force as possible. As Allied troops prepared to tackle Iraqi land forces, these shelters (and, from the 16 February 1991, other airfield targets) were of particular

importance in order to eliminate the possibility of a surprise airborne biological or chemical attack. The majority of LGB attacks were successful, although nearly 25% were aborted due to weather conditions over target areas.

One Tornado was lost during this phase on 14 February 1991, the final combat loss to be suffered by the RAF. During a Buccaneer-led strike by the Muharraq Detachment on Al Taqaddum AB, two SAMs (either SA-2 Guidelines or SA-3 Goas) struck GR1 ZD717. The pilot, Flt Lt Rupert Clark, managed to eject and was taken prisoner, whilst navigator Flt Lt Steven Hicks was killed in the aircraft. The relative sanctuary of medium altitude may have engendered some complacency, and the aircraft was lost while flying in a package which was, in retrospect, too large, too unwieldy and too vulnerable, with four Buccaneers and eight Tornados attacking shelters on a single airfield. Some reports suggest that SAM warnings were not heard in the general chatter by 12 participating aircraft.

By the end of the war, the Buccaneers had 'lased' for a total of 619 LGBs; 288 of these were dropped by the Dhahran Detachment and 283 by Muharraq, the remaining 48 being released by the Buccaneers themselves. Before and during the LGB missions, all three Tornado Detachments also expended a large number of 1,000 lb iron bombs. Leading the table was Muharraq, whose aircraft dropped 1,700, followed by Tabuk with 1,451 and finally Dhahran with 1,045.

Flying serenely over Southern Iraq, 'Bacardi and Coke' (ZD848/BC) was one of five aircraft modified under the TIALD Accelerated Programme for deployment to the Gulf. It is seen here carrying one of the two available TIALD pods, one of which was trials equipment, the other having been built from spare parts!

TIALD – From test-bench to war

The availability of the a handful of Pave Spike-equipped Buccaneers was insufficient to fulfill the requirements of the three Tornado bomber detachments for laser designation capability. GEC-Ferranti's TIALD pod was identified as offering tremendous potential, though it was still at an early stage of development. Despite this, GEC and the DRA worked miracles to get two pods deployed to the Gulf, providing one of the most incredible stories of the war.

The Royal Aircraft Establishment at Farnborough, using the 'Nightbird' Buccaneer (XV344) concluded a three-year, five-phase, 116-sortie initial TIALD flight trial on 10 December 1990. The tests culminated in the Buccaneer designating a target for attack by a No 13 Squadron Tornado, using a Paveway II bomb. In parallel to the final trials flights, the manufacturer and MoD embarked upon a TIALD accelerated programme. This aimed to give a small number of deployed Tornados the ability to carry the pod, providing the *Granby* Tornado force with an autonomous day/night laser designator capability.

GEC-Ferranti, with sub-contractor EASAMS, undertook to re-write the Operational Flight Programme software to accommodate TIALD within a six-week timescale, after BAe's estimate of six months for a software re-write. Following a series of plenary meetings by the contractors and relevant RAF, RAE and A&AEE parties, Project *Albert* commenced on 30 November 1990, following issue of a contract on 19 November (Day 1).

Five *Granby*-modified Tornado GR1s (ZA393, ZA406, ZD739, ZD844 and ZD848) were transferred from Brüggen to Honington for work to begin on installing the necessary wiring and cockpit modifications, using control panels supplied by Farnborough prior to flight and rig-testing by the

A&AEE at Boscombe Down. GEC-Ferranti released the first of two pods to the A&AEE Boscombe Down on 14 January 1991 (Day 27), with the first Tornado/TIALD integration test flight taking place four days later. Strike/Attack OEU crews undertook these initial tests, working in conjunction with (and eventually handing over to) two crews from No 617 Squadron (including Wg Cdr Bob Iveson) plus four from No 13 Squadron, who all arrived at Boscombe Down over 20-23 January 1991. The first laser designation flight took place on 30 January 1991, with the first 'live' LGB drop occurring on 2 February 1991 (Day 46). Concluding on 6 February 1991 (Day 50), with the despatch of four of the five aircraft to the Gulf, Project *Albert* has since been estimated as being two years work condensed into six weeks, a tribute to all involved.

The urgent requirement for TIALD in theatre necessitated that four of the five aircraft flew direct to Tabuk on 6 February 1991. The two pods were transported to the theatre by RAF

The same aircraft sitting on the line at Tabuk immediately after the mission above. The sensor head of the precious TIALD pod has already been covered up, but the groundcrew have yet to add another mission mark, in the form of a laser 'sparkle'.

Hercules, accompanied by volunteer GEC-Ferranti support personnel. Within a few days, and as part of the Gulf War trend to apply nose art to most RAF aircraft, the pods themselves were named Sandra and Tracy and appropriate artwork (taken from the British adult comic *Viz*) applied.

Led by Wg Cdr Iveson, the six crews formed 'TIALD Flight' of the Tabuk Detachment. Two of the Tornados, ZD739 and ZD844 (*Dundee 40/41*), crewed respectively by Iveson with Flt Lt Chris Purkiss and Flt Lts Gareth Walker with Adrian Frost, flew the first TIALD theatre familiarisation sortie on 7 February 1991. The following day saw two TIALD-equipped aircraft (again ZD739 and ZD844) and two LGB-armed standard GR1s (ZD810 and ZD851) fly a practice mission with live weapons on the Saudi's Badr ranges.

After two more training sorties, Iveson was ready to take TIALD into combat. On 10 February 1991, two cells of three Tornados (callsigns *Lincoln 71/73* and *Stamford 77/79*,) took off for an attack against H-3 airfield. Each cell consisted of the TIALD aircraft, accompanied by two 'bombers' each of the latter carrying three Paveway II LGBs. Iveson and Purkiss, flying ZD848 in the first cell, suffered equipment problems and their accompanying bombers dropped their weapons 'dumb' (without laser designation). Walker and Frost, in ZD739, successfully 'lased' for the bombs released by GR1s ZA447 and ZD748, destroying two HASs in the process. A further successful mission was flown against H-3 later that day, and twice on 11 February 1991.

Most TIALD attacks were made against airfields, primarily targeting shelters and aircrew briefing facilities, though also against runway intersections. Some attacks were also made against ammunition and fuel storage areas and against bridges. TIALD Flight usually mounted three sorties of two aircraft per day, normally divided equally between three different targets. Perhaps the most spectacular result came on 19 February 1991, when Sqn Ldr Greg Monaghan and Flt Lt Harry Hargreaves flying ZD844 (*Halifax 03*) designated for the initial wave attacking an ammunition and fuel depot at Ubaydah bin al Jarrah. The secondary explosions resulted in a plume of smoke which rose some 15,000 ft into the air, to form a classic 'mushroom cloud', prompting reports of a nuclear explosion.

TIALD missions were usually flown by pairs of designator aircraft, each accompanied by pairs of bombers, with a third TIALD aircraft being readied (but not obviously launched) as a spare. This meant that the two available pods had to be regularly switched between aircraft. The normal procedure adopted for TIALD attacks was for the designator aircraft to identify the target on radar at a range of about 20 to 25 nautical miles, with TIALD slaved to the radar. The narrow field-of-view would then be selected about 15 miles from the target, with the navigator satisfied that the TIALD was tracking the right target. Flying above the two bomber aircraft (normally in excess of 20,000 ft), the TIALD aircraft would fly a gentle orbit some four miles from the target, the pod being placed in automatic track mode to keep the laser on the desired point of impact, closely monitored by the navigator who could refine the aim point using his hand controller as

necessary. The laser itself was fired for periods of up to 30 seconds for each flight of bombs, with the navigator rapidly slewing the seeker onto a second target while the second stick of bombs were in flight. Very occasionally, the TIALD aircraft carried a single LGB on its own starboard underfuselage station, and self-designated for this.

The six original crews were joined by four more (one each from Nos 2 and 14 Squadrons, plus two from No 16 Squadron) and the fifth aircraft, ZA406, arrived from the UK on 20 February 1991. This allowed five two-crew shifts to be formed, with each shift flying one day and one night sortie, before having a 'day off'. Poor weather over target areas on 20/21 February 1991 hampered operations on both those days, although most missions were still flown in the hope that breaks in the cloud cover would permit an attack.

The final TIALD missions came on 27 February 1991, with raids on the airfields of Al Asad and Habbaniyah. The latter was attacked during the evening, the bombers being ZA473, ZA492 and ZA491 (all as *Boston 02/04*). The TIALD aircraft were ZD739 (*Boston 05*, flown by Monaghan and Hargreaves) and ZD848 (*Boston 06*, with Flt Lts Bohill and Ross on board). Of particular note was that one of the targets 'lased' by ZD739 was a hangar built by the RAF before the British left Iraq. The Iraqi helicopters inside were all destroyed.

By the end of the war, the TIALD-equipped Tornados flew 72 sorties (39 successful missions) designating targets for 229 direct hits with their LGBs. Some 23 sorties, were aborted due to weather. TIALD also proved to be a useful reconnaissance and bomb damage assessment tool, though video imagery was best viewed on the ground, using a 625-line monitor, rather than the 200-line cockpit TV Tab.

Operation Locusta – Italy's Strike Force

Twelve Tornados, drawn from various AMI units to form the Autonomous Flight Detachment at Al Dhafra in Abu Dhabi, had arrived in the region from 2 October 1990, under Operation *Locusta*. Like their British counterparts, the Italian Tornados underwent a host of modifications including the application of an overall desert camouflage scheme. The

This Italian Tornado is seen carrying the standard Operation Locusta loadout of four Mk 83 GP bombs under the fuselage. The 14 aircraft deployed operated from Al Dhafra in Abu Dhabi.

Homeward bound after a bombing mission, one Italian Tornado waits while his wingman refuels from a USAF KC-135. The Italian aircraft sometimes flew with their own tanker support, in the form of other Tornados equipped with buddy refuelling pods.

aircraft were initially assigned to the low-level strike role, using US-made Mk 83 1,000 lb bombs. Some problems were encountered, particularly with regard to aerial refuelling, though these were soon solved. AAR tanker support for the Italian Tornados was mostly provided by USAF KC-135s. On the first Italian Tornado mission, on 17 January 1991, only one aircraft (MM7074, crewed by Major Mario Betlini and Captain Maurizio Cocciolone of 50•Stormo) out of a formation of seven managed to take on fuel from a KC-135, due to very severe turbulence and poor weather. Pressing on to the target alone, with commendable professionalism and great courage, the aircraft was shot down by enemy AAA and both crew members were taken prisoner. Subsequently the Italian Tornados played a vital role in the Allied air campaign, albeit without much press or PR coverage.

Little information has come to light on the role played by Royal Saudi Air Force Tornado IDSs. No 7 Squadron, based at Dhahran and forward-deployed to Taif, is known to have undertaken anti-airfield attacks employing JP233. The first of these missions appears to have been as part of a US-led attack on H-3 airfield on the night of 17/18 January 1991. Low-level bombing missions, apparently using US-made Mk 84 2,000 lb bombs, were also undertaken. One non-combat loss, involving Tornado 765, took place on the night of 19/20 January 1991 with both occupants ejecting safely.

A cease-fire was announced by US President George Bush at 0800hr Gulf time on 28 February 1991; six weeks of war had come to an end. Over 100,000 Iraqi troops had lost their lives, compared to only 500 of the Allies.

At the cessation of hostilities, the 61 RAF Tornado GR1s operational in-theatre during *Desert Storm* had flown an estimated 1,617 sorties including aborts. The Muharraq Detachment's 17 aircraft flew 400 of these. Dhahran, with 15 bomber and six recce aircraft, flew 567 sorties, whilst Tabuk

(operating 23 Tornados) flew 650 sorties. The 12 Italian Tornados at Al Dhafra mounted 226 sorties, dropping 565 Mk 83 bombs.

By comparison, the RAF Tornado F3s and Saudi ADVs operating from Dhahran had a 'quiet' war. The RAF aircraft flew some 360 combat air patrols during the conflict, all of which were 'barrier' missions to protect Saudi airspace. The better-equipped (IFF and JTIDS) USAF F-15 Eagles and Saudi forces flew the fighter escort and fighter sweep missions which accounted for virtually all of the air-to-air victories scored during the conflict. There is little doubt that had the allied bombers not been so effective in grounding the Iraqi Air Force, then the F3's Gulf War story might have been somewhat different.

The use of air power proved crucial to the coalition's swift and decisive victory over Iraq. The Tornado in particular proved itself to be a reliable and highly effective weapon, with British Aerospace giving an estimated combined total of over 3,250 sorties being flown by the three nations who operated it. Known figures for British and Italian aircraft amount to just over 2,200, inferring that the BAe figure includes *Desert Shield* training as well as the Saudi participation. But sortie numbers alone tell only part of the story. The seven Tornado combat losses demonstrated the dangerous nature of the missions assigned to the Tornado, especially during the first few nights of the war. At the same time, the Tornados proved devastatingly effective against their assigned targets, and even in the newly embraced medium-level role, proved to be one of the war's great success stories. The TIALD Tornados, hastily deployed, with hastily trained crews, achieved better accuracy rates than the USAF's dedicated F-117As and F-111Fs, with a lower weather-abort rate. All of those who flew, supported and manufactured the Tornado could be justifiably proud of their achievements.

Sea strike

Smart in overall sea grey, one of No 12 squadron's GR1Bs blasts past the Old Man of Hoy, a prominent Scottish landmark and a favourite backdrop for photographs. The aircraft carries a pair of Sea Eagles, and the massive ADV-type 'Hindenburger' fuel tanks.

The Tornado has always had an important maritime strike/attack role with one of the original customers for the aircraft being the German Navy's air arm, the Marineflieger. In German Navy service, the Tornado was seen as a replacement for some 135 ageing F-104Gs, used in the anti-shipping and reconnaissance roles by Marinefliegergeschwaderen 1 and 2 at Schleswig-Jagel and Eggebek. Rather fewer of the more capable and more expensive Tornados were acquired, though the 112 aircraft were sufficient to give each unit 48 Tornados, plus reserves. Only 12 of the total were twin-stickers, reflecting the fact that Marineflieger Tornado aircrew would be trained under Luftwaffe auspices.

When it became clear that the Tornado would not be available in 1975, as once intended, the Luftwaffe replaced its oldest F-104Gs (two recce wings, two fighter wings, and two fighter-bomber wings) with F-4E Phantoms, but the Marineflieger soldiered on with F-104Gs, ensuring that it was

accorded a high priority once the Tornado was available.

During their run-on, the Marineflieger F-104Gs replaced their AS30 ASMs with the more modern AS34 Kormoran, 350 of which were ordered, at a cost of DM469 m. When the Tornado entered service with the Marineflieger, the Kormoran missile became the primary anti-shipping weapon, though the aircraft also carried BL755 CBUs, and a wide range of bombs.

Integration of Kormoran was extremely straightforward, and apart from their sea grey topsides and white undersurfaces, the Marineflieger Tornados hardly differed from the aircraft delivered to the Luftwaffe. MFG 1 flew its last F-104G mission on 29 October 1981, and stood down while aircrew underwent conversion with the TTTE. The Marineflieger received its first four Tornados on 2 July 1982, when MFG 1 was formally recommissioned. MFG 2 soldiered on with its F-104Gs until May 1987, though it received its first Tornado on 11 September 1986. MFG 2 took delivery of the

The initial customer for the Tornado in the maritime strike role was the Marineflieger, who used the Kormoran ASM as its primary anti-ship weapon, and who integrated AGM-88 HARM on later aircraft. The HARM-shooters served primarily with the second of the two wings, though this HARM test aircraft wears an MFG 1 badge.

Navy's 48 HARM-capable Batch 5 aircraft, and the second Staffel took on a SEAD/HARM-shooting role. The first Staffel operated in the reconnaissance role, using 26 MBB/Aeritalia reconnaissance pods. The digital Kormoran 2 ASM entered service in 1989 (174 being delivered) this offering a heavier 220-kg warhead and a 5-km increase in range, to 35-km. MFG 1 eventually gained some Batch 6 Tornados, and began integrating HARM into its operations, but disbanded as a

The first Italian prototype (P.05) launching a Kormoran missile. In frontline AMI service, the weapon is used primarily by the 36° Stormo's 156° Gruppo.

result of post Cold War defence cuts on 1 January 1994. This left MFG 2 as the Marineflieger's sole surviving Tornado operator. The unit took over some of MFG 1's aircraft, growing to a strength of about 60 aircraft, and the first unit's Sea Eagle badge.

Since it had no land border with any Warsaw Pact nation, the primary war role of Italy's Tornados was one of maritime strike in the Mediterranean, with an overland role supporting forces in Austria or Yugoslavia, had these countries been invaded. The importance of the maritime role led to an early acquisition of about 60 Kormoran 1 missiles and the assignment of 156° Gruppo (the first frontline squadron) to the TASMO (Tactical Support to Maritime Operations) role.

In Britain, plans to use the Tornado in the maritime role were formulated at an early stage of the programme, but two squadrons of Buccaneers were actually run-on in the role in order to maximise the number of Tornados available for use in the overland role. The Tornado was always viewed as being the probable successor to the Buccaneer in the maritime strike/attack role, though many expected to see a new-build variant based on the ADV airframe, with its increased fuel capacity.

With the end of the Cold War and the disbandment of the

Even Britain was involved in the early carriage trials of the Kormoran missile, though it was always apparent that any British maritime Tornado variant would carry the indigenous Sea Eagle. This aircraft is P.03, the second British prototype.

Laarbruch wing, the RAF suddenly had surplus Tornado GR1s on its hands, and it made sense to use some of these aircraft to re-equip the maritime Buccaneer squadrons, taking over the BAe Sea Eagle ASMs used by the Buccaneer force. This meant that the RAF's maritime Tornado variant would by necessity be a minimum change conversion of the standard, Batch 3 Tornado GR1.

The first (Proof Installation) GR1B was ZA407, which was converted by BAe at Warton. A further 25 aircraft (ZA374, 375, 399, 409, 411, 446, 447, 450, 452, 453, 455, 456, 457, 459, 460, 461, 465, 469, 471, 473, 474, 475, 490, 491 and 492) were

converted at RAF St Athan, two of them (ZA409 and 411) twin-stickers. The conversion was relatively straightforward, covering the installation of a new stores management system, a Sea Eagle control panel, and pylon adaptors providing an interface between the Sea Eagle missile and the launch aircraft. This allows the missile's onboard navigation system to be updated with data from the launch aircraft, making it possible to use the missile's computed launch mode, allowing off-boresight attacks and giving the ability to attack specific targets within a group. If carried on a non-dedicated pylon, the Sea Eagle can only be used in its reversionary mode, having to be fired at a boresighted target, and attacking the first target it 'sees' after popping up and turning on its own active radar seeker.

Sea Eagle is a genuinely fire and forget missile, flying towards the target using inertial navigation, before using its own active radar seeker. It also has a range in excess of 50 miles, giving the launch aircraft a useful stand-off range.

Compared to the Buccaneer it replaced, the Tornado GR1B does not have quite the same payload/range capability, and there have been schemes to increase mission radius. One useful addition would be to provide a buddy-refuelling pod (such a store was used by the Buccaneers). During the Gulf War, nine RAF Tornados (one of them later converted to GR1B configuration) were modified to carry 15 Sargent Fletcher 28-300 inflight refuelling pods acquired from the Marineflieger, before the programme was abandoned.

Subsequently, Flight Refuelling were awarded a contract to convert a number of the 70 surplus Mk 20B, C, D and E refuelling pods (previously carried by redundant Victor (Mk 20B) and Buccaneer (Mk 20C and D) tankers) for use on the Tornado. The new Mk 20H pod was designed to incorporate

Looking decidedly non-maritime in standard grey-green camouflage, this GR1B wears the markings of No 12 Squadron. 'Shiny Twelve' gained a black, white and green fin flash and a green nose arrow when it transitioned to the Tornado. The squadron's previous Buccaneers had contented themselves with the fox-head badge, but applied it very large! KEVIN WILLS

One of No 617 Squadron's first GR1Bs sits outside its HAS, ready for a Sea Eagle trial firing. The aircraft carries a pair of standard 330-gal underwing tanks. JEREMY FLACK/API

the Sargent Fletcher pod was carried on the centreline.

Rather than simply delivering the new Tornado GR1Bs to the Lossiemouth Buccaneer squadrons, the decision was taken to use the airframes to re-equip the two Marham-based Tornado GR1 squadrons, until then tasked with the overland strike/attack role. No 27 Squadron at Marham re-numbered as No 12 Squadron on 1 October 1993, on the disbandment of the first of the Lossiemouth Buccaneer squadrons. The new No 12 squadron moved to Lossiemouth on 1 January 1994. No 617 at Marham received its first GR1B on 14 April 1994, moving to Lossiemouth on 27 April and taking over from No 208 Squadron which disbanded on 30 April 1994.

Nos 27 and 617 were not replaced in the overland role, and once the GR1B conversion programme was complete, the unit's original aircraft were reallocated to other units or placed in storage. This surplus of aircraft has proved enormously useful as aircraft are cycled through the GR4 upgrade by BAe at Warton. With the introduction of the GR 4 the need for the dedicated GR1B will disappear, since all GR4s will be Sea Eagle compatible. The maritime role is sufficiently different for there still to be a requirement for dedicated or part-dedicated maritime squadrons, however, since crews still require intensive training in the role, and must practise tactics and techniques if they are to stay proficient.

While extremely useful for attacks on enemy capital ships, the Sea Eagle is less well optimised for littoral warfare, and although a modernisation/refurbishing programme for the

a larger integral tank, doubling from 1,000 to 2,000-lb capacity (275 gals). Originally due for delivery in 1996, the Mk 20H was cancelled as the configuration was being finalised, with funding being transferred elsewhere. Some 30 pods were to have been converted, some being used for trials (including a jettison) with 24-25 entering service. The plan was for the pod to be carried on one of the Tornado's shoulder pylons, balanced by a 'Hindenburger' on the other shoulder, whereas

This Tornado GR1B, wearing the colours of No 12 Squadron, was borrowed by the SAOEU for a long trials deployment to Yuma and Indian Springs during late 1997. Here the aircraft has an unusual three-tank fit, with one under the fuselage and two under the wings. KEVIN WILLS

The use of ADV-style 465-gal tanks first became routine during the Gulf War, and has become increasingly common, as seen on this No 617 Squadron GR1B. Their use significantly improves the Tornado's radius of action. SGT RICK BREWELL

Sea Eagle is underway, some believed that the maritime Tornado squadrons might be the most likely victim of any force reductions imposed as part of the Strategic Defence Review. Fortunately this did not happen, although the Lossiemouth aircraft's maritime commitments have reportedly reduced. Instead, the two Lossiemouth-based units have been used to reduce the over-stretch on the force as a whole, taking their turn in manning the deployments in Turkey, Kuwait and Saudi Arabia. The two maritime Tornado squadrons already reportedly spent less than 40% of their training time practising for the maritime role, and have used GP(1) recce pods and TIALD laser designators during their overseas deployments, and not the Sea Eagle missile. The two squadrons always maintained a full overland capability, although the nuclear strike role has been relinquished, with the final withdrawal of the WE177.

Although the Tornado GR1B is theoretically capable of carrying a load of four Sea Eagles, it is more usual to carry fuel tanks underwing. Without such tanks, the Tornado is lacking in range, and the drag of two extra missiles degrades performance figures further.

Peacekeepers

Laden with ADV-style 'Hindenburgers' and a Vicon pod, this No II (AC) Squadron GR1A is seen en route to Northern Iraq from its temporary home at Incirlik. SQN LDR MARK KNIGHT

Since the end of Operation *Desert Storm*, RAF Tornados have continued to fly operational missions over Iraq, and have also been involved in operations over the former Yugoslavia. In the latter operation, RAF Tornados have been joined by Tornados from the AMI and the Luftwaffe – the first time that all three Tornado operators have participated in military operations together.

Many criticised the fact that Saddam Hussein remained in power in Iraq after the conclusion of Operation *Desert Storm*, though in truth, it is doubtful whether the integrity of the broad allied coalition could have been maintained once the Allied war aims (of removing Iraqi forces from Kuwait) had been achieved. Driving forward to Baghdad itself was probably never a realistic or practical proposition. But as a result the Iraqi leader has continued to be a thorn in the side of the international community ever since. He has continued to threaten Iraq's neighbours and has continued to persecute minorities within his own country, while ruthlessly suppressing all dissent or opposition.

Saddam Hussein's persecution of the Shiite Arabs in southern Iraq, and of the Kurds in the north prompted the establishment of UN-defined 'No Fly Zones' in both areas, enforced by coalition air power. Infringements of these areas, interference with allied aircraft patrolling them and a continuing reluctance to be bound by the terms of the surrender agreement have caused frequent concern in the UN, and have generated a host of military responses. On two occasions, Iraq has even suffered further airstrikes.

The RAF has maintained a commitment to the operations enforcing both the northern and southern No Fly Zones, virtually since the end of the war. A rotationally manned detachment has been maintained at Incirlik as a part of Operation *Warden*, first by the Jaguar force, then by Harrier GR7 squadrons, and most recently by Tornado GR1 units. In the south, Britain's contribution to the US-led Operation *Southern Watch* was known as Operation *Jural*. This has always been staffed by Tornado IDS squadrons, predominantly from those based in Germany.

But ironically enough, neither *Jural* nor *Warden* flowed on directly from *Granby*. With the end of Operation *Desert Storm*, most allied forces were rapidly withdrawn from the region, and especially from Saudi Arabia, where the heavy Western presence promised to provide opposition groups with a focus for dissatisfaction, complaint and hostility to the regime. Thus the RAF withdrew its Tornados from Dhahran and Tabuk in March 1991, with a small detachment remaining at Muharraq in Bahrain for slightly longer.

The Muharraq detachment led directly from the wartime deployment in Bahrain, but consisted of only twelve aircraft (ZA455, 463, 471, 472, 475, 490, 491, ZD790, 792, 809, 844, and 890), some of them drawn from Tabuk and Dharhan, allowing those aircraft with 'longest to go' before overhaul to stay in-theatre. A couple of replacement aircraft (which had not participated in *Desert Storm*, but which had full *Granby* modifications) were sent out before the Detachment (officially No IX (Composite) Squadron disbanded and its aircraft and aircrew returned to their parent units. The detachment formally came to an end on 22 May 1991, following a farewell flypast over Manamah with elements of the Bahrain Defence Force.

During late 1991 at least 15 RAF Germany Tornados were prepared for deployment to the Middle East for a show of force (in support of UN efforts to gain access for its weapons inspectors). These were painted in desert camouflage, and each briefly visited RAF Marham, before passing back to their own units, wearing their original squadron codes, but with a No 617 Squadron lightning flash added to their fin caps. The aircraft comprised ZD851/AJ and ZD789/AM of No IX Squadron, ZD714/BE of No 14, ZD793/CA, ZD849/CC and ZA393/CQ of No 17, ZD811/DF and ZA406/DN of No 31, ZA472/EE, ZA453/EG, ZA459/EL, and ZA462/EM of No 15 and ZA458/FB, ZA470/FC and ZA470/FL of No 16, together with ZA491/GC of No 20 Squadron.

But while that crisis passed without requiring a Tornado deployment to the area, it was not long before Iraqi brinkmanship necessitated an RAF deployment to the region.

The brutal crushing of a Kurdish rising in the northern part of Iraq led to a mass exodus of Kurds in the south-eastern part of Turkey. The UN established a secure area in northern Iraq to allow the Kurds to return to their homes, and this was protected by forces from 13 nations under Operation *Provide Comfort*, beginning on 5 April 1991. Allied ground forces withdrew from the Safe Haven in mid-July 1991, when the UN focus shifted from relief operations to the deterrence of Iraqi encroachment of the Safe Haven. Air elements continued to monitor and enforce a No Fly Zone over the area under Operation *Provide Comfort II*.

US and Turkish air force units were already in place in Turkey to police the No Fly Zone, and were joined by a detachment of French Dassault Mirage F1CR reconnaissance aircraft under Operation *Aconit* in July 1991. British Jaguars flew out from RAF Coltishall on 4 September 1991, under what the RAF called Operation *Warden*.

The Northern No Fly Zone was established north of the 36th Parallel, with a small Military Co-ordination Centre on the ground in the town of Zakho. The latter was abandoned on 2 September 1996 in the face of an Iraqi ground offensive. Operation *Provide Comfort II* continued, however, and became Operation *Northern Watch* on 1 January 1997, when France withdrew from the operation.

Tornados had finally taken over the *Warden* commitment in April 1995 (from Harrier GR7s), with six aircraft arriving at Incirlik on 3 April. These consisted of three No II (AC) Squadron GR1As and three No 617 Squadron GR1Bs, supported by a No 101 Squadron VC-10. Air and ground crews deployed to Incirlik for eight-week detachments, with support personnel for the 158-man detachment deploying for four-month periods.

Primarily a reconnaissance operation (with the limited air-to-ground role being lost when the MCC at Zakho was evacuated), *Warden* is based around the use of the W. Vinten Ltd Vicon 18 Series 601 GP(1) reconnaissance pod, three of which are deployed to Incirlik as theatre assets. The pod is

Two of the first six Tornados deployed to Dhahran on 27 August 1992 to take part in Operation Southern Watch *(the RAF element of which was known as Operation* Jural*). The six aircraft included three TIALD-capable GR1s, two of which are seen 'on patrol' over the southern deserts of Iraq.*

In the early days of Operation Jural*, the Tornados deployed routinely wore desert pink ARTF camouflage, with a No 617 Squadron fin flash and codes which echoed those used during the 1942 Dams Raid. This aircraft was seen after returning from the Gulf, and carries an ML CBLS200 practise bomb carrier.*

described in greater detail in Chapter 5. The mission is one flown almost exclusively at medium altitude, and for this reason the low-level optimised GR1A does not use its TIRRS when deployed. In fact, TIRRS is normally removed and replaced by ballast on GR1As deployed on the operation. The *Warden* deployment has tended to be manned by UK-based Tornado squadrons, leaving *Jural* in the South in the hands of the Brüggen-based units. But while Tornados were slow to return to Iraqi skies in the northern No Fly Zone, in the south, Tornados returned to Dharhan much sooner.

In the summer of 1992, Shia Muslims living in the marshlands near Basrah (the so-called Marsh Arabs) were bombed by Saddam Hussein's forces after an anti-government uprising (the majority of Iraqi Muslims are from the Sunni sect, and have a traditional antipathy to Shiites). To stop Iraqi government oppression of the Marsh Arabs, the UN set about establishing a NFZ south of the 32nd Parallel to protect them from aerial attack, much like that already established in the north to protect the Kurds. The zone itself would be patrolled by coalition aircraft deployed to Saudi Arabia, under Operation *Southern Watch*. HQ Strike Command issued a Warning Order to the Marham wing on 18 August 1992,

Two Jural *Tornados refuel from a No 10 Squadron VC-10 C1K high above the featureless desert. The far aircraft carries a TIALD laser designator, while the other has a Vinten GP(1) reconnaissance pod. The picture was taken by a third Tornado, using another GP(1) pod.* VIA SGT 'TINY' BRIGGS

detailing three TIALD-capable Tornado GR1s (ZD849 AJ-F, ZA462/AJ-M and ZA393/AJ-T) and three recce Tornado GR1As (ZA371/C, ZA398/S and ZA400/T) to make ready for deployment to the Gulf. With three crews drawn from No 617 Squadron, and others from No II (AC) and No 13, the aircraft left Marham at dawn on 27 August 1992, flying direct to Dhahran in time for the promulgation of the NFZ at 1415 hrs UTC that day.

Although the US codename for the operation was *Southern Watch*, the RAF deployment was codenamed Operation *Jural*. The role of the RAF Tornados was to monitor Iraqi compliance with UN Security Council Resolution 688 and to be ready to mount PGM strikes if necessary. LGB deliveries were practised on the Udairi range in September 1992, with the Tornados achieving a creditable 100% success rate.

All six of the aircraft deployed could carry out both strike and recce roles, with TIALD being seen as surveillance and observation tool rather than simply as a designator for laser-guided PGMs. TIALD had demonstrated its post-strike analysis capability during the Gulf War, when two prototype pods had been hastily integrated and deployed. This second

In recent years, aircraft participating in Operations Warden, Jural *and* Deny Flight *have tended to do so with unit insignia removed, but in standard camouflage. This* Jural *aircraft's 'BT' tailcode reveals it as belonging to No 14 Squadron.* SGT 'TINY' BRIGGS

TIALD deployment was a similar contingency operation, in advance of the planned 'production' integration of the system. Under an ITC (Interim TIALD Capability) programme, production TIALD pods were integrated on a number of aircraft using the existing Gulf War TAP 2 (TIALD Accelerated Programme) software, specifically for use on Operation *Jural*.

Monitoring of Iraqi forces was the detachment's main task, checking for compliance with the UN Security Council resolutions imposed on Iraq. As 1992 drew to a close, it became apparent that Saddam Hussein intended to mark the final days in office of US President George Bush with a show of defiance. On 27 December 1992, two Iraqi MiG-25 'Foxbats' engaged USAF F-16s inside the NFZ, leading to one of the Iraqi fighters being shot down. On the ground, Iraqi forces redeployed SAMs to threaten allied aircraft within the NFZ, and the mood began to look progressively more ugly. In the days that followed, Iraqi troops made several cross-border incursions into Kuwait. By 3 January 1993, plans were in place to mount selective air strikes against key targets within the No Fly Zone, mostly directly connected with air defence. Diplomatic measures failed to secure the removal of the SAM batteries, and the Allied nations agreed upon a strike by their forces on 11 January 1993.

RAF participation in the raid was codenamed Operation *Ingleton*, and drew on aircraft and personnel from the *Jural* detachment at Dhahran. The majority of aircrew were from No 31 Squadron, which had taken over the deployment only a fortnight before. No 617 Squadron had actually flown on the dress rehearsal, but rotated home before the actual attack. The use of TIALD was relatively new to No 31 Squadron, and a TIALD-experienced crew from No 617 Squadron (who had used the system during *Desert Storm*) bolstered the detachment. Following weather delays, 100 coalition aircraft launched from their bases and ships on the night of 13 January 1993. Four RAF Tornados (Callsigns *Bulldog, 11, 12, 13* and *14*) took part in the raid, bombing targets within the Al

This No II (AC) Squadron GR1A carries a GP(1) pod on the centreline, and would have had its low-level optimised TIRRS removed and replaced by ballast. The use of the larger ADV-type fuel tanks is routine on Jural. SGT 'TINY' BRIGGS

As memories of Iraqi aggression in 1991 grew fainter, some sections of Arab opinion swung around to reflect a growing public unease with western policy towards Iraq and a growing concern for the Iraqi people, who were hard hit by sanctions (albeit principally by the actions of their own government). The security of (mainly US) western forces at Dharhan became a matter for increasing concern, due to their high visibility and their perceived vulnerability to attack, sabotage or intelligence operations conducted by Iraqi symapthisers or by anti-American opposition groups.

Accordingly, the focus of operations switched from Dharhan to the massive Prince Sultan Air Base (PSAB) at Al Kharj. An RAF Advance Party moved to the base in August 1996, and the aircraft themselves flew in on 13 September 1996. Some 80 miles south of Riyadh, and at 1,600 ft above sea level, Al Kharj lacked many of the creature comforts enjoyed at Dharhan (where many personnel were accommodated in Western-style hotels) although the massive Harvest Falcon Housing Area was much more than a 'Tent City'. Personnel did live in ten-man tents, but these were extremely high-tech, with timber floors, electric lighting, air conditioning, video recorders and networked US TV channels. The RAF detachment was about 230-strong, working alongside 4,500 American servicemen and 150 French personnel. The Tornados operate from a fenced-in flightline known as the 'Doughnut', with six open-sided sun shelters dispersed within it. In recent years (since about mid-1994), Tornados deployed on Operation *Jural* have tended to include aircraft compatible with the W. Vinten Ltd Vicon 18 Series 601 GP (1) reconniassance pod, three of which are assigned.

Iraq has continued to flout United Nations resolutions, deliberately restricting the movements and hampering the

Amarah integrated operations centre complex. They followed USAF F-15Es (callsign *Stingray*) and were covered by Wild Weasels (*Pearl*) and F-15C fighters (*Mobile*). The TIALD-equipped ZD849/AJ-F 'lased' for the Paveway II LGBs dropped by the lead aircraft ZA492/DJ, while ZA472/AJ-E performed the same service for ZA462/AJ-M. Two further strikes on 17 January and 18 January 1993, against SAM sites and command facilities respectively, saw further action by the RAF Tornados. Iraq announced a ceasefire on 21 January 1993, but even this was so framed as to be a deliberately 'mocking' act to welcome the inauguration of Bill Clinton as the new US President.

The new all-grey colour scheme has become a common sight on Operation Warden, *as shown by this GR1A of No II (AC) Squadron. GR1As participating in* Warden *and* Jural *have their TIRRS removed and replaced by ballast.* SQN LDR MARK KNIGHT

All RAF Tornados deployed to Al Jaber in Kuwait for Operation Bolton, *like this No 12 Squadron GR1B, wore their normal squadron markings, but were flown by No 14 Squadron crews.* CPL JOHN CASSIDY

One of the few unmarked Bolton *Tornados was this No 17 Squadron aircraft, seen here carrying a GEC TIALD laser designator on the port shoulder.* CPL JOHN CASSIDY

efforts of weapons inspectors, continuing to persecute ethnic minorities and opposition groups and regularly intimidating Kuwait with shows of force in 'military exercises' along its border. Ever since the end of Operation *Desert Storm*, teams of UN weapons inspectors have faced intimidation and obstruction. It became clear that Iraq's biological weapons programme could be enormous, with huge quantities of growth medium delivered but unaccounted for. At the same time, inspectors were denied access to Saddam's massive Presidential Palace complexes, heavily bunkered and widespread facilities sometimes as large as small towns. Some teams were prevented from going about their business because

Iraq objected to certain American inspectors. There was a genuine concern that Iraq might be deliberately concealing weapons of mass destruction, but in any case, Saddam could not be allowed to dictate terms as to where inspectors went, and as to who served on the UN teams.

US patience with Iraq wore paper-thin, and preparations were put in place for further military operations. Britain was the first nation to join the renewed effort, as Saddam Hussein once more brought the Middle East to the brink of conflict. The existing Tornado *Jural* and *Warden* detachments in Saudi Arabia and Turkey were augmented through Operation *Bolton*. This saw the deployment of HMS *Invincible* (with RAF

As action became more likely, the Bolton *aircraft received a blue-outlined white tail chevron as a recognition marking. This TIALD-equipped No 12 Squadron Tornado GR1B was one of the aircraft allocated to the No 14 Squadron detachment at Al Jaber.* CPL JOHN CASSIDY

A small Union Jack was added to the white tail chevron of the aircraft operated by the No 14 Squadron detachment during Operation Bolton. *This aircraft is a No 12 Squadron GR1B, several of which are TIALD-capable.* CPL JOHN CASSIDY

Harrier GR7s augmenting its air wing) to the Gulf, and the despatch of what was nominally No 14 Squadron to Ali Al Salim AB at Al Jaber, Kuwait, from 9 February 1998.

The choice of Al Jaber, only 60 km from the Iraqi border, as a base for RAF Tornados was somewhat ironic, as its hardened aircraft shelters remain wrecked, many of them having been destroyed during the Gulf War by Paveway II LGBs dropped by… RAF Tornados. Activated in short order by a team led by Wg Cdr Tom Boyle of HQ No 1 Group (himself a former No 14 Squadron Tornado pilot), after a 48-hour reconnaissance, Ali Al Salim soon became a fully functioning base, hosting the eight aircraft of the No 14 Squadron Detachment. The airfield was prepared for the Tornados by RAF and army personnel, the latter being drawn from 34 Field Squadron (Air Support), Royal Engineers. The RAF detachment was commanded by Gp Capt Mal Prisssick, normallly the Station Commander at RAF Marham.

Although nominally assigned to No 14 Squadron the aircraft deployed were actually drawn from a number of units, and included aircraft equipped for TIALD operation and for reconnaissance. The eight aircraft were drawn from GR1s ZA393/BE (No 14 Squadron), ZD747/AL (No IX Squadron) and ZD843/CJ (No 17 Squadron), plus GR1As ZA370/A, ZA398/S and ZA405/Y (all No II (AC) Squadron) together with GR1Bs ZA450/FB and ZA490/FJ (No 12 Squadron) with ZA457/AJ-J and ZA460/AJ-A (No 617 Squadron). There must have been some change-over of aircraft, or some increase in the number of aircraft deployed, since all the aircraft underlined were seen in theatre at one time or another. All of

Hard-worked groundcrew load AIM-9Ls onto a waiting No IX Squadron Tornado. The damage to Al Jaber's HASs forced the RAF to operate in the open. (The shelters had been bombed by RAF Tornados when in Iraqi hands during the Gulf War). CPL JOHN CASSIDY

the GR1s and GR1Bs (with the possible exception of ZD747) were confirmed as being TIALD-capable, and sufficient pods were deployed for five of the seven Tornados involved in the RAF Anniversary Flypast over Kuwait city on 1 April 1998 to be carrying the equipment.

The aircraft retained their standard wraparound grey/green or LIR two-tone grey colour schemes, with their original squadron markings. This was relatively unusual, since British aircraft involved in operations have usually deployed with

Four Tornados preparing for a mission at Al Jaber during Operation Bolton. *All four come from different squadrons (Nos 14, II, 617 and IX) although all were flown by No 14 Squadron crews.* CPL JOHN CASSIDY

For the RAF's 80th anniversary flypast over Kuwait City, five TIALD-armed Tornados preceded a No 101 Squadron VC-10 tanker and another pair of Tornados. CPL JOHN CASSIDY

squadron markings removed. If Iraqi intelligence monitored UK TV newscasts and looked at the RAF News and British aviation magazines, they might have wrongly inferred that they were facing a force of six Tornado squadrons! The aircraft were eventually decorated with a 'cake-slice' chevron in white (outlined thinly in very dark blue) as a recognition marking. A tiny Union Jack was subsequently superimposed on this.

Saddam Hussein was finally sufficiently intimidated by the Anglo-American show of force to come to a negotiated settlement, brokered by the UN Secretary General. He agreed to allow unrestricted access to the weapons inspectors, after a face-saving personal visit by and face-to-face meeting with the UN Secretary General. During a visit to Al Kharj, Britain's Defence Secretary, the Rt.Hon. George Robertson observed that "British Forces in the region have earned a new Battle Honour as the best peacekeepers in the world, and the British public can be very proud of them." But both Britain and the USA were well used to Iraq's brinkmanship and of its previous failures to abide by international agreements. Accordingly they maintained their forces in the region at a high rate of readiness, including the Tornados at Al Jaber. In fact, when HMS *Illustrious* (which had replaced HMS *Invincible*) returned home, its Harrier GR7s were replaced by four more

Tornados which deployed to Al Jaber, bringing the unit there up to full squadron strength.

Slightly closer to home, the Tornado has also proved its worth in the peacekeeping role, supporting UN operations in and over the former Yugoslavia. But while operations over Iraq have seen the RAF making extensive use of its GR1 bombers (principally in the recce role), the Balkans saw the first operational deployment of the F3 since Operation *Granby*. Following the bloody and complex civil war in the former Yugoslavia, the UN launched a major peacekeeping operation in March 1992, aiming to maintain a ceasefire between the newly independent Croatia and Serbia, but also had to protect and maintain the supply of humanitarian aid in neighbouring Bosnia, which was being fiercely fought over by the Muslim army of Bosnia Herzegovina and the Bosnian Serb Army (supported by the Belgrade regime and the Yugoslav Federal Armed forces). The situation was complex, since Bosnia was not an obviously cohesive nation, with an ethnically diverse population spread throughout the country, with pockets where one grouping was numerically dominant within larger areas where another ethnic group might be dominant. Meanwhile the newly independent Croatia had its own designs on parts of Bosnia – and aimed to take over the ethnically Serbian Krajina region, which had declared itself to be a Serb republic in 1992.

The Bosnian Serbs naturally received much assistance from Serbia (the major part of and successor to the old Yugoslavia), which helped to equip Serbian armed forces in Krajina and Bosnia. These included small air arms, which participated in operations against Croat and Bosnian forces, and which continued to do so even after the UN Security Council ordered a ban on all military flights over Bosnia in October 1992, except as authorised by UNPROFOR. USAF, NATO, Armée de l'Air and RAF E-3s began surveillance of Bosnian airspace on 16 October 1992, monitoring countless violations. The No Fly Zone was finally enforced from March 1993, following Serbian air attacks during the attack on Srebrenica.

NATO's 5 ATAF set up a Combined Air Operation Centre at

Dal Molin, near Vicenza, and began flying round-the-clock fighter CAPs (two permanent CAP stations were maintained over Bosnia) using USAF, RAF, Dutch, French and Turkish fighters based in Italy, and US Navy carrier-borne fighters from vessels operating in the Adriatic. RAF Tornado F3s maintained a detachment at Gioia del Colle from April 1993, with all of the UK-based squadrons taking it in turns to man the detachment on a rotational basis. The first six Tornado F3s flew out to Gioia on 19 April 1993, and were supported by a VC-10 tanker deployment, which quickly moved from hot-and-high Sigonella to Milan Malpensa. The initial deployment was made by No 11 Squadron, under Wg Cdr John Cliffe.

With their NVG-trained, two-man crews, the Tornado F3s were among NATO's most capable night/all-weather fighters, and often found themselves assigned to 'Graveyard shifts', when the operational area was in darkness, and when F-16s and the like were of more limited usefulness. Typically, the Tornado squadrons would launch four aircraft to fulfil a three-hour slot on station, with one pair of aircraft flying direct to the operational area, and the second to a waiting tanker over the Adriatic.

The fighter CAPs had an immediate effect. The Bosnian Serb air force's fast jets remained on the ground at Banja Luka, and while the Krajina Serb ground attack aircraft continued operations from Udbina, they were careful not to venture into Bosnian airspace.

But the allied rules of engagement were very strict, allowing NATO fighters to engage aircraft that were carrying out offensive combat operations, actually firing cannon or rockets, or dropping bombs. All sides continued to conduct intensive helicopter and light aircraft operations, and it was decided that while these movements should be investigated and intercepted wherever possible, helicopters would not actually be shot down. This constraint was due to fears that a casevac helicopter or an aircraft carrying civilians could be shot down, and this

would have given the Serbs a useful propaganda weapon. But although NATO interceptors regularly intercepted helicopters, they achieved very little. The offending aircraft would often leave the NFZ as instructed, or would land, but as soon as the fighters left the area to refuel they would continue with their missions. Moreover, the anti-helicopter mission forced the fighters to descend to very low level, often in dangerously mountainous terrain, where they were more vulnerable to SAMs and AAA. Fuel consumption also rose, and while the Tornado F3 crews had practised low-level fighter affiliation with RAF helicopters prior to deployment, there was no doubt that flinging a heavily laden F3 around at low level, and often at night, was not always a welcome task.

Tornado detachments in support of Operation *Deny Flight* continued as the situation on the ground deteriorated. Squadrons took it in turns to man the deployment, three months at a time. The Leeming wing took the controls first, and No 23 Squadron were in Italy when a formal announcement was made that the unit would disband as a result of the cuts announced in the 'Options for Change' defence review. This was bad news, and was singularly badly timed since the unit was fulfilling an operational commitment (and had received the honour of being only the second F3 squadron to deploy) as the announcement was formally made, on 7 July 1993. The AOC-in-C No 11 Group had flown to Gioia to give the squadron the bad news personally, but Sky News had got there first. No 23 showed its mettle by completing its deployment in exemplary fashion. Fortunately, the Tornado F3s then still deployed to Gioia in full squadron markings, and the unit's red eagle insignia flew operational CAP missions over Bosnia before the squadron returned to Leeming and disbandment.

The collapse of the Vance-Owen plan led to the establishment of a Joint Action Plan which authorised CAS missions by NATO aircraft, but this had little real effect on the

Tornado F3 ZE967 shortly before take-off from Gioia del Colle on 5 February 1994 on a sortie which was to last for over six and a half hours, that would see the Tornado element achieve their 3,000th flight hour since Deny Flight *operations began in April 1993.* BOB ARCHER

Fully armed and connected up to ground power, this No XI Squadron F3 waits for its crew before taking off for a **Deny Flight** *mission over Bosnia. The aircraft has small IDS-type fuel tanks, a Phimat chaff dispenser, three AIM-9s and four SkyFlash missiles.*

tempo of F3 operations. The air war intensified in February 1994, when four Krajina Serb ground attack aircraft were shot down by F-16s. The shootdowns occurred when six Galebs, Oraos or Super Galebs attacked Bosnian weapons factories on 28 February 1994. In November 1994, Serb aircraft from Udbina attacked targets in the Bihac pocket, but were able to return to base before they could be intercepted. This led directly to NATO's attack on Udbina, which involved RAF Jaguars, but not the F3s. The attack was followed, however, by a series of incidents in which NATO attacked Serb SAM radars which illuminated its aircraft, which in turn led to the launching of SAMs against a number of NATO aircraft. A Royal Navy Sea Harrier was almost hit on 22 November, and on 24 November two No 11 Squadron Tornados were fired upon by a SAM-2 and a SAM-6. The F3s escaped unharmed, but the incident led to a crash programme to improve the

Armourers load a SkyFlash onto a Tornado F3 during Operation Deny Flight. *The way in which the upper fin of the missile recesses into a slot in the lower fuselage is noteworthy.* JEREMY FLACK/API

type's defensive aids, with the rapid integration of the GEC Aerial Towed Radar Decoy.

Italy's first F3s joined *Deny Flight* after 36° Stormo's 12° Gruppo was declared combat ready in February 1995. The Italian F3s, co-located beside the RAF detachment at Gioia, flew intensive CAP missions, and the unit's aircrew rapidly built up an invaluable level of operational experience. Italian Tornado IDS aircraft had already been quite heavily committed to UN operations, though they were initially prohibited from actually operating over the former Yugoslavia. 36° Stormo, in particular, had assisted allied navies in maintaining the naval arms blockade of Yugoslavia, flying low-level reconnaissance and show-of-force missions over the Adriatic. On more than one occasion, the sight of a pair of Kormoran-armed Tornados sweeping past was enough to halt Serb ships in their tracks! Fortunately, the aircraft were never called upon to actually engage enemy shipping. The Italian participation in Operation *Sharp Guard* was rotated between 154°, 155° and 156° Gruppi, with Kormoran missiles being 'borrowed' from 156° Gruppo.

1995 saw no improvement in the situation in Bosnia, and it became increasingly apparent that it would only be a matter of time before NATO would have to use its air power to make a decisive intervention to break the deadlock and force the sides to negotiate. With NATO aircraft encountering increasingly effective Serbian air defences, Germany deployed a composite unit of eight JBG 32 ECRs and six recce-configured aircraft from AKG 51 to Piacenza in August 1995, beginning operations on 31 August. NATO's Operation *Deliberate Force*, a pre-prepared contingency plan, had been launched on 30 August 1995, in response to a Serb mortar attack on a market in Sarajevo. This gave the Tornado its first opportunity to expend live ordnance in the conflict, though the German aircraft were destined to return home without

German Tornados deployed to Piacenza for operations over Bosnia in August 1995. They consisted of ECRs from JBG 32 and recce-roled IDS aircraft from AKG 51, as seen here. The aircraft were nominally assigned to Einsatzgeschwader 1. DAVE BOWERS

In September 1995, 6° Stormo started mounting rotational deployments to Gioia del Colle for missions over Bosnia. 6° Stormo's 154° Gruppo flew an armed reconnaiisance mission over Bosnia on 2 September 1995. On 7 September, the same unit mounted its first bombing mission, using free-fall Mk 83 bombs. The *Deliberate Force* series of attacks forced the warring factions to the negotiating table, and began the long road to peace, but also demonstrated shortfalls in Italian Tornado capabilities, prompting the acquisition of Thomson-CSF CLDP (Combined Laser Designator Pod) pods to allow autonomous designation for GBU-16 Paveway II LGBs. Aircraft from 6°, 36° and 50° Stormos have participated in missions over Bosnia, in support of Operation *Joint Endeavor* (to which eight AMI Tornados were assigned, on a rotational basis). The RAF's Tornado F3 deployments to Gioia ended in February 1996, and the ECRs assigned to Einsatzgeschwader 1 returned home on 22 November 1996, but other German and Italian Tornados continued to operate over Bosnia, and the F3s and ECRs remained on standby to return to the theatre if required.

firing a shot in anger. The deployment of Einsatzgeschwader 1 (the German composite unit) was Germany's first operational deployment, and German reluctance to use its forces outside her own borders was reflected in the unit's Rules of Engagement. These ensured that a German officer at the CAOC had power of veto over any mission proposed for the German Tornados, while the RoE governing actual weapons release were almost impossibly tight. The reconnaissance aircraft were able to operate in their primary role virtually without restriction, however, and proved useful in the daylight reconnaissance role.

Both Iraq and the former Yugoslavia were destined to remain in the news, and both became the scene of further action by the hard-worked Tornados, as described in the final chapter of this book. The post-Cold War world has been a busy one for NATO air forces, and cutbacks imposed to secure a 'Peace Dividend' now look increasingly cynical and short-sighted.

This Tornado ECR was one of those assigned to Einsatzgeschwader 1 between August 1995 and November 1996. The recce aircraft remained in-theatre rather longer. The aircraft deployed to Bosnia were painted in a new light grey camouflage. WERNER GREPPMEIR

Upgrading the IDS

The first prototype GR4 (ZD708) gets smartly airborne on its first flight, on 29 May 1993, carrying the bold GR4 logo on the fin, and an empty FLIR fairing below the forward fuselage.

Throughout its service life, the Tornado has been subject to a near-constant stream of improvements, modifications and enhancements, such that the latest Batch 9 aircraft rolled off the line for Saudi Arabia were surprisingly different from the first production aircraft delivered to the TTTE. But the changes instituted during production were largely evolutionary, and generally helped the aircraft to perform its existing role more effectively. But the passage of time, and a changing international environment, led to the need for a more far-reaching and ambitious upgrade, if the Tornado was to remain viable beyond the end of the Cold War. Although all three of the original Tornado partners would need to upgrade their Tornados at roughly the same time, and would require similar capability enhancements, it soon became clear that agreeing a joint MLU requirement would impose unacceptable delays and prevarication.

The RAF began looking at a Mid-Life Update for the Tornado in the early 1980s, aiming to enhance the aircraft's operational capabilities, and to extend the type's OSD (Out-of-Service Date). Staff Requirement SR(A)-417 was drawn up for a Tornado upgrade which would enhance the aircraft's ability to penetrate hostile airspace, to use more accurate new-generation weapons, and to attack targets from greater stand-off range.

Britain remained committed to low-level penetration tactics, and conceived its upgraded Tornado as an aircraft able to make a covert, electronically silent penetration of enemy airspace, using a variety of non-emitting (or low emission)

systems for navigation and terrain following, instead of the Terrain Following and Attack radars. It was soon decided that the new Tornado variant would use a GEC Spartan Terrain Referenced navigation system together with a GEC TICM II FLIR. Spartan used a radar altimeter to compare terrain features overflown with a comprehensive terrain database in order to ascertain the aircraft's position (it was of course integrated with GPS and INS), and could also give predictive warning of terrain features in the aircraft's path, giving a nominally electronically silent automatic terrain following capability. Spartan was first flown in a Jetstream testbed, then later in an F-16, and finally in one of BAe's own Tornados, XZ630.

In the early days of the project, the extent of the upgrade was ambitious. The GR4 as originally planned would even have looked different from the standard, baseline IDS. With a stretched forward fuselage (giving room for new avionics and perhaps extra fuel) the aircraft would have also featured 'stealthy' air intakes, a gold-coated canopy, and other RCS-reduction features. It was proposed that the new variant might make increased use of composite materials, including the all-composite taileron developed by BAe and flown in 1982. Some even proposed that the upgraded aircraft would be re-engined with the Eurojet EJ200 developed for the Eurofighter. Lighter than the RB199, with half the number of moving parts and 50% greater dry thrust, the EJ200 had been designed to be 'installationally compatible with the RB199'. While this compatability later allowed prototype Eurofighters to fly under RB199 power, the requirement had originally been put in place to allow the engine to be offered as a Tornado retrofit option. The EJ200 would have been an excellent engine for Tornado, producing almost as much dry thrust as the RB199 produced in maximum reheat. More modestly, it was suggested that the GR4 might use the RB199 Mk 105 fitted to German Tornado ECRs, or the frugal RB199 Mk 103B.

Other elements of the planned MLU Tornado included new stub pylons on the outboard face of each underwing pylon, these being dedicated to carriage of the BAe ALARM anti-radar missile. The aircraft would also feature provision for TIALD, and for the carriage of massive new 592-Imp gal (2,691 litre) underwing fuel tanks. Less obviously, the new variant would feature a new Stores Management System, a Ferranti wide-angle holographic HUD, a new MFD HDD from Smiths Industries for the pilot, Marconi Zeus RHAWS and a digital FBW flight control system.

A feasibility study for a Tornado MLU (Mid-Life Update) was first approved in 1984, and the so-called MLU-88, which identified a need to upgrade the Tornado weapons systems. This was followed by a development and investment contract on 16 March 1989. This eventually resulted in a planned programme to update 165 aircraft for service entry in 1993, to be preceded by 26 new-build aircraft being built to the same standard as part of Batch Eight. The first 70 upgrades were to be converted by BAe at Warton in a Return to Works programme, with the next 15 to be produced by joint BAe/RAF working parties at St Athan, and with the last 80 to be converted by whichever organisation provided the best competitive tender. The total cost of the programme was then estimated at around £1bn, each upgrade taking ten months, and with 20 aircraft on the conversion line at any one time.

The end of the Cold War and the associated 'Options for Change' defence review led to the cancellation of the new-build Batch Eight aircraft on 18 June 1990, and the programme (already running behind schedule as a result of 'shifting goalposts' and technical problems) came under threat of cancellation or 'trimming'. Even as the dust settled after 'Options for Change' the Tornado force found itself caught up in the Gulf War. Operation *Granby* saw the Tornado pressed into service in the medium level role, using PGMs, and seemed to cast some doubt on the long-term relevance of low level penetration tactics. In fact, it did nothing of the sort, since the original anti-airfield campaign was best conducted at low level, and the ability of aircraft to operate safely at medium level subsequently was the result of the unchallenged allied air supremacy – a state of affairs which could not always be expected. However, it was clear that medium level operations could not be ruled out, and that the Gulf War medium level air campaign had revealed some 'sub-optimal areas' for the Tornado GR1, whose sensors were perhaps too narrowly optimised for low level use, and which lacked autonomous laser designation capability.

Thus the Gulf War certainly had its effect on the Tornado MLU-88. The operation prompted re-examination of the project by the Operational Requirements Branch and by the Treasury! Moreover the loss of aircraft during Operation *Granby* meant that to update 165 aircraft (161 according to some recent sources) would now require the modification of some older, first production batch aircraft (which lacked LRMTS and centreline pylons, and which still had the original engines). Throughout 1993, the final outcome standard of the MLU aircraft was discussed and it became clear that the extent of the upgrade, and the number of aircraft to be upgraded

One of the aircraft used intensively in support of the GR4 programme has been BAe Warton's ZA354. The aircraft is seen here with JP233 under the fuselage, standard IDS fuel tanks, ALARM missiles on the outboard stub pylons, and with Sky Shadow and BOZ outboard. A patch of primer on the fin shows the position of the GR4's new ADV heat exchanger. It also has low-intensity strip-type formation lights fitted. DEREK BOWER

One weapon mooted for the GR4 was a derivative of Rockwell's AGM-130, a rocket-boosted guided bomb seen here under the wing of an SAOEU Tornado. VIA ROBERT F DORR

would have to be reduced further. The budget was reduced by 25% (to £750 m), and the major airframe modifications were abandoned. On 4 May 1993 (the very day that XZ631 made its maiden flight in support of the MLU), the Chief of the Air Staff, Sir Michael Graydon, announced the cancellation of the GEC Spartan TRNS. But worse was to follow when the MLU contract was finally awarded on 14 July 1994, following the Government's Front Line First defence review.

The £640m order covered the upgrade of only 80 aircraft, with an option to convert 62 more during 2000-2002. The decision had been taken to reduce the number of aircraft to be upgraded to 142, generating a much-needed cost-saving estimated at £109m. At the same time the reduced content of the upgrade was finally revealed. The GEC TICM II FLIR was retained (in a fixed forward-looking mounting), together with

a pilot's MFD which could display either a FLIR picture (with or without HUD symbology) or a digital moving map display. The upgraded aircraft also featured a new wide-angle holographic HUD which could display the FLIR picture, GPS and a new video-based recording system.

It was hard to see the reduced scope of the extent as anything other than a cynical exercise in cost-saving. The changing international situation faced the RAF's Tornado force with a less well-defined (but no less capable) threat, and a wider range of possible scenarios. RAF Tornados might have to operate in new roles, and might have to operate without the USAF fighter escort or SEAD support which could once have been taken for granted. This demanded increased flexibility and enhanced capability, rather than the reverse. If there was a bright side for BAe it was that the tender element of the MLU had disappeared, and that BAe would get all of the upgrade work, and perhaps that the MLU had not been cancelled entirely.

But despite the cutbacks, the core aims of the upgrade remained the same. These aims were to provide integrated avionics and weapons (including compatability with future weapons systems), an improved DASS, improved 24 hour capability, and to standardise the Tornado fleet. The latter aim was of crucial importance, since by 1997, the Tornado Force was hindered by a severe 'Fleets within Fleets' or Mini Fleet problem, with at least seven different standards of aircraft, each with slightly different equipment fits and capabilities. By giving each GR4 compatability with the widest possible range of weapons, sensors, and systems, the present situation with a handful of TIALD aircraft, a handful of Sea Eagle aircraft, etc. should be avoided.

At the heart of the GR4 is its GEC FLIR. Although dismissed by some as obsolescent in its application on the Harrier GR7, the FLIR will give Tornado crews a much-needed boost in

ZA354 again, this time getting airborne at Warton during Paveway III trials. The Texas Instruments Paveway III was selected to meet the RAF's requirement for a low-level stand-off bomb.

An unidentified Tornado GR1 rushes along a valley in the Lake District. One vital (but often overlooked) fact about the GR4 upgrade is that it leaves the Tornado's existing foul weather, ultra low-level capabilities in place. FRANK HOUSBY

night attack capability, freeing them from reliance on radar to find their targets. When used in conjunction with NVGs, FLIR will also free pilots from relying on timing or external lights for separation from other aircraft, for finding the tanker, or for safe formation keeping. The equipment will give a degree of fine weather non-radar covert night attack capability, while established TFR and attack radar capabilities will be retained for bad weather night operation.

Fortunately, most of the requirements for the range of new weapons planned for the upgraded Tornado survived the cuts, and various specific weapons were finally selected, after intense competitive evaluations. The requirement for a new stand-off nuclear weapon (SR(A) 1244) was the exception, being abandoned after evaluation of the Martin TASM, the Boeing SRAM 2, and the Aerospatiale ASLP. The abandonment of SR(A) 1244 may not have been entirely unconnected with the final relinquishing of the RAF's nuclear role, and the premature retirement in early 1998 of the WE177 freefall nuclear bomb.

In the conventional attack role, three new generation weapons were planned for the upgraded Tornado. SR(A)-1238 called for a new stand-off anti-armour weapon. Many expected this to be a dispenser weapon system, like a winged, powered JP233, but the weapon selected was the AGM-114 Hellfire-based Brimstone missile. Small and relatively light in weight, Brimstone can be carried in clusters of three on most fast jet hardpoints, allowing a Tornado equipped with the weapon to engage multiple targets. SR(A)-1242 called for a low level stand-off bomb. The preferred option was once believed to be GEC's rocket boosted Lancelot, but this carried a 50% higher price tag than the freefall Texas Instruments Paveway III LGB, which was selected in July 1994, and whose big wings give it a measure of glide performance.

Arguably the most important of the new weapons

Based on the Matra Apache, the Storm Shadow was selected to meet the RAF's requirement for a Conventionally Armed Stand-Off Missile to be carried by the GR4.

requirements for the MLU Tornado was SR(A)-1238 – for a Conventionally Armed Stand-Off Missile (CASOM). It certainly attracted the largest number and variety of competing weapons, which ranged from extended-range boosted glide-bombs to full-up cruise missiles. Apparent favourite at one stage seemed to be the GEC Pegasus or Centaur (derived from the Al Hakim weapons supplied to the UAE), a turbofan-powered, imaging infra-red missile. It is believed that the weapon fell victim to licencing difficulties with the Microturbo powerplant, Sagem INS and SNPE warhead. The weapon eventually selected to meet the requirement was the BAe/Matra Storm Shadow, a development of the German

Although looking superficially identical, the two GR4 prototypes differed in minor details. ZD708 (nearest the camera) had a forward-looking camera mounted in the RWR fairing on the fin leading edge, a white belly, and camera calibration markings. It also carried a Sky Shadow pod painted in Saudi camouflage.

Apache. Other weapons proposed included the German Benz Aerospace KEPD 350, the Israeli Popeye, the Hunting/ McDonnell Douglas Grand Slam (a derivative of the AGM-84), the Shorts/Texas Instruments JSOW P31, a derivative of the Rockwell AGM-130 and the Hughes Airhawk. SR(A) 1240 calls for a short-range ARM, and remains unfulfilled.

Warton has used three primary trials aircraft in support of the Tornado GR4 programme. The first of these was XZ631 (P.15) the final British pre-production aircraft, which was

The SAOEU is already developing tactics and procedures for the GR4. The unit (whose Tornados are seen here en route to the USA in September 1997) has a single aircraft equipped with a podded FLIR. This is ZG706, a converted GR1A, seen here closest to the camera and known as the Nightfox Tornado. KEVIN WILLS

brought up to virtual Block 11 standards, but which was not converted to GR4 configuration. Used primarily for Defensive Aids Sub-System clearances, the aircraft did feature an aerodynamic mock-up of the undernose FLIR fairing which made it appear like a full-standard GR4. The aircraft first flew in support of the GR4 programme on 4 May 1993, in the hands of John Turner and Peter Huett, flying FLIR fairing aerodynamic assessments in June and July.

Apart from XZ631, two production GR1s were converted to serve as GR4 prototypes, with work on these beginning in April 1992. The first of these was ZD708, which made its maiden flight on 29 May 1993. ZG773 followed on 1 September 1993, in the hands of Pete Orme and Garth Gardner. ZD708 and ZG773 were almost identical in external appearance, and supported one another in the trials programme. ZD708 had a forward-facing test camera in place of the forward RHAWS antenna on the fin, and had camera calibration markings along the lower 'corners' of the forward fuselage. ZG773 has a full NVG cockpit and standard tail-mounted RWR antenna fairings, however, and only ZG773 is slated to be included in the 142 aircraft total for delivery to the RAF. The aircraft is actually scheduled to be the last on the GR4 'production' line, though it has already been converted, since its installations are prototype standard. Both ZD708 and ZG773 are destined to spend an extended period at Warton.

The two GR4 prototypes carried large GR4 logos in red and blue on the fuselage in front of the intakes and on the tailfin (with a reduced-size, high fin flash), and each also had a white Tornado logo on the forward fuselage. This logo has also been applied to at least one unmodified Tornado (GR1A ZA401) for static display purposes at the 1996 Farnborough Air Show.

A number of other Tornados have been used in support of the GR4 programme, without having been converted to GR4 standards. Warton's ZA354 has been heavily involved in weapons clearances (including Paveway III) and has also trialled strip-type low intensity formation lights. Even more significant has been the SAOEU's GR1A, ZG706, known as the Nightfox Tornado. Converted as a one-off trials aircraft, the Nightfox Tornado was intended for frontline operational evaluation of FLIR (like the Nightrider Harrier). It was also to provide the Strike Attack OEU with a FLIR-equipped Tornado in advance of the GR4, allowing the frontline to be better prepared to exploit FLIR when the new variant entered service. At one time, the Nightfox Tornado was to have been an early equivalent to the 'full monty' GR4, but FLIR integration was addressed first, due to timescales.

Following a July 1993 MoD (PE) contract, the Avionics and Sensors Department (AVS) at DRA Farnborough provided ZG706 with a podded GEC 1010 FLIR, a new GR4-type GEC Marconi Raster-capable HUD, a new HDD, a MIL STD 1553B digital databus, multiplexed video recording and HOTAS control of the FLIR, using a new F/A-18 type stick-top. The aircraft was modified by the Air Fleet Department at Boscombe Down, which also acted as the Design Authority. The Nightfox aircraft was produced rapidly and at low cost, by pooling the RAF's Tornado operating experience with DERA's extensive experience of project management, systems design and integration, flight test and aerodynamic/airworthiness clearance.

Nightfox is not an operational aircraft, since its FLIR is high quality trials equipment, which may not be robust enough for frontline use. It is also mounted in a large, heavy and high-drag pod, which takes up a stores station. Similarly, while the GR4 has a multi-function display screen for FLIR imagery or a moving map display, the Nightfox Tornado can either be fitted with the normal GR1 moving map display or a Head-Down Display for FLIR imagery (with or without HUD symbology overlaid).

The Nightfox Tornado was delivered to the SAOEU on 12 January 1996, in time for the unit to conduct trials in the USA that summer. The aircraft was grounded briefly at the end of 1996 for revisions to the HOTAS functionality, but soon resumed trials flying. This gave the RAF a GR4 'simulator' more than two years before the actual GR4 entered service with the unit.

While the GR4 prototypes were converted 'from scratch' at Warton, where they are destined to stay, aircraft to be converted and returned to service undergo a slightly more convoluted process. Before going to Warton, aircraft are delivered to RAF St Athan for what is known as a PIMP (Pre-Input Maintenance Programme), a pre-MLU lay-up during which aircraft are brought to their theoretically correct production standard. They receive a major or minor servicing, as appropriate, and have any missing modifications incorporated, and have any STFs removed. The procedure now usually includes a repaint in black primer (for corrosion

The GR4 is fitted with an NVG compatible cockpit, as seen here. The use of NVGs complements the fixed, forward-looking FLIR.

Plans for a batch of new-build GR4s were abandoned in 1990, placing the onus of development on a pair of converted GR1s, which had to serve as prototypes. TERRY SENIOR

protection) with control surfaces finished in the new grey colour scheme.

The aircraft are then delivered to Warton, where they stay in their assigned bay rather than flowing along a conversion line. Three Hangars (2, 3 and 4) will eventually participate in the programme, each with six bays and one or two Receipt, Fuel and PFAT (Pre-Flight/Air Test) positions. Each bay will have its own IT links, while mobile test equipment will move from bay to bay. Single 40-man teams will look after three aircraft simultaneously, overseeing the conversion from delivery to dispatch. Movement of individual aircraft will be kept to an absolute minimum. The GR4 line will represent the finest Return-to-Works facility in Europe.

Warton received its first Tornado for upgrade on 1 April 1996, and will receive the last in February 2002. This will finally be re-delivered in October 2002. The delivery schedule called for six GR4s to be delivered in 1997, nineteen in 1998, 29 in 1999, 32 in 2000 and 2001, and 24 in 2002. The procedure will be streamlined as the teams gain experience, and will fall

The second GR4 prototype, ZG773, makes its maiden flight on 1 September 1993. The GR4s are rarely photographed from this side, since their GR4 logos slope 'the wrong way'!

from 252 to 157 days. Breakdown and equipment removal will fall from ten to five days, for example, while modification embodiment will be reduced from 143 to 64 days, and systems functionality testing will fall from 45 to 38 days. The peak rate (which will be achieved in 1999) will see aircraft leaving the line every eight days.

Following conversion, the GR4s return to St Athan for a POMP (Post-Output Maintenance Programme) which includes re-painting, any necessary rectification, and sometimes the re-incorporation of STFs removed before the aircraft went to St Athan. Such STFs could include Sea Eagle or TIALD modifications, or GP(1) reconnaissance pod compatability – service modifications which were not the responsibility of BAe.

The first true 'production' GR4 was ZG750, which was formally handed over to the RAF at Warton on 31 October 1997. Programme insiders regarded this as a 'Major Smilestone' – happy that it marked the end of the project's first phase. Already re-painted in the new grey colour scheme, the aircraft had GR4 logos on the nose and tail, together with a Tornado logo in yellow on the forward fuselage, and a yellow fin flash on which were the words 'First Production'. Delivered to Boscombe Down the aircraft subsequently made high profile visits to Brüggen and Leuchars (the latter for a Tactical Leadership Training exercise, concentrating on night operations). Handed over to the RAF on the same occasion was ZA557, the third 'production' GR4.

The first aircraft to return to St Athan for the 37-day POMP (Post Output Maintenance Programme) was ZG710/D of No 13 Squadron, the first GR4A and second aircraft off the line). Although this process was due to be completed on 23 April 1998, it was planned that the aircraft would then remain at St Athan until the release to service document was signed.

The first GR4 to be delivered from St Athan to the frontline (ZD847/AA) went to No IX Squadron at Brüggen on 11 May 1998. As far as can be ascertained, the variant did not then have a full release to service (though this was due on 31 March 1998), and the usefulness of the aircraft to No IX must be open to question. Cynics suggested that the delivery was made in order to be able to say that delivery to the frontline had been achieved in 1998, since the programme was already rather delayed (the original ISD had been June 1993). The 63-month

Unlike ZD708, the second GR4 retained its forward RWR fairing, providing an immediate recognition aid between the two prototypes. The GR4 as flown was a very much more modest advance on the baseline Tornado than had once been expected.

The first 'production' Tornado GR4 (ZG750) is seen here in the PFAT position of one of the first two GR4 hangars. Behind are six line positions, in which further GR4s and 4As are taking shape. The GR4s stay in one bay, and do not flow along a 'production line'.

Graham Wardell (previously the RAF's first F-117A exchange pilot) and Phil Compton stand in front of ZG750.

delay was broken down by the NAO, who attributed 24 months of the delay to 'technical difficulties and additional time for competitive tendering', a further 28 months to 'funding constraints, the need to seek reapproval because of cost escalation and the resultant need for project redefinintion' (the latter adding a further 11 months to the overall figure). The aircraft was expected to meet its revised ISD of September 1998, following a final software upgrade, but the latter was still being cited as a problem in February 2000, when the British national press highlighted the GR4's alleged continuing inability to perform certain roles.

The first GR4s were destined to equip the Brüggen Wing and delivery of ZD847 to Brüggen preceded publication of the National Audit Office's Ministry of Defence Major Projects Report 1997 by two days. This document revealed the current cost estimates for the project as £403m for development and £543m for production, giving a unit production cost of £3.82m, or a unit programme cost of £6.66m. Costs were increased by the cancellation of the planned production Batch Eight, which resulted in the GR4 conversion programme requiring more dedicated design work. Costs were also increased by the RAF's requirement to integrate TIALD, and by the provision of what was described as 'Extra Government Furnished Equipment'.

The RAF's GR1A reconnaissance aircraft are being upgraded to similar standards, and will differ from the GR4 only in retaining TIRRS in place of the internal cannon. Some of the earliest aircraft on the conversion line were GR1As, and the first were re-delivered to No 13 Squadron as GR4As in late 1998. The new RAPTOR pod can be carried by both the GR4A and the GR4 'bomber'.

The first GR4s and GR4As in service will not be to the full planned standard. The MLU is a multi-stage programme, with certain weapons/equipment integration to be provided after re-delivery of the upgraded aircraft. These integrations are

divided into numbered packages. Package 1 (with wiring provided from aircraft No 49, and with full incorporation 'on the Warton line' from aircraft No 61) will introduce the six-channel Video Recording System, and will finally provide compatability with the Raytheon/Texas Instruments Paveway III laser-guided bomb, the upgraded TIALD 400 Series pod and will introduce fleet-wide compatability with Sea Eagle. Deliveries of Package 1 aircraft will coincide with Tornado GR4 deliveries to Lossiemouth, after which the bulk of the GR1Bs will be cycled through the upgrade.

Package 2 (to be incorporated 'on the line' from aircraft No 109, in September 2002) will add provision for Storm Shadow,

The first and third GR4s (the second aircraft was actually a GR4A) were officially handed over to the RAF in a ceremony at Warton on 31 October 1997. The third aircraft is seen here, with TIALD, Brimstone and Storm Shadow mock-ups. DEREK BOWER

ZG750 (the first production GR4) gets airborne on its maiden flight on 31 October 1997. Areas of primer show much of the extent of structural work on the new variant, including the faired-over left-hand cannon port.

A close up of the new FLIR fairing fitted below the port forward fuselage of all Tornado GR4s and GR4As. The fairing contains a GEC 1010 FLIR based on TICM II, as used in the Harrier GR7. DEREK BOWER

Brimstone, ALARM on the stub pylons, and (on the GR1As) the new RAPTOR reconnaissance pod. RAF Marham, home to the two Tornado recce squadrons, will be the last of the three frontline Tornado Main Operating Bases to re-equip with upgraded aircraft. Package 2 will incoprorate some airframe modifications, aimed primarily at protecting the airframe from the missile plume. Further upgrade packages may incorporate an integrated LINS/GPS/GPWS, MIL STD 1760 compatibility, a new successor IFF, JTIDS or MIDS, fast jet MAWS, and greater HOTAS functionality.

When all of its elements are fully integrated, the Tornado GR4 will tepresent one of the most capable air-to-ground aircraft in service, more advanced and more capable than aircraft like the F-15E in some key respects. The baseline GR1 will reach its OSD in 2010 (by which time it will be limited to the conversion training role), while the GR4 will be able to soldier on until at least 2018. This length of service obviously has implications for the Tornado's airframe. Fatigue is apparently being 'looked at separately'. The Tornado's fatigue life has already been extended from 4,000 to 4,500 flying hours, and should be extended further to 8,000 hours.

There is every likelihood that the Royal Saudi Air Force will become a customer for the GR4 upgrade, while BAe has even made attempts to sell new-build GR4s to new Tornado customers. In 1996, for example, the company offered 24 such aircraft to the UAE, with provision for an interim lease of 12 GR1s. Such an order would mark a neat end to the Tornado story (production of the aircraft stands at 26 short of the 1,000 aircraft mark) but would give any customer a remarkably efficient and cost-effective strike attack aircraft, whose strengths have seldom been widely acknowledged.

Germany has always kept at the forefront of upgrade activity on the Tornado. During the late 1980s, early German aircraft were upgraded to virtual Batch 5 standards through the Tornado First Upgrade programme, which provided a MIL STD 1553B digital databus, a new HARM compatible SMS, improved EW/ECM, a mission data transfer system and DECUs for the engines. But this was little more than ensuring that all in-service aircraft were to a common (high) standard, avoiding the potential 'Mini-Fleet' problem inherent in operating a large fleet of aircraft built in batches over an extended period. But Tornado First was not a solution to the aircraft's increasing obsolescence, nor, most crucially, to its unsuitability for post-Cold War operations, which inferred medium level attacks using PGMs.

Luftwaffe strike/attack Tornados (not the ECRs, and

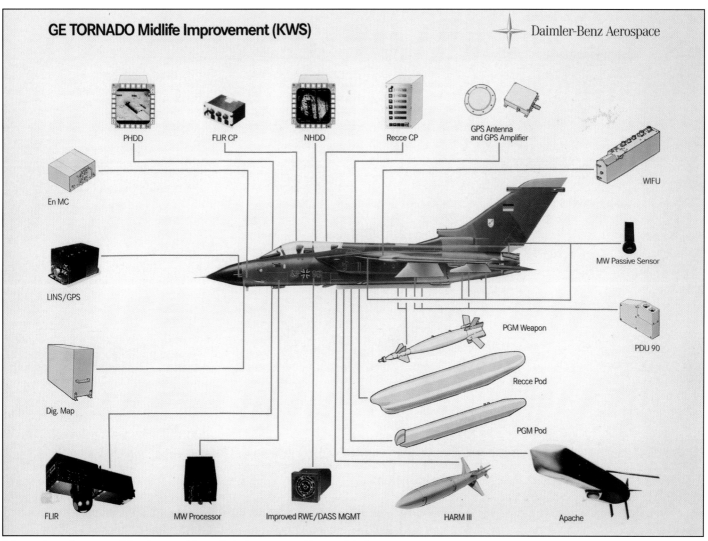

The various elements of the German Tornado MLI presented in graphic form.

probably not the recce-roled aircraft of AKG 51) are therefore receiving a further multi-stage MLU known as the KWS (Kampfwertanpassungsprogramm or Combat Efficiency Enhancement Programme) at the hands of Daimler-Benz Aerospace. The first phase (known as the Neue Avionikstruktur) will see the installation of a MIL STD 1760 databus and a new main computer using ADA software rather than the original Assembler. These improvements will allow the subsequent integration of various new sensors, weapons and systems in phase two, known as KWE (Kampfwerterhaltungsprogramm or Combat Efficiency Upgrade Programme). This stage of the upgrade also added a new defensive aids computer, with a new MAWS, improved RHAWS and enhanced ECM.

The upgraded aircraft will be able to use the new improved HARM III ARM, and the modular Apache stand-off ASM/dispenser weapon. Germany has selected (but has not purchased) the Rafael Litening laser designator, and if procured, this could be fitted to KWE-modified aircraft.

Italy has also announced a Mid-Life Upgrade for its Tornados, though this is relatively modest. The AMI has a stated requirement for an enhanced main computer with ADA software, advanced RHAWS, improved Active ECM (ELT-553

While the RAF's Tornado GR4 will use the Storm Shadow ASM, upgraded German Tornados will use the Matra Apache from which Storm Shadow was derived. Two Apaches are seen here under the fuselage of a German IDS.

A key element in the modernisation of the Luftwaffe Tornado force is the new GAF Recce Pod, which combines optical cameras with the Honeywell IIS systems stripped from Tornado ECRs. This ex-MFG 2 Tornado IDS has served as the trials platform for the new pod.

AECM Mk 3), an autonomous PGM capability, compatability with HARM III and a microwave landing system. The requirement for an autonomous PGM capability was underlined by combat experience in *Desert Storm*. It has already partly been addressed through the acquisition of 20 Thomson-CSF CLDP laser designators delivered from 1995, and by the purchase of Paveway II kits. These allow Mk 83 bombs to be converted to GBU-16 configuration. Dropping trials were undertaken during 1994 and 1995 and 154° and 156° Gruppi achieved IOC with Paveway II in the autumn of 1995. The whole active fleet is now to be modified to use the CLDP pod and Paveway II. CLDP can be used co-operatively, 'spiking' targets for other aircraft, or can be used to designate for bombs carried by the designating aircraft. In the latter case, the CLDP pod is carried on the port shoulder, with a GBU-16 to starboard.

There have been proposals for more ambitious upgrades and more radically modified Tornados or Tornado derivatives. In the immediate aftermath of Operation *Desert Storm*, a 'Tornado 2000' configuration was studied. Described as an 'advanced multi-role penetrator for the 21st Century' the aircraft featured a dramatically stretched fuselage with increased internal volume for fuel, or avionics, or both. The nose was faceted to reduce RCS, and the intakes were redesigned. Under the fuselage, the proposed variant carried a massive semi-conformal ventral fuel tank, and this incorporated provision for semi-conformal weapons carriage on each side.

There are unconfirmed reports that the basic Tornado 2000

formed the basis of an even more advanced Tornado derivative study, reportedly known as the 'Long Range Penetrator'. This used the same fuselage and tail fin, married to a highly swept Delta wing, with prominent LERXes. There remains the possibility that a Tornado derivative might be considered to meet the RAF's FOAS requirement, though this seems unlikely.

None of the upgrades actually being applied to the Tornado IDS will transform the aircraft into an all-aspect Stealth attacker like the F-117A, but that's probably no bad thing. All-aspect low-observability imposes massive constraints of high unit cost, very high fuel consumption, limited payload/range capability, and maintainability problems. Expensive and fragile stealth coatings have to be carefully cosseted and require endless patching and constant repair. Furthermore, the dedicated Stealth aircraft's reliance on passive EO targeting systems and sensors imposes severe limitations on all-weather capability. In most weather conditions the new Tornado GR4 is a superb medium altitude PGM delivery platform, but if necessary, the aircraft is still able to penetrate at very low altitude, using TRNS and/or TFR. This makes the aircraft extremely versatile, and arguably more useful to a force commander than more glamorous (and more hyped) more narrowly specialised types.

Thus the tri-national Tornado force is approaching the new millenium in excellent shape, with a long and promising future ahead to add to the aircraft's distinguished history and combat record.

Tornado Resurgent

The last production Tornado was this IDS for the Royal Saudi Air Force (8319), ceremonially rolled out with 8318 in September 1998.

In 1999, Panavia were able to celebrate two anniversaries, though both slipped past without much formal recognition. The year marked the 30th anniversary of the foundation of Panavia itself, and also the 25th anniversary of the Tornado's first flight. At one of the partner companies, 1999 also saw the 50th anniversary of one of its products – BAe at Warton celebrating 50 years since the first flight of the Canberra.

This neat coincidence invites comparisons, but the most useful is that in 1974, at the 'grand old age' of 25, the Canberra was a much-loved 'has been', already phased out of service in its primary bombing role by the RAF, and hanging on to frontline credibility only with export customers and in the recce role. The Tornado at 25 is, by contrast, still very much alive, vital and viable in its primary roles, and remains the most important aircraft type in service with each of its operators. And while the handful of remaining RAF Canberra operators gathered 25 aircraft together for a celebratory bash at RAF Cottesmore in August 1999, Tornados were too busy going about their job ("denying aggression and genocide and restoring peace", as Panavia's Managing Director, Dipl-Ing Reinhold Falthauser put it) for aircraft to be available for a similar commemoration.

1999 was a busy year for the Tornado, for each of the five air arms in the Tornado's four customer countries. The RAF Tornado detachment at Al Jaber, established in February 1998 as part of Operation *Bolton* (described in more detail in the 'Peacekeepers' chapter), did not have long to wait before being called into action.

Nominally aimed at destroying what remained of Iraq's capability to produce weapons of mass destruction, Operation *Desert Fox* has been said by some to have been a deliberate attempt to 'decapitate Iraq's leadership' and that it was quite deliberately timed to coincide with a *coup* by the Iraqi Army's own 3rd Corps. Others believed that the operation represented no more than an impotent media opportunity to showcase certain weapons systems and to demonstrate a particular resolve and seriousness. Some even claimed that the operation was timed to distract attention away from an impending and scheduled House of Representatives debate on the impeachment of US President Bill Clinton over the so-called 'Zippergate' scandal, like a real-world version of the Hollywood motion picture *Wag the Dog*.

Nothing could have halted the impeachment of President Clinton however, and by launching *Desert Fox* he merely gave

After delays and problems, the GR4 is now in full squadron service. No IX Squadron at Brüggen were the first recipients. SGT JACK PRITCHARD

his opponents more ammunition. Similar accusations were made against British Prime Minister Tony Blair, suggesting that he committed British forces simply to enhance his reputation as a world leader. But any balanced interpretation of the facts would conclude that President Clinton and Mr Blair acted perfectly correctly and honourably in mounting airstrikes against Iraq, and were not simply courting easy popularity, either domestically or internationally.

The premature cessation of hostilities in 1991, which left Saddam Hussein still in control in Iraq with his power base largely intact, left the problem of Iraq unresolved. The Iraqi leader has maintained his grip on power by putting down rebellions, uprisings and mutinies with customary brutality. Saddam's personal prestige has been enhanced by the failure of the United Nations to destroy his arsenal of chemical and bacteriological weapons, and his nuclear weapons programme. UN inspectors played an extraordinary game of cat and mouse with the Iraqi authorities, obstructed at every turn as they attempted to catalogue and verify the elimination of Iraq's weapons of mass destruction.

Meanwhile, NATO aircraft flew reconnaissance missions over Iraq, enforcing no-fly zones over the northern and southern parts of the country, where internal opposition to Saddam was greatest. When Iraqi SAM sites locked up allied aircraft they were attacked, but such attacks were small-scale and sporadic. Saddam's continued obstruction of the UNSCOM (UN Special Commission) weapons inspectors, and his ongoing refusal to comply with UN Security Council resolutions led to the US and UK approving airstrikes.

On 11 November Clinton approved a massive build-up of forces in the region, and on 14 November a major attack on Iraq – Operation *Desert Viper* – was actually launched. US aircraft were already airborne, approaching 'the fence' (the border between Iraq and Saudi Arabia), and British Tornados were only two hours from take off when Iraq climbed down and pledged to resume co-operation with the UN. Britain and America warned the Iraqis that any failure to keep this promise would result in airstrikes with 'little or no warning'.

However, obstruction of the inspectors continued and was officially reported by the chief inspector, Richard Butler. Although the report emerged within a few days of the start of the Moslem holy festival of Ramadan, hasty plans were drawn up for a four-day air campaign, using only those assets already in-theatre – principally ship-launched cruise missiles, ALCM-carrying B-52s from Diego Garcia, the USS *Enterprise*, and USAF and RAF aircraft based in Kuwait. Operation *Desert Fox* began with a wave of 280 cruise missiles, the first of which hit their targets shortly before 10.00pm (GMT) on Wednesday 16th December. By comparison, only 291 cruise missiles were fired during the whole of Operation *Desert Storm*.

Further cruise missiles were fired the following night, when the RAF Tornados joined the campaign. These aircraft, flown by crews drawn from No 12 Squadron and based at Ali Al Salem, flew three waves of attacks – targeting a radar site, a radio antenna, and the Iraqi airfield at Talil, near Baghdad.

The Tornado attack on Talil targeted a hangar housing a number of Aero L-29s, modified as drones. These were reportedly intended to be used for spraying chemical or bacteriological warfare agents, and were described by UK Defence Secretary George Robinson as the 'drones of death'. A single photo released by the MoD of an Iraqi L-29 did show 'unidentified underwing stores' – though these looked much like fuel tanks, while there was no sign of spray gear or of the command antenna required for unmanned operation, although the L-29s had been identified as priority targets by UNSCOM inspectors. One pilot did not release his bombs after suffering an unspecified 'system failure', worried by the possibility of colateral damage.

The *Desert Fox* Tornados were armed with Paveway II laser-guided bombs (LGBs) and supported by VC-10 tankers flying from Muharraq. Six of the Tornados were TIALD 400-equipped, and these spiked for their wingmen. The TIALD-equipped aircraft each carried one or two LGBs, while the others carried two or three bombs. The Tornados flew again on Friday 18 December, and on the last day of the operation, Saturday 19 December.

The RAF Tornados flew their first attack using 2,000lb Paveway III LGBs (one per TIALD-equipped aircraft, while the bombers each carried two). The first wave of Tornados that night took off at 2.57pm GMT (5.57pm Local), but the second wave turned back after getting airborne, to avoid any chance of operating after the dawn start of Ramadan, and the third wave was scrubbed. By the end of the operation, the RAF's 12 Tornados had flown 28 sorties against eleven targets – three air defence sites, three air defence missile facilities, two command and control facilities, two Republican Guard targets and Talil airfield. They had dropped 55 Paveway II bombs and six Paveway IIIs, representing about 10% of the air-dropped bomb total. The MoD claimed a 'better than 75%' success rate for the TIALD/Tornado combination.

Iraq claimed to have suffered only 62 military casualties killed, including two Special Republican Guard officers and sixteen men, plus one Republican Guard officer and nineteen soldiers, while the US DoD claimed 1,600 Republican Guard casualties alone. Civilian casualties were very low, though Iraq

Although regarded principally as a reconnaissance unit, No 13 Squadron practises reconnaissance and ground attack missions with its new GR4As. SGT JACK PRITCHARD

claimed heavy losses. Operation *Desert Fox* has been described as the most humane bombing campaign ever carried out, and the Allies certainly made every possible effort to avoid civilian casualties. The possibility of causing civilian casualties was considered when planning, briefing and flying all missions. But even the most modern precision guided weapons are not 100% reliable, and when dropping 1,000lb or 2,000lb HE bombs, some 'collateral' damage is inevitable. An agricultural college was entirely destroyed, along with a grain silo containing 2,600 tons of rice, while UN sources suggest that about a dozen hospitals and schools suffered minor damage. A stray cruise missile also ruptured one of Baghdad's main water mains, briefly cutting off the water supply to an estimated 300,000 civilians! But hardships to the civil population caused by the bombing were minimal.

Of 93 military targets attacked during *Desert Fox*, 14 were claimed as destroyed, 26 more as 'severely damaged', 30 as 'moderately damaged' (a more severe category than the name suggests) and 12 as suffering 'light damage'. Some 10-15 targets were attacked but remained undamaged. Unfortunately, only one of the weapons of mass destruction (WMD) targets received severe damage, and five received moderate damage. It was initially assessed that this would put back Iraq's WMD

programme by only one year.

The Iraqi MoD building in Baghdad was 'reduced to rubble' though, as was the Ba'ath Party HQ (hit by eight cruise missiles on a single night), but this was 'gesture warfare' and marked no more than a largely pointless but highly visible response to Iraqi provocation. But the allied response at least ensured that Saddam Hussein was seen to have been punished.

There was massive international opposition to the allied bombing campaign. Russia withdrew its ambassadors from London and Washington, and boycotted a planned NATO meeting, while the action was vigorously condemned by the Arab League and by individual Arab governments, and even by France. Egypt urged a halt to the bombing, while Saudi Arabia, Bahrain and Turkey refused to allow their airfields to be used. Turkey had already suspended all but *Northern Watch* reconnaissance missions over Northern Iraq at the end of 1996, having pressed for an early end to airstrikes in 1991. Even Kuwait was reticent in its support of allied actions, with Kuwaiti State television denying that Kuwaiti airfields had been used by the British and American bombers. Support for UN sanctions against Iraq was eroded, and it became certain that no UNSCOM inspector would ever again be allowed in

Iraq, so that monitoring Saddam's weapons of mass destruction became virtually impossible. The UNSCOM inspection regime was probably already 'dead in the water' anyway – unwelcome and marginalised, and described by one unnamed senior inspector as 'the skunk at the garden party'. Saddam's survival enhanced his reputation among anti-Western extremists throughout the Arab world, turning him into a heroic and iconic figure.

Following the end of Operation *Desert Fox*, things remained tense, with the focus of attention switching to the No Fly Zones. On Boxing Day, an RAF Tornado was fired upon by AAA as it patrolled the Southern No Fly Zone. On Sunday 27 December, Iraq's Vice-President, Taha Yassin Ramadan, warned that Iraq did not recognise the right of British and American warplanes to patrol the No Fly Zones, perhaps worried that these might become the location of a successful rising against the regime (at least in the south), leading to the establishment of a separate state. The following day, an Iraqi SAM site engaged four USAF F-16Cs from Incirlik as they

patrolled the Northern NFZ and these reacted to being fired upon by evading the missiles. An attack on the SAM site involved was mounted immediately. Much the same thing happened on 30 December, when RAF Tornados were fired upon by SAM-6s. They escaped unscathed before USAF F-16C/Js retaliated, and there have been many similar incidents since then.

With the Tornado GR4 conversion programme gathering pace, and with increasing numbers of aircraft joining BAe's conversion line at Warton, or going to St Athan for pre- and post-upgrade maintenance, the RAF began to experience a growing shortage of Tornado GR1 airframes. The *Bolton* commitment did not help, especially since it was in addition to the normal Operation *Jural* detachment of six Tornado GR1s and GR1As at Al Kharj in Saudi Arabia. But with the Jaguar Force supporting Operation *Warden* at Incirlik, and the Harrier Force maintaining a detachment in Italy for *Deliberate Forge*, it was difficult to see how the Tornado IDS force commitments could be reduced.

This BAe-operated GR1 has been used extensively in support of the GR4, and is seen here laden with Brimstone ATGMs.

The Tri-national Tornado Training Establishment finally closed its doors at the end of March 1999.

A solution was eventually found in February 1999, with the deployment of six Tornado F3s (flown by No 25 Squadron crews) to Al Kharj to take over the *Jural* commitment, which has also been referred to under the operational name *Bolton South*. This was a remarkable step, since the RAF's role on *Jural* had previously been one of reconnaissance, with some bombing sorties being flown against Iraqi SAM sites which illuminated the Tornados as they 'went about their business.' It was thus difficult to see quite how the Tornado F3 fighter could take over the same commitment. This was not made clear because, unfortunately, the changeover between GR1 and F3 was made at the very time that Saudi Arabia was becoming more sensitive about the allied aircraft stationed on its soil, and the F3 deployments were made against what amounted to a news blackout. There were suggestions that the aircraft were cleared for the carriage of the W. Vinten Ltd GP(1) reconnaissance pod, and even that the aircraft were carrying (or had at least been cleared to use) the BAe ALARM anti-radar missile.

Away from the frontline over Iraq, the Tri-national Tornado Training Unit (TTTE) at Cottesmore disbanded on 31 March 1999, after which each of the three partner nations took charge of its own Tornado conversion training. This step became inevitable after the roles and equipment standards of the three partner nations' Tornados began to diverge as a result of post Cold War restructuring and markedly different upgrade programmes, which translated into the need for a growing proportion of 'national specific' training, and which reduced the benefits of sharing a common training unit. By the

beginning of 1999, the TTTE had 29 aircraft on charge, plus two 'full mission' simulators, and a staff of 50 pilots and 29 navigators. Twenty-eight of the aircraft were drawn up in a massive two deep semi-circle for the disbandment ceremony photograph, with personnel standing in blocks in the shape of the letters 'TTTE'. By the time of its disbandment, the TTTE had trained 3,347 Tornado aircrew, plus 930 instructors.

In Britain, the TWCU (usually known as No XV (Reserve) Squadron) took over the aircraft and role of the British element of the TTTE, retaining the same Reserve Squadron identity but picking up the new designation of NTOCU (National Tornado Operational Conversion Unit), and gaining a new integrated syllabus. Lossiemouth is to be the home of one of two GR4 simulators forming part of a new £175m Private Finance Initiative contract covering the provision of GR4 simulator training at Marham and Lossiemouth. Reductions in the size of the RAF Tornado Force also reduced the need for Tornado aircrew, allowing the training task to be carried out more easily by a single unit. Since Operation *Desert Storm*, the RAF had lost Nos XV, 16, 20 and 27 Squadrons through disbandment, as well as a single ADV unit, No 23 Squadron.

In Germany, training duties previously performed by the TTTE have passed entirely to the Ausbildungsstaffel Tornado, part of the Taktische Ausbildungskommando Luftwaffe USA at Holloman AFB, New Mexico, which previously provided weapons instructor training and 'top-up' training (especially low-level flying) for frontline aircrew from the German-based wings. The Holloman-based unit will also take over most of the weapons-conversion training syllabus from JBG 38, effectively re-locating all conversion training to the USA. Interestingly, the German Tornados are the only foreign-owned military aircraft permanently based in the USA permitted to retain their own national insignia.

In Italy, Tornado aircrew now go direct from the MB 339s of the 61° Stormo at Lecce or the T-37s and T-38s of the ENJJPT at Shepherd AFB, Texas, to the 6° Stormo's 102° Gruppo at Ghedi. Tornado F3 aircrew for the Italian Air Force continue to train with the RAF's No 56 (Reserve) Squadron at Coningsby, Lincs, which was unaffected by the end of the TTTE.

On the very same day that the TTTE officially disbanded, so too did No 17 Squadron at RAF Brüggen. This left only Nos IX, 14 and 31 in RAF Germany, and these units will re-deploy to the UK when Brüggen closes in 2001 or 2002. No 14 Squadron will move to Lossiemouth, while Nos IX and 31 will take up station at Marham. The F3 force had already been reduced by one unit, Coningsby-based No 29 Squadron having disbanded on 30 October 1998.

Quite apart from supporting the multinational peace-keeping and enforcement operations which have proliferated since the end of the Cold War, the Tornado force has continued to undertake a regular cycle of exercises and training deployments – though operational commitments have sometimes led to a scaling down of such efforts. In 1999, however, four Tornados of JBG 33 were deployed to Powidz in Poland for Exercise *Ozelot*, while the Marineflieger sent aircraft for training at Puerto Rico's NAS Roosevelt Roads. The RAF's deployments included one by three Tornado F3s (plus two VC-10 and one TriStar tankers, two Nimrods and a C-130 Hercules) to Brazil, mounted as a diversion to a regular 'roulement' of fighters for No 1435 Flight in the Falklands.

Having played a significant part in *Desert Storm* (flying 226 sorties and dropping 565 bombs) and in operations over the Adriatic and former Yugoslavia, the Aeronautica Militare Italiana's Tornado force also flew in support of Operation *Allied Force* in 1999. Ten standard IDS 'bombers' drawn from 6° Stormo's 102° and 154° Gruppi and 53° Stormo's 156° Gruppo flew combat missions from Ghedi and Gioia del Colle, equipped with Thomson CSF CLDP laser designators and armed with pairs of GBU-16 Paveway II LGBs. Six of the new Italian ECRs of 50° Stormo's 155° Gruppo flew intensive SEAD sorties from Piacenza, armed with AGM-88 HARM ARMs. The Italian Tornados flew a total of 600 sorties (1,930 flying hours) during *Allied Force*.

At Piacenza, the newly converted Italian ECR aircrew were not short of expert advice, since their Piacenza base also

This CSP development aircraft (ZE155) was the first to carry AIM-120 AMRAAM missiles, which are installationally compatible with the standard SkyFlash missile recesses.

Although No 29 Squadron disbanded during 1998, its markings adorned the second CSP development aircraft, ZG797, seen here with a pair of AIM-120s under the belly.

accommodated the Luftwaffe's Einsatzgeschwader 1, which included eight (and later ten) JBG 32 Tornado ECRs and six (later four) recce-configured 'standard' IDSs from AG 51. After initial political difficulties (which required an amendment to the constitution), the Luftwaffe has become a regular participant in international peacekeeping and enforcement operations outside Germany, and during *Allied Force*, the German Tornados flew 500 sorties (430 by the ECRs), amassing 2,260 flying hours and firing 236 AGM-88 HARM missiles (one third of the wartime total) against enemy SAM installations.

The Luftwaffe (and Italian) Tornado ECRs shared the SEAD task with US Navy Grumman EA-6B Prowlers and F/A-18s, USMC F/A-18s and USAF F-16s, but with their Emitter Locator System and datalinks allowing them to transmit information directly to AWACS aircraft, they proved to be among the most useful and most autonomous of the SEAD platforms used.

The capabilities of the Tornado ECR make Germany's Luftwaffe a much sought after partner. There is a great shortage of SEAD platforms, which are a necessity in the kind of medium altitude PGM missions which have characterised post-Cold War operations. The German Tornados also offer a useful tactical reconnaissance capability (another area in

A close up of two AIM-120s 'in situ' below a CSP development aircraft. Although it looks like the SkyFlash, AMRAAM delivers a quantum improvement in capability.

No 17 Squadron disbanded at the end of March 1999, leaving only three Tornado squadrons in RAF Germany. JAMIE HUNTER

which there is a shortage of assets), especially since the new DASA 'GAF Recce' and 'Telelens' pods have entered service. From 2000, the AG51 Tornados will also offer a radar reconnaissance capability, using new Radar Aufklärungs Behälter (RABE) pods with SAR/MTI (Synthetic Aperture Radar/Moving Target Indicator) capability.

The German government has established the KRK (Krisenreaktionskräfte – rapid reaction force) which includes AG 51, JBG 31, JBG 32 and JBG 34, as well as the F-4F equipped JG 71 and JG 74 and miscellaneous transport, helicopter and SAM units. The KRK's Tornado units have been accorded priority when it comes to receiving modernised and upgraded Tornados, and they have already begun to replace the ageing Cerberus III jammer with an improved Tornado Self Protection Jammer, and will soon be fully operational with the Paveway III LGB (guidance kits having been delivered for use with 2,000lb Mk 84 bombs in 1999).

Also operating in support of Operation *Allied Force* were eight of the Tornado F3s of the 36° Stormo's 12° Gruppo and 21° Gruppo (the latter formerly part of the 53° Stormo at Cameri), both units having been concentrated at Gioia del Colle since 1999. The Italian-operated ADVs flew extended-duration CAPs over the Adriatic, usually armed with four AIM-9 Sidewinders and four SkyFlash AAMs, while F-104ASA-Ms stood 'strip alert' armed with a single Aspide BVR AAM and a single AIM-9.

RAF Tornado F3s were not committed to Operation *Allied Force*, although eight Tornado GR1s from Nos IX, 14 and 31

Squadrons did fly operational sorties (with tanker support) from their Brüggen base, before 12 aircraft (with No IX and No 31 Squadron crews) were deployed to the French base at Solenzara (on the island of Corsica) between 29 and 31 May. These were commanded by Northolt's Station Commander, Group Captain Jerry Witts, who had previously commanded the Dharhan Tornado detachment during *Desert Storm*. The squadron-sized detachment was led by Wing Commander Greg Bagwell, OC No IX Squadron. The move somewhat reduced the transit times flown by the Tornados.

Interestingly, the brunt of the Tornado bombing campaign was borne by the 'old' GR1, with some suggestions that the GR4 was 'not ready' for operations with some of the weapons used. It has been suggested that the Brüggen sorties included at least two by the new GR4 variant, though this cannot be confirmed. What is certain, however, is that the RAF Tornados flew 160 sorties – averaging between six and seven hours each – during the operation.

In an increasingly unstable world, it would be a brave man who predicted that the Tornado could look forward to a quiet end to its career. Powerful, versatile and effective, the Tornado seems likely to be called upon to do its job again (perhaps many times) before it is retired. As these words were written, Tornados and their crews stand 'ready for action' over Iraq, flying from bases in Kuwait and Saudi Arabia. Back in their home countries, Tornado squadrons remain aware that their next deployment to a 'combat zone' could still be just a phone call away.

TORNADO PRODUCTION – UK

One of the 'non-recce' standard GR1s (ZA449) operated by No II (AC) Squadron, showing off its overall grey colour scheme. KEVIN WILLS

Serial	Type	Build No/ Plane set	c/n Batch	First flt	Delivery	Operator, location or fate
XX946	-	P.02		30-Oct-74	-	RAF Museum, Hendon (8883M)
XX947	- (T)	P.03		05-Aug-75	-	DARA, RAF St Athan, BDRT (8797M)
XX948	-	P.06		19-Dec-75	-	RAF No 1 SoTT, Cosford (8879M) [P]
XX950	- (T)	P.08		15-Jul-76	-	Cr 12-Jun-79; Irish Sea 44 miles West of Blackpool (BAe)
XZ630	GR1	P.12		14-Mar-77	03-Feb-78	DARA, RAF St Athan, BDRT(8976M)
XZ631	GR1	P.15		24-Nov-78	-	DPA/BAe Warton
ZA254	F2	A.01/003	-/1	27-Oct-79	-	RAF, stored Coningsby
ZA267	F2	A.02/018	-/1	18-Jul-80	-	RAF Marham, instructional use
ZA283	F2	A.03/033	-/1	18-Nov-80	-	DPA/BAe Warton
ZA319	GR1	BT.001/001	3001/1	10-Jul-79	15-Nov-79	RAF, stored St Athan [B-11]
ZA320	GR1	BT.002/005	3002/1	14-Dec-79	01-Jul-80	RAF No 15(R) Sqn, Lossiemouth [TAW]
ZA321	GR1	BS.001/007	3003/1	14-Mar-80	08-Jun-81	RAF No 15(R) Sqn, Lossiemouth [TAB]
ZA322	GR1	BS.002/009	3004/1	23-May-80	01-Jul-80	RAF No 15(R) Sqn, Lossiemouth [TAC]
ZA323	GR1	BT.003/011	3005/1	03-Aug-83	03-Nov-83	RAF No 15(R) Sqn, Lossiemouth [TAZ]
ZA324	GR1	BT.004/013	3006/1	25-Jun-80	02-Sep-80	RAF No 15(R) Sqn, Lossiemouth [TAW]
ZA325	GR1	BT.005/014	3007/1	08-Sep-80	13-Oct-80	RAF, stored St Athan [B-03]
ZA326	GR1	BT.006/016	3008/1	31-Mar-83	26-May-83	DPA/AFD, DERA Boscombe Down (conv to GR1B)
ZA327	GR1	BS.003/020	3009/1	15-Sep-80	16-Nov-80	DPA/BAe, Warton
ZA328	GR1	BS.004/022	3010/1	13-Jul-81	03-Feb-82	DPA/BAe, Warton
ZA329	GR1	BS.005/024	3011/1	08-Oct-80	18-Nov-80	Cr 09-Aug-88; collided with ZA593 near Milburn, Cumbria (TTTE)
ZA330	GR1	BT.007/025	3012/1	15-Oct-80	06-Jan-81	Cr 21-Jan-99; collided with a Cessna 152 over Everton and crashed near Mattersey, Notts (TTTE)
ZA352	GR1	BT.008/027	3013/1	05-Nov-80	04-Dec-80	RAF, stored St Athan [B-04]
ZA353	GR1	BS.006/028	3014/1	10-Nov-80	17-Dec-80	DPA/AFD, DERA Boscombe Down [B-53]
ZA354	GR1	BS.007/030	3015/1	13-Jan-82	-	DPA/BAe, Warton
ZA355	GR1	BS.008/032	3016/1	28-Nov-80	08-Jan-81	RAF No 15(R) Sqn, Lossiemouth [TAA]
ZA356	GR1	BT.009/035	3017/1	15-Dec-80	06-Mar-81	RAF No 15(R) Sqn, Lossiemouth [TP]
ZA357	GR1	BT.010/037	3018/1	02-Feb-81	06-Mar-81	RAF No 15(R) Sqn, Lossiemouth [TS]
ZA358	GR1	BT.011/038	3019/1	27-Jan-81	06-Mar-81	DPA/BAe, Warton

A white fin chevron identifies this No 12 Squadron aircraft (ZA450) as one of those originally deployed for Operation **Bolton**. KEVIN WILLS

Serial	Type	Build No/ Plane set	c/n Batch	First flt	Delivery	Operator, location or fate
ZA359	GR1	BS.009/040	3020/1	30-Jan-81	05-Mar-81	BAe Warton, Overseas Customer Training Centre
ZA360	GR1	BS.010/041	3021/1	06-Mar-81	22-Apr-81	RAF No 15(R) Sqn, Lossiemouth [TC]
ZA361	GR1	BS.011/042	3022/1	27-Feb-81	28-Apr-81	RAF, stored St Athan [B-57]
ZA362	GR1	BT.012/043	3023/1	20-Mar-81	28-Apr-81	RAF No 15(R) Sqn, Lossiemouth [TR]
ZA365	GR1	BT.029/156	3079/3	07-Jul-82	20-Sep-82	DPA/BAe, Warton (conv to GR4)
ZA366	GR1	BT.030/159	3080/3	23-Jul-82	16-Sep-82	Cr 03-Jun-87, Manby, Lincs (TWCU)
ZA367	GR1	BT.031/161	3081/3	29-Jul-82	16-Sep-82	DARA, RAF St Athan [II]
ZA368	GR1	BT.032/163	3082/3	23-Jul-82	20-Sep-82	Cr 19-Jul-94, Moray Firth 10 miles N of Lossiemouth (617 Sqn)
ZA369	GR1	BS.051/166	3083/3	26-Aug-82	13-Oct-82	RAF No 13 Sqn, Marham [U] (conv to GR1A then GR4A)
ZA370	GR1	BS.052/168	3084/3	18-Aug-82	29-Sep-82	RAF No 2 Sqn, Marham [A] (conv to GR1A)
ZA371	GR1	BS.053/172	3085/3	18-Aug-82	11-Oct-82	DPA/AFD, DERA Boscombe Down (conv to GR1A then GR4A)
ZA372	GR1	BS.054/173	3086/3	27-Aug-82	11-Oct-82	RAF No 2 Sqn, Marham [E] (conv to GR1A) *[E] Sally T
ZA373	GR1	BS.055/175	3087/3	10-Sep-82	20-Oct-82	RAF No 2 Sqn, Marham [H] (conv to GR1A)
ZA374	GR1	BS.056/178	3088/3	16-Sep-82	27-Oct-82	RAF No 617 Sqn, Lossiemouth [AJ-L] (conv to GR1B) *[CN] Miss Behavin'
ZA375	GR1	BS.057/180	3089/3	29-Sep-82	29-Oct-82	RAF No 617 Sqn, Lossiemouth [AJ-W] (conv to GR1B)
ZA376	GR1	BS.058/183	3090/3	04-Oct-82	23-Nov-82	Cr 10-May-91, near Lubberstedt, Germany (20 Sqn) * Mrs Miggins
ZA392	GR1	BS.059/185	3091/3	14-Oct-82	17-Nov-82	Cr 17-Jan-91; possibly shot down while attacking Shaibah AB, near Basrah, Iraq (617 Sqn)
ZA393	GR1	BS.060/188	3092/3	14-Oct-82	11-Nov-82	RAF No 14 Sqn, Brüggen [BE] *[CQ] Cool Queen, later Sir Galahad
ZA394	GR1	BS.061/190	3093/3	26-Oct-82	02-Dec-82	Cr 09-Jan-90; collided with Jaguar XZ108 3 miles E of Hexham, Northumberland (2 Sqn) (conv to GR1A)
ZA395	GR1	BS.062/192	3094/3	27-Oct-82	13-Dec-92	RAF No 2 Sqn, Marham [N] (conv to GR1A)
ZA396	GR1	BS.063/194	3095/3	03-Nov-82	07-Dec-82	Cr 20-Jan-91; shot down by Roland SAM while attacking Tallil AB, Iraq (27 Sqn)
ZA397	GR1	BS.064/197	3096/3	12-Nov-82	11-Feb-83	Cr 01-Aug-94; collided with ZD844 over Quebec, Canada (2 Sqn) (conv to GR1A)
ZA398	GR1	BS.065/199	3097/3	19-Nov-82	11-Feb-83	RAF No 2 Sqn, Marham [S] (conv to GR1A)

Serial	Type	Build No/ Plane set	c/n Batch	First flt	Delivery	Operator, location or fate
ZA399	GR1	BS.066/202	3098/3	30-Nov-82	15-Feb-83	RAF No 617 Sqn, Lossiemouth [AJ-C] (conv to GR1B) *[G] *Grannie*
ZA400	GR1	BS.067/204	3099/3	26-Nov-82	17-Feb-83	DPA/BAe, Warton (conv to GR1A then GR4A)
ZA401	GR1	BS.068/206	3100/3	13-Dec-82	17-Feb-83	RAF No 2 Sqn, Marham [R] (conv to GR1A)
ZA402	GR1	BS.069/209	3101/3	10-Dec-82	17-Feb-83	DPA/AFD, DERA Boscombe Down (conv to GR1A)
ZA403	GR1	BS.070/211	3102/3	07-Jan-83	12-Dec-89	Cr 24-Jan-91; lost in action when bomb exploded immediately after release, Iraq (17 Sqn)
ZA404	GR1	BS.071/214	3103/3	06-Jan-83	22-Feb-83	RAF No 13 Sqn, Marham (conv to GR1A then GR4A)
ZA405	GR1	BS.072/216	3104/3	19-Jan-83	15-Mar-83	RAF No 2 Sqn, Marham [Y] (conv to GR1A)
ZA406	GR1	BS.073/217	3105/3	20-Jan-83	01-Mar-83	RAF No 14 Sqn, Brüggen [CI] *[DN] *Dog's Nob*
ZA407	GR1	BS.074/219	3106/3	30-Mar-83	01-Jun-83	RAF No 617 Sqn, Lossiemouth [AJ-G] (conv to GR1B)
ZA408	GR1	BS.075/222	3107/3	01-Mar-84	30-Mar-84	Cr 12-Jul-84; collided with Jaguar XZ393 2 miles W of Sheringham, Norfolk (TWCU)
ZA409	GR1	BT.033/224	3108/3	12-Feb-83	07-Apr-83	RAF No 12 Sqn, Lossiemouth [FQ] (conv to GR1B)
ZA410	GR1	BT.034/227	3109/3	03-Mar-83	27-Apr-83	DARA, RAF St Athan [FZ]
ZA411	GR1	BT.035/229	3110/3	11-Feb-83	24-Mar-83	RAF No 617 Sqn, Lossiemouth [AJ-S] (conv to GR1B)
ZA412	GR1	BT.036/232	3111/3	03-Mar-83	05-May-83	RAF No 2 Sqn, Marham
ZA446	GR1	BS.076/234	3112/3	08-Mar-83	13-Apr-83	RAF AWC/SAOEU, DERA Boscombe Down [U] (conv to GR1B)
ZA447	GR1	BS.077/235	3113/3	17-Mar-83	20-Apr-83	RAF No 12 Sqn, Lossiemouth [FA] (conv to GR1B) *[EA] *MiG Eater*
ZA448	GR1	BS.078/237	3114/3	29-Mar-83	12-May-83	Cr 30-Mar-88, on Nellis range, USA (15 Sqn)
ZA449	GR1	BS.079/240	3115/3	08-Apr-83	01-Jun-83	RAF No 2 Sqn, Marham [Q]
ZA450	GR1	BS.080/242	3116/3	15-Apr-83	09-Jun-83	RAF No 12 Sqn, Lossiemouth [FB] (conv to GR1B)
ZA451	GR1	BS.081/245	3117/3	29-Apr-83	16-Jun-83	Cr 06-Feb-84, 15 miles SW of Wilhelmshaven, Germany, after lightning strike (15 Sqn)
ZA452	GR1	BS.082/247	3118/3	05-May-83	15-May-84	RAF No 15(R) Sqn, Lossiemouth [FC] (conv to GR1B) *[GK] *Gulf Killer/I Luv Gaynor XX*
ZA453	GR1	BS.083/249	3119/3	17-May-83	22-Jul-83	RAF No 617 Sqn, Lossiemouth [AJ-M] (conv to GR1B)
ZA454	GR1	BS.084/252	3120/3	27-May-83	07-Jul-83	Cr 30-Apr-90, 20 miles NE of Goose Bay, Canada (15 Sqn)
ZA455	GR1	BS.085/254	3121/3	03-Jun-83	14-Jul-83	RAF No 12 Sqn, Lossiemouth [FE] (conv to GR1B)
ZA456	GR1	BS.086/257	3122/3	06-Apr-84	09-May-84	RAF No 617 Sqn, Lossiemouth [AJ-Q] (conv to GR1B) *[M] *Mel*

No 31 Squadron Tornado GR4 ZA542 accompanied No 14 Squadron aircraft on the APC to Cyprus in November 1999. DARRON HALL

Serial	Type	Build No/ Plane set	c/n Batch	First flt	Delivery	Operator, location or fate
ZA457	GR1	BS.087/259	3123/3	21-Jun-83	04-Aug-83	RAF No 617 Sqn, Lossiemouth [AJ-J] (conv to GR1B) *[CE] *Bob*
ZA458	GR1	BS.088/262	3124/3	12-Sep-83	13-Dec-83	DPA/BAe, Warton (conv to GR4)
ZA459	GR1	BS.089/264	3125/3	23-Jun-83	01-Sep-83	RAF No 617 Sqn, Lossiemouth [AJ-B] (conv to GR1B)
ZA460	GR1	BS.090/266	3126/3	05-Jul-83	16-Aug-83	RAF No 617 Sqn, Lossiemouth [AJ-A] (conv to GR1B) *[FD] *Fire Dancer*
ZA461	GR1	BS.091/269	3127/3	06-Jul-83	18-Aug-83	RAF No 12 Sqn, Lossiemouth [FD] (conv to GR1B)
ZA462	GR1	BS.092/271	3128/3	29-Jul-83	07-Sep-83	RAF No 14 Sqn, Brüggen [BV]
ZA463	GR1	BS.093/273	3129/3	03-Aug-83	14-Sep-83	RAF No 12 Sqn, Lossiemouth [CR] *[Q] *Flying High XV*
ZA464	GR1	BS.094/276	3130/3	17-Aug-83	21-Sep-83	Cr 14-Aug-90; collided with ZA545 and crashed into North Sea 12 miles E of Spurn Head (20 Sqn)
ZA465	GR1	BS.095/278	3131/3	23-Aug-83	11-Oct-83	RAF No 12 Sqn, Lossiemouth [FF] (conv to GR1B) *[FK] *Foxy Killer*
ZA466	GR1	BS.096/281	3132/3	08-Sep-83	25-Oct-83	Cr 09-Oct-90, Tabuk, Saudi Arabia, having snagged runway crash barrier (16 Sqn) DARA, RAF St Athan, BDRT <ff>

TTTE Tornado GR1 ZA560 wore this black scheme for display appearances. The tri-national unit closed at the end of March 1999. PETER R MARCH

New grey camouflage and reduced size markings adorn this GR1 of No 17 Squadron, which disbanded in 1999. HARTMUT FELDMANN

Only the small tailcode identifies this Tornado GR1 (ZD739) as belonging to No 14 Squadron. KEVIN WILLS

Serial	Type	Build No/ Plane set	c/n Batch	First flt	Delivery	Operator, location or fate
ZA467	GR1	BS.097/283	3133/3	03-Dec-83	14-Feb-84	Cr 22-Jan-91; lost in action during attack on Ar Rutbah radar station, Iraq (16 Sqn)
ZA468	GR1	BS.098/285	3134/3	05-Sep-83	18-Oct-83	Cr 20-Jul-89, nr Bergen, Netherlands, shortly after take-off from Laarbruch (15 Sqn)
ZA469	GR1	BS.099/288	3135/3	15-Sep-83	03-Nov-83	RAF, stored St Athan [AJ-O] (conv to GR1B)
ZA470	GR1	BS.100/290	3136/3	11-Oct-83	05-Jan-84	RAF No 14 Sqn, Brüggen [BQ]
ZA471	GR1	BS.101/293	3137/3	06-Oct-83	10-Nov-83	RAF No 617 Sqn, Lossiemouth [AJ-K] (conv to GR1B) *[E] Emma
ZA472	GR1	BS.102/295	3138/3	18-Oct-83	17-Nov-83	RAF No 617 Sqn, Lossiemouth [CT]
ZA473	GR1	BS.103/298	3139/3	25-Oct-83	23-Nov-83	RAF No 12 Sqn, Lossiemouth [FG] (conv to GR1B) *[FM] Foxy Mama
ZA474	GR1	BS.104/300	3140/3	04-Nov-83	01-Dec-83	RAF No 617 Sqn, Lossiemouth [AJ-F] (conv to GR1B)
ZA475	GR1	BS.105/302	3141/3	15-Nov-83	12-Jan-84	RAF No 12 Sqn, Lossiemouth [FH] (conv to GR1B)
ZA490	GR1	BS.106/305	3142/3	10-Nov-83	07-Dec-83	RAF No 12 Sqn, Lossiemouth [FJ] (conv to GR1B) *[GG] Gigi
ZA491	GR1	BS.107/307	3143/3	24-Nov-83	17-Jan-84	RAF No 12 Sqn, Lossiemouth [FK] (conv to GR1B) *[N] Nikki
ZA492	GR1	BS.108/310	3144/3	06-Dec-83	27-Jan-84	RAF No 12 Sqn, Lossiemouth [FL] (conv to GR1B)
ZA493	GR1	BS.109/312	3145/3	08-Dec-83	01-Feb-84	Cr 17-Jun-87; collided with Jaguar XZ116, Walla Crag, Cumbria (20 Sqn)
ZA494	GR1	BS.110/314	3146/3	08-Dec-83	14-Feb-84	Cr 18-Jul-84 after control loss, Goose Bay, Canada (27 Sqn)
ZA540	GR1	BT.013/047	3024/2	02-Apr-81	06-Aug-81	Cr 12-Sep-91, Bristol Channel (27 Sqn)
ZA541	GR1	BT.014/048	3025/2	15-Apr-81	10-Jul-81	RAF No 31 Sqn, Brüggen [DZ] (conv to GR4)
ZA542	GR1	BS.012/050	3026/2	21-Apr-81	30-Jun-81	RAF No 31 Sqn, Brüggen [DM] (conv to GR4)
ZA543	GR1	BS.013/052	3027/2	19-Jun-81	16-Jul-81	DPA/BAe Warton (conv to GR4)
ZA544	GR1	BT.015/054	3028/2	22-May-81	07-Jul-81	RAF No 13 Sqn, Marham [VII]
ZA545	GR1	BS.014/057	3029/2	02-Jun-81	02-Jul-81	Cr 14-Aug-90; collided with ZA464 and crashed into North Sea 12 miles E of Spurn Head (TWCU)
ZA546	GR1	BS.015/058	3030/2	12-Jun-81	23-Jul-81	RAF No 13 Sqn, Marham [W]
ZA547	GR1	BS.016/060	3031/2	17-Jun-81	03-Aug-81	RAF No 31 Sqn, Brüggen [DC] (conv to GR4)
ZA548	GR1	BT.016/061	3032/2	03-Jul-81	11-Sep-81	DPA/BAe Warton [TQ] (conv to GR4)
ZA549	GR1	BT.017/063	3033/2	10-Jul-81	03-Sep-81	RAF No 13 Sqn, Marham [III] (conv to GR4)
ZA550	GR1	BS.017/064	3034/2	24-Jul-81	27-Aug-81	RAF No 31 Sqn, Brüggen [DC] (conv to GR4)
ZA551	GR1	BT.018/067	3035/2	12-Aug-81	11-Sep-81	DARA, RAF St Athan (conv to GR4)
ZA552	GR1	BT.019/068	3036/2	27-Aug-81	24-Sep-81	DARA, RAF St Athan [TS] (conv to GR4)
ZA553	GR1	BS.018/070	3037/2	07-Aug-81	24-Sep-81	RAF No 31 Sqn, Brüggen [DI] (conv to GR4)
ZA554	GR1	BS.019/071	3038/2	13-Aug-81	21-Sep-81	RAF No 31 Sqn, Brüggen [DF] (conv to GR4)
ZA555	GR1	BT.020/074	3039/2	20-Aug-81	04-Dec-81	Cr 02-Dec-86, Wortham, Suffolk after engine failure (TWCU)
ZA556	GR1	BS.020/075	3040/2	08-Sep-81	06-Mar-84	DPA/BAe, Warton (conv to GR4)

The No IX Squadron CO's aircraft wears the legend and nose art 'Still Going Strong' – echoing the markings carried by one of the unit's wartime Lancasters. ZD748 has been replaced by a new GR4. KEVIN WILLS

Serial	Type	Build No/ Plane set	c/n Batch	First flt	Delivery	Operator, location or fate
ZA557	GR1	BS.021/077	3041/2	09-Sep-81	21-Jan-82	RAF No 9 Sqn, Brüggen [AC] (conv to GR4)
ZA558	GR1	BS.022/078	3042/2	25-Sep-81	03-Nov-81	Cr 28-Oct-83, into North Sea 10 miles NW of Cromer after pilot became unconscious (617 Sqn)
ZA559	GR1	BS.023/081	3043/2	13-Oct-81	27-Nov-81	RAF No 9 Sqn, Brüggen [AD] (conv to GR4)
ZA560	GR1	BS.024/082	3044/2	09-Oct-81	06-Nov-81	RAF AWC/SAOEU, DERA Boscombe Down [O] (conv to GR4)
ZA561	GR1	BS.025/084	3045/2	23-Oct-81	17-Dec-81	Cr 16-Aug-90, into North Sea 10 miles E of Spurn Head (27 Sqn)
ZA562	GR1	BT.021/085	3046/2	05-Nov-81	30-Nov-81	RAF No 15(R) Sqn, Lossiemouth [TT]
ZA563	GR1	BS.026/088	3047/2	28-Oct-81	04-Dec-81	RAF No 9 Sqn, Brüggen [AG] (conv to GR4)
ZA564	GR1	BS.027/090	3048/2	16-Oct-81	27-Nov-81	RAF No 14 Sqn, Brüggen [CK]
ZA585	GR1	BS.028/091	3049/2	09-Nov-81	17-Dec-81	RAF No 9 Sqn, Brüggen [AH] (conv to GR4)
ZA586	GR1	BS.029/093	3050/2	24-Nov-81	06-Jan-82	Cr 27-Sep-83, 6 miles N of King's Lynn after electrical failure (9 Sqn)
ZA587	GR1	BS.030/096	3051/2	20-Nov-81	14-Jan-82	RAF No 15(R) Sqn, Lossiemouth (conv to GR4)
ZA588	GR1	BS.031/098	3052/2	04-Dec-81	21-Jan-82	RAF No 15(R) Sqn, Lossiemouth [TM]
ZA589	GR1	BS.032/099	3053/2	04-Dec-81	04-Feb-82	DPA/BAe, Warton (conv to GR4)
ZA590	GR1	BS.033/101	3054/2	23-Dec-81	11-Feb-82	RAF, stored St Athan
ZA591	GR1	BS.034/104	3055/2	06-Jan-82	04-Feb-82	RAF No 31 Sqn, Brüggen [DJ] (conv to GR4)
ZA592	GR1	BS.035/105	3056/2	11-Jan-82	19-Feb-82	RAF No 2 Sqn, Marham [C]
ZA593	GR1	BS.036/107	3057/2	21-Jan-82	24-Feb-82	Cr 09-Aug-88; collided with ZA329 near Milburn, Cumbria (617 Sqn)
ZA594	GR1	BT.022/110	3058/2	22-Feb-82	30-Mar-82	RAF No 13 Sqn, Marham [XI] (conv to GR4)
ZA595	GR1	BT.023/112	3059/2	13-Jan-82	01-Feb-82	DARA, RAF St Athan [TV] (conv to GR4)
ZA596	GR1	BS.037/113	3060/2	08-Feb-82	05-Mar-82	DPA/BAe, Warton (conv to GR4)
ZA597	GR1	BS.038/116	3061/2	11-Feb-82	15-Mar-82	RAF No 15(R) Sqn, Lossiemouth [TA]
ZA598	GR1	BT.024/118	3062/2	24-Feb-82	23-Mar-82	DPA/BAe, Warton [TN] (conv to GR1B then GR4)
ZA599	GR1	BT.025/120	3063/2	24-Feb-82	11-May-82	RAF No 15(R) Sqn, Lossiemouth [TX]
ZA600	GR1	BS.039/122	3064/2	18-Mar-82	07-Jun-82	RAF No 15(R) Sqn, Lossiemouth [TH]
ZA601	GR1	BS.040/124	3065/2	23-Mar-82	23-Apr-82	DPA/BAe, Warton [TI] (conv to GR4)
ZA602	GR1	BT.026/127	3066/2	31-Mar-82	19-May-82	DARA, RAF St Athan (conv to GR4)
ZA603	GR1	BS.041/129	3067/2	20-Apr-82	17-May-82	Cr 08-Nov-84, 13 miles S of Schweinfurt, Germany after navigator initiated ejection of crew in belief that aircraft was out of contol (27 Sqn)
ZA604	GR1	BT.027/131	3068/2	19-Apr-82	11-May-82	DARA, RAF St Athan [TY]
ZA605	GR1	BS.042/134	3069/2	28-Apr-82	07-Jun-82	Cr 10-Dec-86, near Thorney, Cambs after collision with ZA611 (617 Sqn)
ZA606	GR1	BS.043/136	3070/2	30-Apr-82	14-Jun-82	DARA, RAF St Athan (conv to GR4)
ZA607	GR1	BS.044/138	3071/2	10-May-82	01-Jul-82	RAF No 9 Sqn, Brüggen [AB] (conv to GR4)

Serial	Type	Build No/ Plane set	c/n Batch	First flt	Delivery	Operator, location or fate
ZA608	GR1	BS.045/141	3072/2	14-May-82	21-Jun-82	RAF No 15(R) Sqn, Lossiemouth [TK]
ZA609	GR1	BS.046/143	3073/2	20-May-82	29-Jun-82	RAF No 13 Sqn, Marham [Z]
ZA610	GR1	BS.047/147	3074/2	08-Jun-82	22-Jul-82	Cr 12-Dec-85, into North Sea 30 miles E of Flamborough Head while attempting air-to-air refuelling with a Buccaneer (617 Sqn)
ZA611	GR1	BS.048/148	3075/2	16-Jun-82	02-Aug-82	RAF No 15(R) Sqn, Lossiemouth [TG]
ZA612	GR1	BT.028/150	3076/2	06-Jul-82	13-Aug-82	DARA, RAF St Athan [TZ]
ZA613	GR1	BS.049/152	3077/2	28-Jun-82	13-Aug-82	RAF No 15(R) Sqn, Lossiemouth [TL]
ZA614	GR1	BS.050/153	3078/2	22-Jun-82	22-Jul-82	RAF No 15(R) Sqn, Lossiemouth [TB]
ZD707	GR1	BS.111/319	3148/4	06-Jan-84	17-Apr-84	RAF No 14 Sqn, Brüggen [BU]
ZD708	GR1	BS.112/321	3149/4	13-Jan-84	29-Feb-84	DPA/BAe, Warton (conv to GR4)
ZD709	GR1	BS.113/324	3150/4	19-Jan-84	14-Mar-84	DARA, RAF St Athan [DG]
ZD710	GR1	BS.114/326	3151/4	09-Feb-84	04-Apr-84	Cr 14-Sep-89, near Drayton,Oxon after bird strike (14 Sqn) Robertsbridge Aviation Society, Mayfield <ff>
ZD711	GR1	BT.037/329	3152/4	10-May-84	20-Jun-84	DARA, RAF St Athan (conv to GR4)
ZD712	GR1	BT.038/331	3153/4	01-Mar-84	11-Apr-84	DPA/BAe, Warton (conv to GR4)
ZD713	GR1	BT.039/334	3154/4	13-Feb-84	24-Jan-85	DARA, RAF St Athan [TW]
ZD714	GR1	BS.115/336	3155/4	13-Mar-84	08-Sep-87	RAF No 31 Sqn, Brüggen [DL] (conv to GR4)
ZD715	GR1	BS.116/339	3156/4	30-Mar-84	23-May-84	DPA/BAe, Warton (conv to GR4) *[DB] *Luscious Lizzie!*
ZD716	GR1	BS.117/341	3157/4	04-Apr-84	16-May-84	RAF No 14 Sqn, Brüggen [JM]
ZD717	GR1	BS.118/344	3159/4	09-Apr-84	06-Jun-84	Cr 14-Feb-91; shot down while attacking Al Taqaddum AB,Iraq (15 Sqn)
ZD718	GR1	BS.119/346	3160/4	27-Apr-84	22-Jun-84	Cr 13-Jan-91, 140 miles W of Masirah, Oman (14 Sqn)
ZD719	GR1	BS.120/348	3161/4	17-May-84	06-Jul-84	RAF No 31 Sqn, Brüggen [DE] *[AD] *Check Six....*
ZD720	GR1	BS.121/352	3162/4	21-May-84	04-Jul-84	RAF No 14 Sqn, Brüggen [BH] (conv to GR4)
ZD738	GR1	BS.122/354	3163/4	08-Jun-84	19-Jul-84	Cr 27-Jul-87, near Sadmoor, N Yorks after controls locked (31 Sqn)
ZD739	GR1	BS.123/358	3165/4	14-Jun-84	13-Jul-84	RAF No 14 Sqn, Brüggen [BI] *[AC] *Armoured Charmer*
ZD740	GR1	BS.124/360	3166/4	05-Jul-84	27-Jul-84	RAF No 9 Sqn, Brüggen [AF] (conv to GR4) *[DA] *Dhahran Annie!!*
ZD741	GR1	BT.040/361	3167/4	20-Jul-84	14-Sep-84	DARA, RAF St Athan (conv to GR4)
ZD742	GR1	BT.041/364	3168/4	11-Jul-84	16-Apr-84	DARA, RAF St Athan (conv to GR4)
ZD743	GR1	BT.042/366	3169/4	26-Jul-84	30-Aug-84	RAF No 31 Sqn, Brüggen [CX]
ZD744	GR1	BS.125/371	3171/4	24-Jul-84	20-Sep-84	RAF No 12 Sqn, Lossiemouth [BD] *[BD] *Buddha*
ZD745	GR1	BS.126/373	3172/4	08-Aug-84	13-Sep-84	RAF No 31 Sqn, Brüggen [DA] (conv to GR4) *[BM] *Black Magic*

Although this No IX Squadron GR4 (ZD847) is carrying ALARM, the weapon may not at the time have been cleared for use by the GR4. KEVIN WILLS

Serial	Type	Build No/ Plane set	c/n Batch	First flt	Delivery	Operator, location or fate
ZD746	GR1	BS.127/376	3173/4	27-Aug-84	28-Sep-84	DPA/BAe, Warton (conv to GR4) *[AB] *Alarm Belle*
ZD747	GR1	BS.128/379	3175/4	31-Aug-84	02-Oct-84	RAF No 9 Sqn, Brüggen [AL] (conv to GR4) *[AL] *Anna Louise*
ZD748	GR1	BS.129/382	3176/4	07-Sep-84	08-Oct-84	RAF No 9 Sqn, Brüggen [AK] *[AK] *Anola Kay!*
ZD749	GR1	BS.130/384	3177/4	28-Sep-84	30-Oct-84	RAF No 14 Sqn, Brüggen [BG]
ZD788	GR1	BS.131/389	3179/4	03-Oct-84	29-Nov-84	RAF No 14 Sqn, Brüggen [BT]
ZD789	GR1	BS.132/391	3180/4	29-Oct-84	06-Dec-84	RAF, stored St Athan (damaged - CAT.3) *[AM] *Hindenburger's ALARM*
ZD790	GR1	BS.133/394	3181/4	30-Oct-84	22-Nov-84	DPA/BAe, Warton (conv to GR4) *[D] *Debbie*
ZD791	GR1	BS.134/400	3183/4	06-Nov-84	30-Nov-84	Cr 16-Jan-91; shot down during an attack on Shaibah AB, near Basrah, Iraq [Peters/Nichol crew] (15 Sqn)
ZD792	GR1	BS.135/402	3184/4	13-Nov-84	20-Dec-84	DPA/BAe, Warton (conv to GR4) *[CF] *Nursie*
ZD793	GR1	BS.136/405	3185/4	16-Nov-84	14-Dec-84	RAF No 17 Sqn, Brüggen [JH]
ZD808	GR1	BS.137/409	3187/4	05-Dec-84	25-Feb-85	Cr 10-May-88, near Berge-Heseke, Germany (17 Sqn)
ZD809	GR1	BS.138/411	3188/4	06-Jan-85	14-Nov-85	RAF No 14 Sqn, Brüggen [BA] *[A] *Awesome Annie*
ZD810	GR1	BS.139/414	3189/4	10-Jan-85	05-Feb-85	RAF No 31 Sqn, Brüggen [DB]
ZD811	GR1	BS.140/416	3190/4	18-Jan-85	08-Mar-85	DPA/BAe, Warton (conv to GR4)
ZD812	GR1	BT.043/420	3192/4	13-Feb-85	27-Mar-85	DARA, RAF St Athan [BW]
ZD842	GR1	BT.044/423	3193/4	14-Feb-85	11-Apr-85	RAF No 31 Sqn, Brüggen [DX]
ZD843	GR1	BS.141/426	3194/4	15-Feb-85	03-Apr-85	RAF No 14 Sqn, Brüggen
ZD844	GR1	BS.142/429	3196/4	21-Mar-85	20-Apr-85	RAF No 31 Sqn, Brüggen [DH] *[DE] *Donna Ewin*
ZD845	GR1	BS.143/432	3197/4	28-Mar-85	10-May-85	Cr 26-Feb-96, near Issum, Germany, following engine failure (9 Sqn) *[AF] *Angel Face*
ZD846	GR1	BS.144/434	3198/4	02-Apr-85	03-May-85	Cr 11-Jan-96, near Munster, Germany after an equipment failure (14 Sqn)
ZD847	GR1	BS.145/437	3199/4	18-Apr-85	03-Jun-85	RAF No 9 Sqn, Brüggen [AA] (conv to GR4) *[CH] *Where do you want it?*
ZD848	GR1	BS.146/441	3201/4	30-Apr-85	10-Jun-85	DPA/BAe, Warton (conv to GR4) *[BC] *Bacardi & Coke*
ZD849	GR1	BS.147/444	3202/4	31-May-85	27-Jun-85	RAF No 12 Sqn, Lossiemouth [CM]
ZD850	GR1	BS.148/447	3204/4	22-May-85	21-Jun-85	DPA/BAe, Warton (conv to GR4) *[CL] *Cherry Lips*
ZD851	GR1	BS.149/450	3205/4	07-Jun-85	08-Jul-85	RAF No 14 Sqn, Brüggen [BO] *[AJ] *Amanda Jane*
ZD890	GR1	BS.150/452	3206/4	03-Jun-85	28-Jan-85	DARA, RAF St Athan [AE]
ZD891	GR1	BS.151/455	3208/4	18-Jun-85	18-Jul-85	Cr 13-Jan-89; collided with Alpha Jet 40+87 near Wiesmoor, Germany (14 Sqn)
ZD892	GR1	BS.152/460	3210/4	03-Jul-85	07-Aug-85	RAF No 617 Sqn, Lossiemouth [BJ] *[H] *Helen*
ZD893	GR1	BS.153/463	3211/4	09-Jul-85	25-Jul-85	Cr 20-Jan-91, Tabuk, Saudi Arabia, following control problems after take-off (20 Sqn)
ZD894	GR1	BS.154/471	3214/4	22-Jul-85	22-Aug-85	Cr 30-Mar-87, near Hunxe, Germany (14 Sqn)
ZD895	GR1	BS.155/477	3216/4	27-Aug-85	30-Sep-85	RAF No 12 Sqn, Lossiemouth [BF]

No 11 Squadron's Tornado F3s (ZE160 illustrated) are now among the most colourful in use, with the bold black and yellow markings standing out more in the new small size. KEVIN WILLS

No 43 Squadron's current markings (seen here on ZE291) consist of a small decal and a black and white checkered fin band. KEVIN WILLS

Serial	Type	Build No/ Plane set	c/n Batch	First flt	Delivery	Operator, location or fate
ZD899	F2	AT.001/318	3147/4	12-Apr-84	-	DPA/BAe Warton
ZD900	F2	AT.002/342	3158/4	05-Mar-84	02-Oct-89	RAF, stored St Athan (comp ZE343)
ZD901	F2	AT.003/356	3164/4	14-Jun-84	05-Nov-84	RAF, stored St Athan (comp ZE154)
ZD902	F2	AT.004/367	3170/4	04-Sep-84	10-May-85	DPA/AFD, DERA Boscombe Down (conv to F2A(TIARA))
ZD903	F2	AT.005/377	3174/4	21-Sep-84	05-Nov-84	RAF, stored St Athan (comp ZE728)
ZD904	F2	AT.006/387	3178/4	30-Jan-85	24-May-85	RAF, stored St Athan (comp ZE759)
ZD905	F2	AS.001/397	3182/4	11-Jan-85	19-Feb-85	RAF, stored St Athan (comp ZE258)
ZD906	F2	AS.002/408	3186/4	05-Feb-85	10-May-85	RAF, stored St Athan (comp ZE294)
ZD932	F2	AS.003/418	3191/4	22-Mar-85	29-Apr-85	RAF, stored St Athan (comp ZE255)
ZD933	F2	AS.004/428	3195/4	16-Apr-85	24-May-85	RAF, stored St Athan (comp ZE729)
ZD934	F2	AT.007/438	3200/4	17-Apr-85	20-May-85	RAF, stored St Athan (comp ZE786)
ZD935	F2	AT.008/446	3203/4	16-May-85	21-Jun-85	RAF, stored St Athan (comp ZE793)
ZD936	F2	AS.005/453	3207/4	14-Jun-85	26-Jul-85	RAF, stored St Athan (comp ZE251)
ZD937	F2	AS.006/459	3209/4	28-Jun-85	14-Aug-85	DARA, RAF St Athan, BDRT (comp ZE736)
ZD938	F2	AS.007/464	3212/4	02-Aug-85	02-Sep-85	RAF, stored St Athan (comp ZE295)
ZD939	F2	AS.008/469	3213/4	08-Aug-85	18-Sep-85	RAF, stored St Athan (comp ZE292)
ZD940	F2	AS.009/474	3215/4	19-Aug-85	02-Oct-85	RAF, stored St Athan (comp ZE288)
ZD941	F2	AS.010/479	3217/4	02-Sep-85	09-Oct-85	RAF, stored St Athan (comp ZE254)
ZD996	GR1	BS.156/480	3218/5	25-Oct-86	04-Dec-86	RAF No 2 Sqn, Marham [I] (conv to GR1A)
ZE116	GR1	BS.160/502	3227/5	19-Dec-86	02-Jan-87	RAF No 13 Sqn, Marham [X] (conv to GR1A then GR4A)
ZE154	F3	AT.009/486	3220/5	20-Nov-85	24-Dec-85	DARA, RAF St Athan [AN] (comp ZD901)
ZE155	F3	AS.011/493	3223/5	16-Oct-86	-	DPA/BAe Warton
ZE156	F3	AS.012/497	3225/5	06-Feb-87	03-Mar-87	DARA, RAF St Athan [E]
ZE157	F3	AT.010/500	3226/5	14-Jan-86	25-Apr-86	RAF No 43 Sqn, Leuchars [GK]
ZE158	F3	AS.013/505	3228/5	25-Sep-86	30-Oct-86	RAF No 111 Sqn, Leuchars [Z]
ZE159	F3	AS.014/509	3229/5	27-Jun-86	29-Jul-86	RAF No 111 Sqn, Leuchars [R]
ZE160	F3	AT.011/513	3231/5	02-Jul-86	08-Aug-86	RAF No 11 Sqn, Leeming [DV]
ZE161	F3	AS.015/519	3234/5	07-Jul-86	01-Aug-86	DARA, RAF St Athan
ZE162	F3	AS.016/524	3236/5	16-Jul-86	13-Aug-86	RAF No 25 Sqn, Leeming [FK]
ZE163	F3	AT.012/529	3238/5	06-Jul-87	11-Sep-87	DARA, RAF St Athan (spares use)

Photographed late in 1998, the nearest aircraft (ZE165) carries special 'airshow' markings, whereas the furthest aircraft in the formation wears No 25 Squadron's normal markings, which are now confined to the tailfin. KEVIN WILLS

Serial	Type	Build No/ Plane set	c/n Batch	First flt	Delivery	Operator, location or fate
ZE164	F3	AS.017/532	3239/5	22-Jul-86	18-Sep-86	DARA, RAF St Athan [DA]
ZE165	F3	AS.018/538	3242/5	11-Aug-86	08-Sep-86	RAF No 111 Sqn, Leuchars [Q]
ZE166	F3	AT.013/542	3244/5	27-Oct-86	12-Nov-86	Cr 10-Jan-96; collided with ZE862 near Sleaford (56(R) Sqn)
ZE167	F3	AS.019/545	3245/5	02-Oct-86	23-Oct-86	Subsequently MM7234
ZE168	F3	AS.020/549	3247/5	31-Oct-86	18-Nov-86	RAF No 25 Sqn, Leeming [FN]
ZE199	F3	AT.014/552	3248/5	19-Nov-86	22-Dec-86	DARA, RAF St Athan [FL]
ZE200	F3	AS.021/555	3249/5	24-Feb-87	06-Mar-87	RAF No 11 Sqn, Leeming [DB]
ZE201	F3	AS.022/559	3251/5	04-Dec-86	17-Dec-86	DARA, RAF St Athan [GA]
ZE202	F3	AT.015/562	3253/5	26-Aug-86	12-Sep-86	Subsequently MM55056 [36-01]
ZE203	F3	AS.023/565	3254/5	29-Aug-86	01-Oct-86	RAF ASF, Leeming [FI] (damaged – CAT.3)
ZE204	F3	AS.024/569	3255/5	10-Sep-86	14-Oct-86	RAF No 11 Sqn, Leeming [DD]
ZE205	F3	AT.016/571	3256/5	18-Sep-86	16-Oct-86	Subsequently MM55061
ZE206	F3	AS.025/574	3257/5	05-Nov-86	28-Apr-87	DARA, RAF St Athan [FH]
ZE207	F3	AS.026/576	3258/5	07-Sep-87	23-Oct-87	DARA, RAF St Athan [GC]
ZE208	F3	AT.017/581	3260/5	27-Nov-86	16-Dec-86	Subsequently MM55060
ZE209	F3	AS.027/583	3261/5	21-Jan-87	06-Feb-87	RAF No 5(R) Sqn, Coningsby [CE]
ZE210	F3	AS.028/586	3262/5	27-Jan-87	12-Feb-87	RAF AMF, Leuchars (spares use – CAT.5)
ZE250	F3	AT.018/590	3264/5	29-Jan-87	24-Feb-87	RAF F3 OCU/No 56(R) Sqn, Coningsby [AM]
ZE251	F3	AS.029/593	3265/5	12-Feb-87	24-Feb-87	RAF No 1435 Flt, Mount Pleasant, FI [C] (comp ZD936)
ZE252	F3	AS.030/595	3266/5	04-Mar-87	19-Mar-87	Subsequently MM7225 [36-04]
ZE253	F3	AT.019/600	3268/5	09-Mar-87	25-Mar-87	RAF F3 OCU/No 56(R) Sqn, Coningsby [AC]
ZE254	F3	AS.031/602	3269/5	12-Mar-87	20-Mar-87	DARA, RAF St Athan [AW] (comp ZD941)
ZE255	F3	AS.032/605	3270/5	24-Mar-87	02-Apr-87	RAF F3 OCU/No 56(R) Sqn, Coningsby [AY] (comp ZD932)
ZE256	F3	AT.020/607	3271/5	31-Mar-87	08-Apr-87	RAF F3 OCU/No 56(R) Sqn, Coningsby [AO]
ZE257	F3	AS.033/610	3272/5	14-Apr-87	28-Apr-87	RAF AWC/F3 OEU, Coningsby
ZE258	F3	AS.034/612	3273/5	21-May-87	12-Jun-87	RAF F3 OCU/No 56(R) Sqn, Coningsby [AQ] (comp ZD905)
ZE287	F3	AT.021/614	3274/5	01-May-87	21-May-87	RAF F3 OCU/No 56(R) Sqn, Coningsby [AF]
ZE288	F3	AS.035/617	3275/5	05-Jun-87	25-Jun-87	RAF F3 OCU/No 56(R) Sqn, Coningsby [AT] (comp ZD940)
ZE289	F3	AS.036/619	3276/5	12-Jun-87	13-Aug-87	RAF F3 OCU/No 56(r) Sqn, Coningsby [C]
ZE290	F3	AT.022/622	3277/5	09-Jul-87	02-Oct-87	RAF F3 OCU/No 56(R) Sqn, Coningsby [AG]
ZE291	F3	AS.037/624	3278/5	30-Jul-87	18-Sep-87	RAF No 43 Sqn, Leuchars [GQ]
ZE292	F3	AS.038/626	3279/5	06-Aug-87	25-Sep-87	RAF F3 OCU/No 56(R) Sqn, Coningsby [AZ] (comp ZD939)
ZE293	F3	AT.023/629	3280/5	26-Aug-87	09-Oct-87	RAF AWC/F3 OEU, Coningsby [HT]

Frequent deployments and changeovers of aircraft brought about a reduction in the size of squadron markings, and common positioning. Fuselage markings have been removed altogether, as seen on F3 ZE788 of No 5 Squadron. KEVIN WILLS

Serial	Type	Build No/ Plane set	c/n Batch	First flt	Delivery	Operator, location or fate
ZE294	F3	AS.039/631	3281/5	18-Sep-87	19-Oct-87	RAF F3 OCU/No 56(R) Sqn, Coningsby [AS] (comp ZD906)
ZE295	F3	AS.040/633	3283/5	01-Oct-87	19-Oct-87	DARA, RAF St Athan [AV] (comp ZD938)
ZE296	F3	AT.024/636	3285/5	27-Sep-87	19-Oct-87	RAF F3 OCU/No 56(R) Sqn, Coningsby [AD]
ZE338	F3	AS.041/638	3286/5	09-Oct-87	26-Oct-87	DARA, RAF St Athan [G]
ZE339	F3	AS.042/641	3287/5	08-Oct-87	26-Oct-87	RAF No 5 Sqn, Coningsby [CK]
ZE340	F3	AT.025/643	3288/5	22-Oct-87	30-Oct-87	RAF F3 OCU/No 56(R) Sqn, Coningsby [AE]
ZE341	F3	AS.043/645	3289/5	28-Oct-87	06-Nov-87	RAF No 111 Sqn, Leuchars [J]
ZE342	F3	AS.044/647	3290/5	10-Nov-87	20-Nov-87	RAF No 111 Sqn, Leuchars [W]
ZE343	F3	AT.026/649	3291/5	12-Nov-87	20-Nov-87	RAF F3 OCU/No 56(R) Sqn, Coningsby [AA] (comp ZD900)
ZE728	F3	AT.027/652	3292/6	14-Oct-87	13-Apr-88	RAF F3 OCU/No 56(R) Sqn, Coningsby [AH]
ZE729	F3	AS.045/654	3293/6	19-Nov-87	21-Dec-87	RAF No 5 Sqn, Coningsby [CF] (comp ZD933)
ZE730	F3	AS.046/656	3294/6	25-Nov-87	21-Dec-87	Subsequently MM7204 [36-05]
ZE731	F3	AS.047/658	3295/6	03-Dec-87	21-Dec-87	RAF No 43 Sqn, Leuchars [GF]
ZE732	F3	AS.048/660	3296/6	17-Dec-87	08-Jan-88	Cr 15-Jun-98, North Sea (29 Sqn)
ZE733	F3	AS.049/662	3297/6	11-Dec-87	08-Jan-88	Cr 30-Oct-95; collided with ZE210 and crashed into North Sea, 60 miles NE of Berwick on Tweed (43 Sqn)
ZE734	F3	AS.050/664	3298/6	07-Jan-88	25-Jan-88	DARA, RAF St Athan [GB]
ZE735	F3	AT.028/666	3299/6	13-Jan-88	02-Feb-88	RAF F3 OCU/No 56(R) Sqn, Coningsby [AL]
ZE736	F3	AS.051/669	3300/6	20-Jan-88	02-Feb-88	DARA, RAF St Athan [AX] (comp ZD937)
ZE737	F3	AS.052/671	3301/6	29-Jan-88	11-Feb-88	RAF No 25 Sqn, Leeming [FF]
ZE755	F3	AS.053/673	3302/6	05-Feb-88	24-Feb-88	RAF No 43 Sqn, Leuchars [GJ]
ZE756	F3	AS.054/674	3303/6	18-Feb-88	15-Mar-88	RAF AWC/F3 OEU, Coningsby
ZE757	F3	AS.055/676	3304/6	19-Feb-88	18-Jan-91	RAF F3 OCU/No 56(R) Sqn, Coningsby [AR]
ZE758	F3	AS.056/677	3305/6	19-Feb-88	09-Mar-88	RAF No 43 Sqn, Leuchars [GO]
ZE759	F3	AT.029/679	3306/6	26-Feb-88	09-Mar-88	Cr 28-Sep-96, off Blackpool on test flight (Bae Warton) (comp ZD904)
ZE760	F3	AS.057/681	3307/6	10-Mar-88	28-Mar-88	Subsequently MM7206 [36-07]
ZE761	F3	AS.058/683	3308/6	14-Mar-88	22-Apr-88	Subsequently MM7203 [36-02]
ZE762	F3	AS.059/685	3309/6	11-Mar-88	30-Mar-88	Subsequently MM7207
ZE763	F3	AS.060/687	3310/6	25-Mar-88	22-Apr-88	RAF No 11 Sqn, Leeming [DG]
ZE764	F3	AS.061/689	3311/6	25-Mar-88	26-Apr-88	RAF No 11 Sqn, Leeming [DH]
ZE785	F3	AS.062/691	3312/6	30-Mar-88	06-May-88	RAF No 111 Sqn, Leuchars [C]
ZE786	F3	AT.030/693	3313/6	31-Mar-88	20-May-88	DARA, RAF St Athan [AG] (comp ZD934)
ZE787	F3	AS.063/695	3314/6	11-Apr-88	13-May-88	Subsequently MM7205 [36-06]

Serial	Type	Build No/ Plane set	c/n Batch	First flt	Delivery	Operator, location or fate
ZE788	F3	AS.064/697	3315/6	18-Apr-88	14-Jun-88	RAF No 11 Sqn, Leeming [DF]
ZE789	F3	AS.065/699	3316/6	25-Apr-88	06-Jun-88	Cr 10-Mar-95, into North Sea off Spurn Head after mechanical failure (56(R) Sqn)
ZE790	F3	AS.066/700	3317/6	06-May-88	16-Jun-88	RAF No 43 Sqn, Leuchars [GD]
ZE791	F3	AS.067/702	3318/6	13-May-88	22-Jun-88	RAF No 111 Sqn, Leuchars [N]
ZE792	F3	AS.068/704	3319/6	27-May-88	12-Jul-88	Subsequently MM7211 [36-16]
ZE793	F3	AT.031/705	3320/6	20-May-88	21-Jul-88	RAF F3 OCU/No 56(R) Sqn, Coningsby [AI] (comp ZD935)
ZE794	F3	AS.069/707	3321/6	03-Jun-88	29-Jun-88	RAF No 111 Sqn, Leuchars [A]
ZE808	F3	AS.070/709	3322/6	10-Jun-88	29-Jul-88	RAF No 25 Sqn, Leeming [FA]
ZE809	F3	AS.071/711	3323/6	23-Jun-88	05-Aug-88	Cr 07-Jun-94, into North Sea 60 miles E of Newcastle (111 Sqn)
ZE810	F3	AS.072/712	3324/6	30-Jun-88	15-Aug-88	RAF No 111 Sqn, Leuchars [P]
ZE811	F3	AS.073/714	3325/6	15-Jul-88	19-Aug-88	Subsequently MM7208
ZE812	F3	AS.074/716	3326/6	22-Jul-88	30-Aug-88	RAF No 5 Sqn, Coningsby [CW]
ZE830	F3	AT.032/718	3327/6	12-Aug-88	19-Sep-88	RAF AWC/F3 OEU, Coningsby
ZE831	F3	AS.075/719	3328/6	17-Aug-88	04-Oct-88	RAF No 43 Sqn, Leuchars [GG]
ZE832	F3	AS.076/721	3329/6	19-Aug-88	07-Sep-88	Subsequently MM7202
ZE833	F3	AS.077/723	3330/6	26-Aug-88	07-Oct-88	Cr 21-Jun-89, into North Sea 30 miles NE of Newcastle (23 Sqn)
ZE834	F3	AS.078/725	3331/6	16-Sep-88	01-Nov-88	RAF No 5 Sqn, Coningsby [CX]
ZE835	F3	AS.079/726	3332/6	21-Sep-88	31-Oct-88	Subsequently MM7209
ZE836	F3	AS.080/728	3333/6	23-Sep-88	22-Nov-88	Subsequently MM7210 [36-14]
ZE837	F3	AT.033/730	3334/6	30-Sep-88	22-Nov-88	Subsequently MM55057 [36-03]
ZE838	F3	AS.081/732	3335/6	09-Nov-88	12-Jan-89	RAF No 43 Sqn, Leuchars [GH]
ZE839	F3	AS.082/733	3336/6	10-Nov-88	25-Nov-88	RAF No 111 Sqn, Leuchars [B]
ZE858	F3	AS.083/735	3337/6	17-Nov-88	15-Dec-88	Cr 21-Oct-93, near Barnard Castle, Co Durham following in-flight fire (No 43 Sqn)
ZE862	F3	AT.034/742	3341/6	02-Dec-88	22-Dec-88	Cr 10-Jan-96; collided with ZE166 near Sleaford (56(R) Sqn)
ZE887	F3	AS.092/753	3347/6	30-Sep-88	02-May-89	RAF No 11 Sqn, Leeming [DJ]
ZE888	F3	AT.035/755	3348/6	16-Dec-88	30-Jan-89	RAF No 111 Sqn, Leuchars [T]
ZE889	F3	AS.093/757	3349/6	21-Feb-89	03-Apr-89	RAF No 1435 Flt, Mount Pleasant, FI [H]
ZE907	F3	AS.098/765	3354/6	02-Feb-89	03-Apr-89	DARA, RAF St Athan [FM]
ZE908	F3	AT.036/766	3355/6	03-Apr-89	24-Apr-89	RAF No 25 Sqn, Leeming [HV]
ZE911	F3	AS.101/772	3358/6	12-Apr-89	27-Apr-89	Subsequently MM7226 [36-12]
ZE934	F3	AT.037/778	3362/6	16-May-89	25-May-89	RAF No 111 Sqn, Leuchars [S]
ZE936	F3	AS.106/781	3364/6	25-Apr-89	11-May-89	RAF No 11 Sqn, Leeming [DL]
ZE941	F3	AT.038/788	3369/6	22-May-89	21-Jun-89	RAF No 25 Sqn, Leeming [FE]

No 13 Squadron GR4A ZG710 wears the reduced sized squadron markings which have become de rigeur *across the Tornado force.* KEVIN WILLS

Tornado F3 ZE908, pictured in October 1999, retains the old high-visibility No 111 Squadron markings. KEVIN WILLS

Serial	Type	Build No/ Plane set	c/n Batch	First flt	Delivery	Operator, location or fate
ZE942	F3	AS.111/790	3370/6	19-May-89	25-Jul-89	RAF AWC/F3 OEU, Coningsby
ZE961	F3	AS.114/794	3373/6	11-Jul-89	28-Jul-89	RAF No 25 Sqn, Leeming [FD]
ZE962	F3	AS.115/796	3374/6	18-Jul-89	28-Jul-89	RAF No 25 Sqn, Leeming [FJ]
ZE963	F3	AT.039/797	3375/6	11-Aug-89	23-Aug-89	DARA, RAF St Athan [GE]
ZE964	F3	AT.040/798	3376/6	27-Sep-89	17-Oct-89	RAF No 11 Sqn, Leeming [DY]
ZE965	F3	AT.041/799	3377/6	23-Oct-89	02-Nov-89	RAF No 43 Sqn, Leuchars [GM]
ZE966	F3	AT.042/800	3378/6	2.-Nov-89	09-Jan-90	RAF No 11 Sqn, Leeming [DX]
ZE967	F3	AT.043/801	3379/6	07-Dec-89	20-Dec-89	RAF No 25 Sqn, Leeming [FU]
ZE968	F3	AS.120/802	3380/6	13-Mar-90	22-Feb-90	RAF No 11 Sqn, Leeming [DM]
ZE969	F3	AS.121/803	3381/6	-90	06-Jun-90	RAF No 11 Sqn, Leeming [DI]
ZE982	F3	AS.122/804	3382/6	-90	28-Aug-90	RAF AWC/F3 OEU, Coningsby
ZE983	F3	AS.123/805	3383/6	24-Oct-90	13-Nov-91	RAF No 11 Sqn, Leeming [DN]
ZG705	GR1A	BS.172/811	3387/7	21-June-89	13-Oct-89	RAF No 13 Sqn, Marham [J]
ZG706	GR1A	BS.173/813	3389/7	07-Sep-89	06-Oct-89	RAF AWC/SAOEU, DERA Boscombe Down [E]
ZG707	GR1A	BS.174/814	3390/7	04-Oct-89	18-Oct-89	RAF No 13 Sqn, Marham [B] (conv to GR4A)
ZG708	GR1A	BS.175/815	3391/7	23-Oct-89	03-Nov-89	Cr 01-Sep-94, near Glen Ogle, Perthshire (13 Sqn)
ZG709	GR1A	BS.176/816	3392/7	10-Nov-89	04-Dec-89	DPA/BAe, Warton (conv to GR4A)
ZG710	GR1A	BS.177/819	3393/7	17-Nov-89	30-Nov-89	RAF No 13 Sqn, Marham [D] (conv to GR4A)
ZG711	GR1A	BS.178/820	3394/7	07-Nov-89	26-Apr-90	DARA, RAF St Athan [O]
ZG712	GR1A	BS.179/822	3395/7	23-Jan-90	26-Apr-90	RAF No 13 Sqn, Marham [F] (conv to GR4A)
ZG713	GR1A	BS.180/824	3396/7	-90	31-May-90	DARA, RAF St Athan [G]
ZG714	GR1A	BS.181/825	3397/7	-90	28-Jun-90	DPA/BAe, Warton (conv to GR4A)
ZG725	GR1A	BS.182/828	3399/7	-90	24-Jul-90	Cr 19-Sep-94, into sea 5 miles N of Cape Frasca, Sardinia (13 Sqn)
ZG726	GR1A	BS.183/829	3400/7	-90	10-Dec-90	RAF No 13 Sqn, Marham [K] (conv to GR4A)
ZG727	GR1A	BS.184/832	3402/7	-90	30-Nov-90	RAF No 13 Sqn, Marham [L]
ZG728	F3	AS.124/834	3403/7	-90	10-Dec-90	Subsequently MM7229
ZG729	GR1A	BS.185/836	3405/7	-90	05-Dec-90	DPA/BAe, Warton (conv to GR4A)
ZG730	F3	AS.125/838	3406/7	-90	10-Jan-91	Subsequently MM7230 [36-11]
ZG731	F3	AS.126/841	3408/7	24-Nov-90	14-Dec-90	DPA/BAe, Warton [BL]
ZG732	F3	AS.127/845	3410/7	-91	30-May-91	Subsequently MM7227 [36-22]
ZG733	F3	AS.128/850	3413/7	-91	23-May-91	Subsequently MM7228
ZG734	F3	AS.129/855	3416/7	-91	07-Jun-91	Subsequently MM7231

Serial	Type	Build No/ Plane set	c/n Batch	First flt	Delivery	Operator, location or fate
ZG735	F3	AS.130/859	3418/7	-91	05-Jul-91	Subsequently MM7232 [36-10]
ZG750	GR1	BT.051/862	3420/7	-91	31-Jul-91	RAF No 31 Sqn, Brüggen (conv to GR4)
ZG751	F3	AS.131/863	3421/7	-91	14-Aug-91	RAF No 5 Sqn, Coningsby [CO]
ZG752	GR1	BT.052/868	3424/7	-91	15-Oct-91	RAF No 13 Sqn, Marham [XIII]
ZG753	F3	AS.132/872	3426/7	-91	08-Oct-91	DARA, stored RAF St Athan (for rebuild)
ZG754	GR1	BT.053/875	3428/7	-91	13-Nov-91	RAF No 13 Sqn, Marham [VI]
ZG755	F3	AS.133/877	3429/7	11-Oct-91	11-Nov-91	RAF No 5 Sqn, Coningsby
ZG756	GR1	BT.054/880	3431/7	-91	22-Nov-91	RAF No 14 Sqn, Brüggen [BX]
ZG757	F3	AS.134/882	3432/7	20-Nov-91	16-Dec-91	RAF No 111 Sqn, Leuchars [U]
ZG768	F3	AS.135/886	3435/7	21-Nov-91	11-Dec-91	Subsequently MM7233
ZG769	GR1	BT.055/889	3437/7	-91	18-Dec-91	RAF No 9 Sqn, Brüggen [AY]

No 29 Squadron's F3s joined the vogue for tiny squadron markings before disbanding, with its 'XXX' moving from the intakes to the fin, as illustrated by ZG778. KEVIN WILLS

TIALD-carrying Tornado GR1 ZG794 wears full No 14 Squadron markings and a Kosovo bomb log on its nose. KEVIN WILLS

These Mount Pleasant-based Tornado F3s of No 1435 Flight wear slightly different fin badges – ZG799 featuring a diving eagle superimposed on the unit's usual Maltese cross symbol (seen on ZG751). KEVIN WILLS

Serial	Type	Build No/ Plane set	c/n Batch	First flt	Delivery	Operator, location or fate
ZG770	F3	AS.136/891	3438/7	-91	11-Dec-91	RAF No 5 Sqn, Coningsby [CC]
ZG771	GR1	BT.056/893	3440/7	-91	19-Dec-91	RAF No 9 Sqn, Brüggen [AZ] (conv to GR4)
ZG772	F3	AS.137/899	3443/7	06-Dec-91	20-Dec-91	RAF F3 OCU/No 56(R) Sqn, Coningsby
ZG773	GR1	BS.186/902	3445/7	-92	21-Feb-92	DPA/BAe, Warton (conv to GR4)
ZG774	F3	AS.138/904	3446/7	26-Feb-92	23-Mar-92	RAF No 1435 Flt, Mount Pleasant, FI [D]
ZG775	GR1	BS.187/907	3448/7	-92	30-Apr-92	DPA/BAe, Warton (conv to GR4)
ZG776	F3	AS.139/908	3449/7	-92	30-Apr-92	RAF No 1435 Flt, Mount Pleasant, FI [F]
ZG777	GR1	BS.188/909	3450/7	-92	11-Jun-92	RAF No 14 Sqn, Brüggen [BS]
ZG778	F3	AS.140/910	3451/7	20-May-92	16-Jun-92	RAF No 5 Sqn, Coningsby
ZG779	GR1	BS.189/911	3452/7	-92	04-Jun-92	DARA, RAF St Athan [DK]
ZG780	F3	AS.141/912	3453/7	-92	09-Jul-92	RAF No 25 Sqn, Leeming [GL]
ZG791	GR1	BS.190/913	3454/7	-92	14-Jul-92	DPA/BAe, Warton (conv to GR4)
ZG792	GR1	BS.191/914	3455/7	-92	13-Jul-92	DPA/BAe, Warton (conv to GR4)
ZG793	F3	AS.142/915	3456/7	-92	06-Aug-92	RAF No 5 Sqn, Coningsby [CY]
ZG794	GR1	BS.192/916	3457/7	-92	19-Nov-92	RAF No 14 Sqn, Brüggen [BP]
ZG795	F3	AS.143/917	3458/7	-92	02-Sep-92	RAF No 5 Sqn, Coningsby [CB]
ZG796	F3	AS.144/918	3459/7	-92	15-Oct-92	RAF F3 OCU/No 56(R) Sqn, Coningsby [D]
ZG797	F3	AS.145/919	3460/7	-92	23-Oct-92	DARA, RAF St Athan [GI]
ZG798	F3	AS.146/920	3461/7	-92	19-Nov-92	DARA, RAF St Athan [AP,F]
ZG799	F3	AS.147/921	3462/7	-92	19-Nov-92	RAF No 5 Sqn, Coninsgby
ZH552	F3	AT.044/922	3463/7	-92	11-Sep-92	RAF No 5 Sqn, Coninsgby [CH]
ZH553	F3	AT.045/923	3464/7		28-Jan-93	RAF F3 OCU/No 56(R) Sqn, Coningsby [AB]
ZH554	F3	AT.046/924	3465/7		27-Jan-93	RAF F3 OCU/No 56(R) Sqn, Coningsby
ZH555	F3	AT.047/925	3466/7		17-Feb-93	RAF No 5 Sqn, Coningsby [CV]
ZH556	F3	AT.048/926	3467/7		27-Jan-93	RAF F3 OCU/No 56(R) Sqn, Coningsby [AK]
ZH557	F3	AT.049/927	3468/7	-93	24-Mar-93	RAF No 111 Sqn, Leuchars [X]
ZH558	F3	AT.050/928	3469/7	-93	24-Mar-93	Cr 08-Jul-94, into sea 15 miles off Akrotiri, Cyprus (No 43 Sqn)
ZH559	F3	AT.051/929	3470/7	-93	24-Mar-93	RAF F3 OCU/No 56(R) Sqn, Coningsby [AJ]

TORNADO PRODUCTION – GERMANY

The disbandment of MFG 1 led to a reshuffle of airframes. 43+58 combines Marineflieger camouflage with JBG 34 markings. HARTMUT FELDMANN

Serial	Type	Build No/ Plane set	c/n Batch	First flt	Delivery	Operator, location or fate
D-9591	-	P.01	-	14-Aug-74		(became 98+04 then 44+48) Luftwaffe, recruiting aid
D-9592	-	P.04	-	02-Sep-75		(became 98+05) Cr 16-Apr-80
98+06	-	P.07	-	30-Mar-76		Luftwaffe, Fassberg, instructional use
98+01	-	P.11	-	05-Feb-77		(became 44+00) Luftwaffe, recruiting aid
98+02	-	P.13	-	10-Jan-78		Luftwaffe, Ingolstadt, instructional use
98+03	ECR	P.16	-	26-Mar-79		Luftwaffe, WTD-61, Ingolstadt
43+01	IDS	GT.001/002	4001/1	27-Jul-79		DASA, Ingolstadt
43+02	IDS	GT.002/004	4002/1	31-Mar-80		DASA, Ingolstadt
43+03	IDS	GT.003/006	4003/1	13-May-80		DASA, Ingolstadt
43+04	IDS	GT.004/008	4004/1	26-Jun-80		Luftwaffe, JbG-33, Büchel
43+05	IDS	GT.005/010	4005/1	22-May-80		DASA, Ingolstadt
43+06	IDS	GT.006/012	4006/1	16-Jul-80		Luftwaffe, JbG-38, Jever
43+07	IDS	GT.007/015	4007/1	07-Apr-82		DASA, Ingolstadt
43+08	IDS	GT.008/017	4008/1	14-Sep-80		Luftwaffe, JbG-32, Lechfeld
43+09	IDS	GT.009/019	4009/1	28-Aug-80		DASA, Ingolstadt
43+10	IDS	GT.010/021	4010/1	08-Oct-80		Luftwaffe, JbG-38, Jever
43+11	IDS	GT.011/023	4011/1	03-Oct-80		DASA, Ingolstadt
43+12	IDS	GS.001/026	4012/1	30-Oct-80		Luftwaffe, Erding, instructional use
43+13	IDS	GS.002/029	4013/1	07-Nov-80		Luftwaffe, Erding, instructional use
43+14	IDS	GS.003/031	4014/1	21-Nov-80		Luftwaffe, Lechfeld, instructional use
43+15	IDS	GT.012/034	4015/1	02-Feb-81		DASA, Ingolstadt
43+16	IDS	GT.013/036	4016/1	17-Feb-81		DASA, Ingolstadt
43+17	IDS	GT.014/039	4017/1	17-Mar-81		DASA, Ingolstadt
43+18	IDS	GS.004/044	4018/2	11-Jun-81		Luftwaffe, JbG-31, Nörvenich
43+19	IDS	GS.005/046	4019/2	28-Apr-81		Cr 10-Jun-97, on White Sands Range, NM (49th FW)
43+20	IDS	GS.006/049	4020/2	29-Jul-81		Luftwaffe, JbG-34, Memmingen
43+21	IDS	GT.015/051	4021/2	24-Sep-81		(became 98+59) Luftwaffe, WTD-61, Ingolstadt
43+22	IDS	GT.016/053	4022/2	15-May-81		Luftwaffe, JbG-38, Jever
43+23	IDS	GT.017/055	4023/2	21-May-81		Luftwaffe, JbG-38, Jever
43+24	IDS	GS.007/059	4024/2	02-Jul-81		Cr 17-Jun-86, near Claerwen reservoir, Powys, UK (TTTE)
43+25	IDS	GS.008/062	4025/2	04-Sep-81		DASA, Ingolstadt
43+26	IDS	GS.009/066	4026/2	20-Jul-81		Cr 27-Jan-99, North Sea, after collision with 44+36 (JbG-38)

Serial	Type	Build No/ Plane set	c/n Batch	First flt	Delivery	Operator, location or fate
43+27	IDS	GS.010/069	4027/2	22-Sep-81		Luftwaffe, JbG-34, Memmingen
43+28	IDS	GS.011/072	4028/2	14-Sep-81		Luftwaffe, 49th FW, Holloman AFB, NM, USA
43+29	IDS	GT.018/076	4029/2	23-Oct-81		Luftwaffe, JbG-31, Nörvenich
43+30	IDS	GS.012/079	4030/2	21-Sep-81		Luftwaffe, JbG-31, Nörvenich
43+31	IDS	GT.019/083	4031/2	24-Sep-81		Luftwaffe, JbG-31, Nörvenich
43+32	IDS	GS.013/087	4032/2	24-Sep-81		DASA, Ingolstadt
43+33	IDS	GT.020/089	4033/2	16-Nov-81		Luftwaffe, JbG-38, Jever
43+34	IDS	GS.014/092	4034/2	29-Oct-81		Luftwaffe, TsLw-1, Kaufbeuren
43+35	IDS	GT.021/095	4035/2	05-Nov-81		Luftwaffe, JbG-38, Jever
43+36	IDS	GS.015/097	4036/2	16-Nov-81		Cr 19-Oct-98, China Lake, Clifornia. (49th FW)
43+37	IDS	GT.022/100	4037/2	16-Nov-81		Luftwaffe, JbG-38, Jever
43+38	IDS	GS.016/103	4038/2	09-Dec-81		Luftwaffe, JbG-33, Büchel
43+39	IDS	GS.017/106	4039/2	24-Nov-81		Cr 05-Jan-84
43+40	IDS	GS.018/109	4040/2	25-Jan-82		Luftwaffe, JbG-33, Büchel
43+41	IDS	GS.019/111	4041/2	13-Jan-82		Luftwaffe, JbG-31, Nörvenich
43+42	IDS	GT.023/115	4042/2	02-Feb-82		DASA, Ingolstadt
43+43	IDS	GT.024/117	4043/2	04-Feb-82		Luftwaffe, JbG-38, Jever
43+44	IDS	GT.025/121	4044/2	24-Feb-82		Luftwaffe, 49th FW, Holloman AFB, NM, USA
43+45	IDS	GT.026/123	4045/2	08-Feb-82		Luftwaffe, 49th FW, Holloman AFB, NM, USA
43+46	IDS	GS.020/126	4046/2	22-Feb-82		Luftwaffe, AkG-51, Schleswig/Jagel
43+47	IDS	GS.021/128	4047/2	12-Mar-82		Luftwaffe, AkG-51, Schleswig/Jagel
43+48	IDS	GS.022/130	4048/2	09-Mar-82		Luftwaffe, AkG-51, Schleswig/Jagel
43+49	IDS	GS.023/132	4049/2	23-Mar-82		Cr 24-Sep-85
43+50	IDS	GS.024/135	4050/2	18-Mar-82		Luftwaffe, AkG-51, Schleswig/Jagel
43+51	IDS	GT.027/137	4051/2	30-Mar-82		Cr 02-Sep-88 into North Sea 20 miles N of Langeoog (MFG-1)
43+52	IDS	GS.025/140	4052/2	05-Apr-82		Luftwaffe, JbG-38, Jever
43+53	IDS	GS.026/142	4053/2	28-Apr-82		Luftwaffe, JbG-34, Memmingen
43+54	IDS	GS.027/145	4054/2	04-May-82		Luftwaffe, JbG-34, Memmingen
43+55	IDS	GS.028/146	4055/2	22-Apr-82		Marineflieger, MFG-2, Eggebek
43+56	IDS	GS.029/149	4056/2	01-Jun-82		Cr 16-Nov-89 into Baltic Sea off Langeland, Denmark (MFG-1)
43+57	IDS	GS.030/151	4057/2	14-May-82		Luftwaffe, 49th FW, Holloman AFB, NM, USA
43+58	IDS	GS.031/155	4058/3	04-Aug-82		Luftwaffe, JbG-34, Memmingen
43+59	IDS	GS.032/157	4059/3	16-Jun-82		Luftwaffe, JbG-38, Jever
43+60	IDS	GS.033/160	4060/3	22-Jun-82		Luftwaffe, JbG-34, Memmingen
43+61	IDS	GS.034/162	4061/3	01-Jul-82		Luftwaffe, TsLw-1, Kaufbeuren
43+62	IDS	GS.035/165	4062/3	01-Jul-82		Luftwaffe, JbG-34, Memmingen
43+63	IDS	GS.036/167	4063/3	07-Jul-82		Luftwaffe, JbG-34, Memmingen
43+64	IDS	GS.037/169	4064/3	07-Jul-82		Luftwaffe, JbG-38, Jever
43+65	IDS	GS.038/171	4065/3	15-Jul-82		Luftwaffe, JbG-38, Jever
43+66	IDS	GS.039/174	4066/3	29-Jul-82		Cr 09-Jan-84 into Baltic Sea off Samsøe Island, Denmark after stalling during practice air combat (MFG-1)
43+67	IDS	GS.040/177	4067/3	03-Aug-82		Luftwaffe, JbG-34, Memmingen
43+68	IDS	GS.041/179	4068/3	25-Aug-82		Luftwaffe, JbG-34, Memmingen
43+69	IDS	GS.042/181	4069/3	31-Aug-82		Luftwaffe, JbG-38, Jever
43+70	IDS	GS.043/184	4070/3	07-Sep-82		Luftwaffe, JbG-38, Jever
43+71	IDS	GS.044/186	4071/3	29-Sep-82		Luftwaffe, JbG-38, Jever
43+72	IDS	GS.045/189	4072/3	23-Sep-82		Luftwaffe, JbG-38, Jever
43+73	IDS	GS.046/191	4073/3	11-Aug-82		Luftwaffe, AkG-51, Schleswig/Jagel
43+74	IDS	GS.047/193	4074/3	20-Dec-82		Luftwaffe, stored AMARC, Davis-Monthan AFB, AZ, USA
43+75	IDS	GS.048/196	4075/3	25-Oct-82		DASA, Ingolstadt
43+76	IDS	GS.049/198	4076/3	25-Oct-82		Luftwaffe, JbG-38, Jever
43+77	IDS	GS.050/200	4077/3	08-Nov-82		Luftwaffe, JbG-34, Memmingen
43+78	IDS	GS.051/203	4078/3	09-Nov-82		Luftwaffe, JbG-38, Jever
43+79	IDS	GS.052/205	4079/3	16-Nov-82		Luftwaffe, AkG-51, Schleswig/Jagel
43+80	IDS	GS.053/208	4080/3	06-Dec-82		Luftwaffe, AkG-51, Schleswig/Jagel

AG 51 applied these striking markings to one of its aircraft (44+88) during 1999.

Serial	Type	Build No/ Plane set	c/n Batch	First flt	Delivery	Operator, location or fate
43+81	IDS	GS.054/210	4081/3	08-Mar-83		Luftwaffe, AkG-51, Schleswig/Jagel
43+82	IDS	GS.055/212	4082/3	15-Dec-82		Luftwaffe, AkG-51, Schleswig/Jagel
43+83	IDS	GS.056/215	4083/3	23-Dec-82		Cr 28-Apr-96, Goose Bay, Canada; skidded off wet runway, overturned and caught fire (AkG-51)
43+84	IDS	GS.057/218	4084/3	21-Jan-83		Cr 31-Oct-91 into the Skagerrak near Denmark; collided with 46+17 (MFG-1)
43+85	IDS	GS.058/221	4085/3	04-Feb-83		Luftwaffe, JbG-38, Jever
43+86	IDS	GS.059/223	4086/3	04-Feb-83		Luftwaffe, JbG-38, Jever
43+87	IDS	GS.060/226	4087/3	17-Feb-83		Marineflieger, MFG-2, Eggebek
43+88	IDS	GS.061/228	4088/3	25-Feb-83		Luftwaffe, 49th FW, Holloman AFB, NM, USA
43+89	IDS	GS.062/230	4089/3	24-Feb-83		(became 98+60) Luftwaffe, WTD-61, Ingolstadt
43+90	IDS	GT.028/233	4090/3	18-Feb-83		Luftwaffe, JbG-38, Jever
43+91	IDS	GT.029/236	4091/3	24-Feb-83		Luftwaffe, 49th FW, Holloman AFB, NM, USA
43+92	IDS	GT.030/239	4092/3	21-Mar-83		Luftwaffe, JbG-31, Nörvenich
43+93	IDS	GT.031/241	4093/3	29-Mar-83		Cr 12-Mar-86, near Pfaffenhousen, Upper Bavaria (JbG-33)
43+94	IDS	GT.032/243	4094/3	08-Apr-83		Luftwaffe, JbG-38, Jever
43+95	IDS	GS.063/246	4095/3	06-Apr-83		Luftwaffe, stored AMARC, Davis-Monthan AFB, AZ, USA
43+96	IDS	GS.064/248	4096/3	30-May-83		Luftwaffe, AkG-51, Schleswig/Jagel
43+97	IDS	GT.033/251	4097/3	26-Apr-83		Luftwaffe, 49th FW, Holloman AFB, NM, USA
43+98	IDS	GS.065/253	4098/3	12-Apr-83		Luftwaffe, AkG-51, Schleswig/Jagel
43+99	IDS	GS.066/256	4099/3	06-May-83		Luftwaffe, 49th FW, Holloman AFB, NM, USA
44+00	IDS	GS.067/258	4100/3	27-May-83		Luftwaffe, JbG-31, Nörvenich
44+01	IDS	GT.034/260	4101/3	13-Jun-83		Luftwaffe, 49th FW, Holloman AFB, NM, USA
44+02	IDS	GS.068/263	4102/3	25-Jul-83		Luftwaffe, JbG-31, Nörvenich
44+03	IDS	GS.069/265	4103/3	22-Jun-83		Luftwaffe, 49th FW, Holloman AFB, NM, USA
44+04	IDS	GS.070/268	4104/3	21-Jun-83		Luftwaffe, AkG-51, Schleswig/Jagel
44+05	IDS	GT.035/270	4105/3	05-Jul-83		Luftwaffe, AkG-51, Schleswig/Jagel
44+06	IDS	GS.071/272	4106/3	14-Jul-83		Luftwaffe, JbG-34, Memmingen
44+07	IDS	GS.072/275	4107/3	30-Aug-83		Luftwaffe, JbG-31, Nörvenich
44+08	IDS	GS.073/277	4108/3	30-Aug-83		Luftwaffe, JbG-38, Jever
44+09	IDS	GS.074/279	4109/3	24-Aug-83		Luftwaffe, JbG-33, Büchel
44+10	IDS	GT.036/282	4110/3	06-Sep-83		Luftwaffe, JbG-38, Jever
44+11	IDS	GS.075/284	4111/3	13-Sep-83		Luftwaffe, JbG-34, Memmingen
44+12	IDS	GS.076/287	4112/3	12-Oct-83		Luftwaffe, 49th FW, Holloman AFB, NM, USA
44+13	IDS	GS.077/289	4113/3	27-Sep-83		Luftwaffe, JbG-31, Nörvenich

Serial	Type	Build No/ Plane set	c/n Batch	First flt	Delivery	Operator, location or fate
44+14	IDS	GS.078/291	4114/3	06-Oct-83		Luftwaffe, JbG-31, Nörvenich
44+15	IDS	GS.079/294	4115/3	12-Oct-83		Luftwaffe, JbG-38, Jever
44+16	IDS	GT.037/296	4116/3	07-Oct-83		Luftwaffe, JbG-31, Nörvenich
44+17	IDS	GS.080/299	4117/3	21-Oct-83		Luftwaffe, AkG-51, Schleswig/Jagel
44+18	IDS	GS.081/301	4118/3	27-Oct-83		Cr 04-Dec-87, Nörvenich; overran runway during emergency landing (JbG-31)
44+19	IDS	GS.082/304	4119/3	14-Nov-83		Luftwaffe, JbG-31, Nörvenich
44+20	IDS	GT.038/306	4120/3	28-Nov-83		Luftwaffe, 49th FW, Holloman AFB, NM, USA
44+21	IDS	GS.083/308	4121/3	28-Nov-83		Luftwaffe, JbG-31, Nörvenich
44+22	IDS	GS.084/311	4122/3	15-Dec-83		Luftwaffe, JbG-31, Nörvenich
44+23	IDS	GS.085/313	4123/3	11-Jan-84		Luftwaffe, JbG-33, Büchel
44+24	IDS	GS.086/316	4124/3	10-Jan-84		Luftwaffe, AkG-51, Schleswig/Jagel
44+25	IDS	GT.039/317	4125/3	19-Jan-84		Luftwaffe, JbG-38, Jever
44+26	IDS	GS.087/320	4126/4	10-Feb-84		Luftwaffe, JbG-31, Nörvenich
44+27	IDS	GS.088/323	4127/4	31-Jan-84		Luftwaffe, JbG-33, Büchel
44+28	IDS	GS.089/325	4128/4	10-Feb-84		Luftwaffe, 49th FW, Holloman AFB, NM, USA
44+29	IDS	GS.090/327	4129/4	21-Feb-84		Luftwaffe, JbG-31, Nörvenich
44+30	IDS	GS.091/330	4130/4	21-Feb-84		Luftwaffe, JbG-31, Nörvenich
44+31	IDS	GS.092/332	4131/4	27-Feb-84		Luftwaffe, JbG-31, Nörvenich
44+32	IDS	GS.093/335	4132/4	14-Mar-84		Luftwaffe, JbG-38, Jever
44+33	IDS	GS.094/337	4133/4	27-Mar-84		Luftwaffe, JbG-33, Büchel
44+34	IDS	GS.095/340	4134/4	30-Mar-84		Luftwaffe, JbG-33, Büchel
44+35	IDS	GS.096/343	4135/4	05-Apr-84		Luftwaffe, JbG-31, Nörvenich
44+36	IDS	GT.040/347	4136/4	17-Apr-84		Cr 27-Jan-99, North Sea, after collision with 43+26 (JbG-38)
44+37	IDS	GT.041/349	4137/4	09-May-84		Luftwaffe, JbG-38, Jever
44+38	IDS	GT.042/351	4138/4	08-May-84		Luftwaffe, 49th FW, Holloman AFB, NM, USA
44+39	IDS	GT.043/353	4139/4	03-May-84		Luftwaffe, 49th FW, Holloman AFB, NM, USA
44+40	IDS	GS.097/355	4140/4	17-May-84		Luftwaffe, JbG-33, Büchel
44+41	IDS	GS.098/359	4141/4	15-May-84		Luftwaffe, JbG-31, Nörvenich
44+42	IDS	GS.099/362	4142/4	28-May-84		Luftwaffe, AkG-51, Schleswig/Jagel
44+43	IDS	GS.100/365	4143/4	29-May-84		Luftwaffe, JbG-34, Memmingen
44+44	IDS	GS.101/368	4144/4	18-Jun-84		Luftwaffe, JbG-31, Nörvenich
44+45	IDS	GS.102/370	4145/4	25-Jun-84		Cr 24-Oct-85
44+46	IDS	GS.103/372	4146/4	27-Jun-84		Luftwaffe, JbG-34, Memmingen
44+47	IDS	GS.104/374	4147/4	04-Jul-84		Cr 22-Oct-86, on Otterburn range, UK (JbG-31)

The second staffel of JBG 38 applied these distinctive special markings to Tornado IDS 44+92. VIA KEVIN WILLS

JBG 38 decorated this aircraft (44+97) in this smart colour scheme during 1997, to commemorate a unit anniversary. HARTMUT FELDMANN

Serial	Type	Build No/ Plane set	c/n Batch	First flt	Delivery	Operator, location or fate
44+48	IDS	GS.105/378	4148/4	31-Aug-84		Luftwaffe, JbG-33, Büchel
44+49	IDS	GS.106/380	4149/4	23-Jul-84		Luftwaffe, JbG-31, Nörvenich
44+50	IDS	GS.107/383	4150/4	31-Jul-84		Luftwaffe, AkG-51, Schleswig/Jagel
44+51	IDS	GS.108/385	4151/4	29-Aug-84		Luftwaffe, JbG-31, Nörvenich
44+52	IDS	GS.109/388	4152/4	07-Sep-84		Luftwaffe, JbG-34, Memmingen
44+53	IDS	GS.110/390	4153/4	19-Sep-84		Luftwaffe, AkG-51, Schleswig/Jagel
44+54	IDS	GS.111/393	4154/4	14-Sep-84		Luftwaffe, JbG-33, Büchel
44+55	IDS	GS.112/395	4155/4	20-Sep-84		Luftwaffe, JbG-38, Jever
44+56	IDS	GS.113/396	4156/4	04-Oct-84		Luftwaffe, JbG-34, Memmingen
44+57	IDS	GS.114/398	4157/4	05-Nov-84		Luftwaffe, JbG-31, Nörvenich
44+58	IDS	GS.115/401	4158/4	31-Oct-84		Luftwaffe, JbG-31, Nörvenich
44+59	IDS	GS.116/403	4159/4	16-Oct-84		Luftwaffe, 49th FW, Holloman AFB, NM, USA
44+60	IDS	GS.117/404	4160/4	12-Nov-84		Luftwaffe, 49th FW, Holloman AFB, NM, USA
44+61	IDS	GS.118/407	4161/4	12-Nov-84		Luftwaffe, AkG-51, Schleswig/Jagel
44+62	IDS	GS.119/410	4162/4	14-Nov-84		Luftwaffe, JbG-33, Büchel
44+63	IDS	GS.120/412	4163/4	23-Nov-84		Luftwaffe, JbG-33, Büchel
44+64	IDS	GS.121/415	4164/4	23-Nov-84		Luftwaffe, AkG-51, Schleswig/Jagel
44+65	IDS	GS.122/417	4165/4	10-Dec-84		Luftwaffe, AkG-51, Schleswig/Jagel
44+66	IDS	GS.123/421	4166/4	10-Dec-84		Luftwaffe, JbG-31, Nörvenich
44+67	IDS	GS.124/422	4167/4			Cr 24-Aug-96, 130km W of Goose Bay, Canada; collided with 45+32 (MFG-2)
44+68	IDS	GS.125/425	4168/4			Luftwaffe, AkG-51, Schleswig/Jagel
44+69	IDS	GS.126/427	4169/4			Luftwaffe, AkG-51, Schleswig/Jagel
44+70	IDS	GS.127/431	4170/4			Luftwaffe, JbG-31, Nörvenich
44+71	IDS	GS.128/433	4171/4			Luftwaffe, JbG-31, Nörvenich
44+72	IDS	GT.044/435	4172/4			Luftwaffe, JbG-33, Büchel
44+73	IDS	GT.045/439	4173/4			Luftwaffe, 49th FW, Holloman AFB, NM, USA
44+74	IDS	GT.046/440	4174/4			Cr 15-Aug-91, near Bad Ems (JbG-33)
44+75	IDS	GT.047/443	4175/4			Luftwaffe, JbG-33, Büchel
44+76	IDS	GS.129/445	4176/4			Luftwaffe, JbG-34, Memmingen
44+77	IDS	GS.130/448	4177/4			Luftwaffe, 49th FW, Holloman AFB, NM, USA
44+78	IDS	GS.131/451	4178/4			Luftwaffe, JbG-31, Nörvenich
44+79	IDS	GS.132/454	4179/4			Luftwaffe, JbG-33, Büchel
44+80	IDS	GS.133/457	4180/4			Luftwaffe, JbG-33, Büchel
44+81	IDS	GS.134/458	4181/4			Luftwaffe, 49th FW, Holloman AFB, NM, USA

Serial	Type	Build No/ Plane set	c/n Batch	First flt	Delivery	Operator, location or fate
44+82	IDS	GS.135/462	4182/4			Cr 03-Feb-98, near Lippstadt (JbG-31)
44+83	IDS	GS.136/465	4183/4			Luftwaffe, JbG-33, Büchel
44+84	IDS	GS.137/466	4184/4			Luftwaffe, JbG-33, Büchel
44+85	IDS	GS.138/468	4185/4			Luftwaffe, JbG-33, Büchel
44+86	IDS	GS.139/470	4186/4			Luftwaffe, AkG-51, Schleswig/Jagel
44+87	IDS	GS.140/472	4187/4			Luftwaffe, AkG-51, Schleswig/Jagel
44+88	IDS	GS.141/475	4188/4			Luftwaffe, AkG-51, Schleswig/Jagel
44+89	IDS	GS.142/476	4189/4			Luftwaffe, JbG-33, Büchel
44+90	IDS	GS.143/481	4190/5			Luftwaffe, JbG-33, Büchel
44+91	IDS	GS.144/482	4191/5			Luftwaffe, JbG-33, Büchel
44+92	IDS	GS.145/484	4192/5			Luftwaffe, JbG-38, Jever
44+93	IDS	GS.146/487	4193/5			Cr 12-Mar-86
44+94	IDS	GS.147/489	4194/5			Luftwaffe, JbG-33, Büchel
44+95	IDS	GS.148/491	4195/5			Luftwaffe, JbG-38, Jever
44+96	IDS	GS.149/494	4196/5			Luftwaffe, JbG-31, Nörvenich
44+97	IDS	GS.150/496	4197/5			Luftwaffe, JbG-38, Jever
44+98	IDS	GS.151/499	4198/5			Luftwaffe, JbG-34, Memmingen
44+99	IDS	GS.152/501	4199/5			Cr 19-Jan-93, near Wader Trudingen (JbG-34)
45+00	IDS	GS.153/504	4200/5			Luftwaffe, JbG-33, Büchel
45+01	IDS	GS.154/506	4201/5			Luftwaffe, JbG-34, Memmingen
45+02	IDS	GS.155/508	4202/5			Luftwaffe, JbG-34, Memmingen
45+03	IDS	GS.156/510	4203/5			Luftwaffe, JbG-34, Memmingen
45+04	IDS	GS.157/512	4204/5			Luftwaffe, JbG-33, Büchel
45+05	IDS	GS.158/516	4205/5			Cr 30-Jul-99, Bøsand, Norway (JbG-33)
45+06	IDS	GS.159/518	4206/5			Luftwaffe, AkG-51, Schleswig/Jagel
45+07	IDS	GS.160/521	4207/5			Luftwaffe, JbG-33, Büchel
45+08	IDS	GS.161/523	4208/5			Luftwaffe, JbG-33, Büchel
45+09	IDS	GS.162/525	4209/5			Luftwaffe, JbG-31, Nörvenich
45+10	IDS	GS.163/528	4210/5			Luftwaffe, JbG-31, Nörvenich
45+11	IDS	GS.164/530	4211/5			Luftwaffe, 49th FW, Holloman AFB, NM, USA
45+12	IDS	GT.048/533	4212/5			Marineflieger, MFG-2, Eggebek
45+13	IDS	GT.049/535	4213/5			Marineflieger, MFG-2, Eggebek
45+14	IDS	GT.050/539	4214/5			Luftwaffe, JbG-38, Jever
45+15	IDS	GT.051/541	4215/5			Marineflieger, MFG-2, Eggebek
45+16	IDS	GT.052/543	4216/5			Marineflieger, MFG-2, Eggebek
45+17	IDS	GS.165/546	4217/5			Luftwaffe, JbG-33, Büchel
45+18	IDS	GS.166/548	4218/5			Luftwaffe, JbG-33, Büchel
45+19	IDS	GS.167/551	4219/5			Luftwaffe, JbG-33, Büchel
45+20	IDS	GS.168/553	4220/5			Luftwaffe, AkG-51, Schleswig/Jagel
45+21	IDS	GS.169/554	4221/5			Luftwaffe, JbG-33, Büchel
45+22	IDS	GS.170/558	4222/5			Luftwaffe, JbG-33, Büchel
45+23	IDS	GS.171/560	4223/5			Luftwaffe, JbG-31, Nörvenich
45+24	IDS	GS.172/564	4224/5			Luftwaffe, JbG-33, Büchel
45+25	IDS	GS.173/566	4225/5			Luftwaffe, AkG-51, Schleswig/Jagel
45+26	IDS	GS.174/568	4226/5			Cr 20-Jan-98, North Sea (MFG-2)
45+27	IDS	GS.175/570	4227/5			Marineflieger, MFG-2, Eggebek
45+28	IDS	GS.176/572	4228/5			Marineflieger, MFG-2, Eggebek
45+29	IDS	GS.177/575	4229/5			Luftwaffe, WTD-61, Ingolstadt
45+30	IDS	GS.178/577	4230/5			Marineflieger, MFG-2, Eggebek
45+31	IDS	GS.179/579	4231/5			Marineflieger, MFG-2, Eggebek
45+32	IDS	GS.180/582	4232/5			Cr 24-Aug-96, 130km W of Goose Bay, Canada; collided with 44+67 (MFG-2)
45+33	IDS	GS.181/584	4233/5			Marineflieger, MFG-2, Eggebek
45+34	IDS	GS.182/587	4234/5			Marineflieger, MFG-2, Eggebek
45+35	IDS	GS.183/589	4235/5			Marineflieger, MFG-2, Eggebek
45+36	IDS	GS.184/592	4236/5			Marineflieger, MFG-2, Eggebek

Serial	Type	Build No/ Plane set	c/n Batch	First flt	Delivery	Operator, location or fate
45+37	IDS	GS.185/594	4237/5			Marineflieger, MFG-2, Eggebek
45+38	IDS	GS.186/596	4238/5			Marineflieger, MFG-2, Eggebek
45+39	IDS	GS.187/599	4239/5			Marineflieger, MFG-2, Eggebek
45+40	IDS	GS.188/601	4240/5			Marineflieger, MFG-2, Eggebek
45+41	IDS	GS.189/604	4241/5			Marineflieger, MFG-2, Eggebek
45+42	IDS	GS.190/606	4242/5			Marineflieger, MFG-2, Eggebek
45+43	IDS	GS.191/608	4243/5			Marineflieger, MFG-2, Eggebek
45+44	IDS	GS.192/611	4244/5			Marineflieger, MFG-2, Eggebek
45+45	IDS	GS.193/613	4245/5			Marineflieger, MFG-2, Eggebek
45+46	IDS	GS.194/616	4246/5			Marineflieger, MFG-2, Eggebek
45+47	IDS	GS.195/618	4247/5			Marineflieger, MFG-2, Eggebek
45+48	IDS	GS.196/620	4248/5			Cr 22-Aug-98, near Tarp, Germany (MFG-2)
45+49	IDS	GS.197/623	4249/5			Marineflieger, MFG-2, Eggebek
45+50	IDS	GS.198/625	4250/5			Marineflieger, MFG-2, Eggebek
45+51	IDS	GS.199/628	4251/5			Luftwaffe, AkG-51, Schleswig/Jagel
45+52	IDS	GS.200/630	4252/5			Marineflieger, MFG-2, Eggebek
45+53	IDS	GS.201/637	4253/5			Marineflieger, MFG-2, Eggebek
45+54	IDS	GS.202/640	4254/5			Marineflieger, MFG-2, Eggebek
45+55	IDS	GS.203/642	4255/5			Marineflieger, MFG-2, Eggebek
45+56	IDS	GS.204/646	4256/5			Marineflieger, MFG-2, Eggebek
45+57	IDS	GS.205/648	4257/5			Luftwaffe, JbG-34, Memmingen
45+58	IDS	GS.206/651	4258/5			Cr 07-Sep-93 into Baltic Sea on test flight (MFG-2)
45+59	IDS	GS.207/653	4259/5			Marineflieger, MFG-2, Eggebek
45+60	IDS	GT.053/655	4260/6			Luftwaffe, JbG-34, Memmingen
45+61	IDS	GT.054/657	4261/6			Luftwaffe, JbG-34, Memmingen
45+62	IDS	GT.055/659	4262/6			Luftwaffe, JbG-38, Jever
45+63	IDS	GT.056/661	4263/6			Cr 19-Nov-91 into North Sea off Vlieland, Netherlands (JbG-38)
45+64	IDS	GS.208/663	4264/6			Luftwaffe, TsLw-1, Kaufbeuren
45+65	IDS	GS.209/665	4265/6			Luftwaffe, 49th FW, Holloman AFB, NM, USA
45+66	IDS	GS.210/667	4266/6			Marineflieger, MFG-2, Eggebek
45+67	IDS	GS.211/668	4267/6			Luftwaffe, AkG-51, Schleswig/Jagel
45+68	IDS	GS.212/670	4268/6			Marineflieger, MFG-2, Eggebek
45+69	IDS	GS.213/672	4269/6			Marineflieger, MFG-2, Eggebek
45+70	IDS	GT.057/675	4270/6			Luftwaffe, JbG-33, Büchel
45+71	IDS	GS.214/678	4271/6			Marineflieger, MFG-2, Eggebek
45+72	IDS	GS.215/680	4272/6			Marineflieger, MFG-2, Eggebek
45+73	IDS	GT.058/682	4273/6			Luftwaffe, JbG-31, Nörvenich
45+74	IDS	GS.216/684	4274/6			Marineflieger, MFG-2, Eggebek
45+75	IDS	GS.217/686	4275/6			(became 98+79) Luftwaffe, WTD-61, Ingolstadt (conv to ECR)
45+76	IDS	GS.218/688	4276/6			Luftwaffe, JbG-38, Jever
45+77	IDS	GT.059/690	4277/6			Luftwaffe, JbG-33, Büchel
45+78	IDS	GS.219/692	4278/6			Luftwaffe, JbG-33, Büchel
45+79	IDS	GS.220/694	4279/6			Luftwaffe, JbG-31, Nörvenich
45+80	IDS	GS.221/696	4280/6			Cr 25-Aug-95, near Babenhausen; collided with 45+97 (JbG-34)
45+81	IDS	GS.222/698	4281/6			Luftwaffe, JbG-34, Memmingen
45+82	IDS	GS.223/701	4282/6			Luftwaffe, JbG-31, Nörvenich
45+83	IDS	GS.224/703	4283/6			Luftwaffe, 49th FW, Holloman AFB, NM, USA
45+84	IDS	GS.225/706	4284/6			Luftwaffe, AkG-51, Schleswig/Jagel
45+85	IDS	GS.226/708	4285/6			Luftwaffe, AkG-51, Schleswig/Jagel
45+86	IDS	GS.227/710	4286/6			Luftwaffe, JbG-33, Büchel
45+87	IDS	GS.228/713	4287/6			Luftwaffe, JbG-34, Memmingen
45+88	IDS	GS.229/715	4288/6			Luftwaffe, JbG-33, Büchel
45+89	IDS	GS.230/717	4289/6			Luftwaffe, JbG-34, Memmingen
45+90	IDS	GS.231/720	4290/6			Luftwaffe, JbG-31, Nörvenich
45+91	IDS	GS.232/722	4291/6			Luftwaffe, AkG-51, Schleswig/Jagel

The Marineflieger's latest darker close-toned disruptive camouflage is seen on Kormoran-equipped Tornado IDS 45+28. HARTMUT FELDMANN

Serial	Type	Build No/ Plane set	c/n Batch	First flt	Delivery	Operator, location or fate
45+92	IDS	GS.233/724	4292/6			Luftwaffe, 49th FW, Holloman AFB, NM, USA
45+93	IDS	GS.234/727	4293/6			Luftwaffe, AkG-51, Schleswig/Jagel
45+94	IDS	GS.235/729	4294/6			Luftwaffe, JbG-33, Büchel
45+95	IDS	GS.236/731	4295/6			Luftwaffe, JbG-34, Memmingen
45+96	IDS	GS.237/734	4296/6			Luftwaffe, 49th FW, Holloman AFB, NM, USA
45+97	IDS	GS.238/736	4297/6			Cr 25-Aug-95, near Babenhausen; collided with 45+80 (JbG-34)
45+98	IDS	GS.239/738	4298/6			Luftwaffe, AkG-51, Schleswig/Jagel
45+99	IDS	GT.060/741	4299/6			Luftwaffe, AkG-51, Schleswig/Jagel
46+00	IDS	GS.240/743	4300/6			Luftwaffe, JbG-34, Memmingen
46+01	IDS	GS.241/745	4301/6			Luftwaffe, JbG-34, Memmingen
46+02	IDS	GS.242/748	4302/6			Luftwaffe, JbG-33, Büchel
46+03	IDS	GT.061/750	4303/6			Luftwaffe, 49th FW, Holloman AFB, NM, USA
46+04	IDS	GT.062/752	4304/6			Luftwaffe, JbG-38, Jever
46+05	IDS	GT.063/754	4305/6			Marineflieger, MFG-2, Eggebek
46+06	IDS	GT.064/756	4306/6			Cr 18-Aug-98, Monheim, Bavaria. (JbG-32)
46+07	IDS	GT.065/759	4307/6			Luftwaffe, JbG-34, Memmingen
46+08	IDS	GT.066/762	4308/6			Luftwaffe, JbG-38, Jever
46+09	IDS	GT.067/764	4309/6			Luftwaffe, JbG-34, Memmingen
46+10	IDS	GS.243/767	4310/6			Luftwaffe, WTD-61, Ingolstadt
46+11	IDS	GS.244/769	4311/6			Marineflieger, MFG-2, Eggebek
46+12	IDS	GS.245/771	4312/6			Marineflieger, MFG-2, Eggebek
46+13	IDS	GS.246/774	4313/6			Luftwaffe, JbG-34, Memmingen
46+14	IDS	GS.247/776	4314/6			Luftwaffe, JbG-34, Memmingen
46+15	IDS	GS.248/779	4315/6			Marineflieger, MFG-2, Eggebek
46+16	IDS	GS.249/783	4316/6			Cr 06-Feb-92, near Ahlhorn (MFG-1)
46+17	IDS	GS.250/786	4317/6			Cr 31-Oct-91 into the Skagerrak near Denmark; collided with 43+84 (MFG-1)
46+18	IDS	GS.251/789	4318/6			Marineflieger, MFG-2, Eggebek
46+19	IDS	GS.252/792	4319/6			Marineflieger, MFG-2, Eggebek
46+20	IDS	GS.253/795	4320/6			Marineflieger, MFG-2, Eggebek
46+21	IDS	GS.254/806	4321/6			Marineflieger, MFG-2, Eggebek
46+22	IDS	GS.255/807	4322/6			Marineflieger, MFG-2, Eggebek
46+23	ECR	GS.256/817	4323/7	26-Oct-89		Luftwaffe, JbG-32, Lechfeld

Serial	Type	Build No/ Plane set	c/n Batch	First flt	Delivery	Operator, location or fate
46+24	ECR	GS.257/818	4324/7			Luftwaffe, JbG-32, Lechfeld
46+25	ECR	GS.258/821	4325/7			Luftwaffe, JbG-32, Lechfeld
46+26	ECR	GS.259/823	4326/7			Luftwaffe, JbG-32, Lechfeld
46+27	ECR	GS.260/827	4327/7			Luftwaffe, JbG-32, Lechfeld
46+28	ECR	GS.261/830	4328/7			Luftwaffe, JbG-32, Lechfeld
46+29	ECR	GS.262/833	4329/7			Luftwaffe, JbG-32, Lechfeld
46+30	ECR	GS.263/837	4330/7			Luftwaffe, JbG-32, Lechfeld
46+31	ECR	GS.264/839	4331/7			Luftwaffe, JbG-32, Lechfeld
46+32	ECR	GS.265/842	4332/7			Luftwaffe, JbG-32, Lechfeld
46+33	ECR	GS.266/844	4333/7			Luftwaffe, JbG-32, Lechfeld
46+34	ECR	GS.267/847	4334/7			Luftwaffe, JbG-32, Lechfeld
46+35	ECR	GS.268/848	4335/7			Luftwaffe, JbG-32, Lechfeld
46+36	ECR	GS.269/851	4336/7			Luftwaffe, JbG-32, Lechfeld
46+37	ECR	GS.270/854	4337/7			Luftwaffe, JbG-32, Lechfeld
46 38	ECR	GS.271/856	4338/7			Luftwaffe, JbG-32, Lechfeld
46+39	ECR	GS.272/858	4339/7			Luftwaffe, JbG-32, Lechfeld
46+40	ECR	GS.273/860	4340/7			Luftwaffe, JbG-32, Lechfeld
46+41	ECR	GS.274/864	4341/7			Luftwaffe, JbG-32, Lechfeld
46+42	ECR	GS.275/866	4342/7			Luftwaffe, JbG-32, Lechfeld
46+43	ECR	GS.276/869	4343/7			Luftwaffe, JbG-32, Lechfeld
46+44	ECR	GS.277/871	4344/7			Luftwaffe, JbG-32, Lechfeld
46+45	ECR	GS.278/873	4345/7			Luftwaffe, JbG-32, Lechfeld
46+46	ECR	GS.279/876	4346/7			Luftwaffe, JbG-32, Lechfeld
46+47	ECR	GS.280/879	4347/7			Luftwaffe, JbG-32, Lechfeld
46+48	ECR	GS.281/881	4348/7			Luftwaffe, JbG-32, Lechfeld
46+49	ECR	GS.282/884	4349/7			Luftwaffe, JbG-32, Lechfeld
46+50	ECR	GS.283/887	4350/7			Luftwaffe, JbG-32, Lechfeld
46+51	ECR	GS.284/890	4351/7			Luftwaffe, JbG-32, Lechfeld
46+52	ECR	GS.285/894	4352/7			Luftwaffe, JbG-32, Lechfeld
46+53	ECR	GS.286/896	4353/7			Luftwaffe, JbG-32, Lechfeld
46+54	ECR	GS.287/898	4354/7			Luftwaffe, JbG-32, Lechfeld
46+55	ECR	GS.288/900	4355/7			Luftwaffe, JbG-32, Lechfeld
46+56	ECR	GS.289/903	4356/7			Luftwaffe, JbG-32, Lechfeld
46+57	ECR	GS.290/906	4357/7			Luftwaffe, JbG-32, Lechfeld

ECR 46+41 of Einsatzgeschwader 1 wears the new two-tone light grey camouflage applied to Luftwaffe Tornados operating over the Balkans.

TORNADO PRODUCTION – ITALY

This AMI Kormoran-armed Tornado IDS of 36° Stormo wears unusual 'stencil-style' codes on the forward fuselage.

Serial	Type	Build No/ Plane set	c/n Batch	First flt	Delivery	Operator, location or fate
MMX586	-	P.05	-	05-Dec-75		(became MM586) AMI, RSV, Pratica di Mare
MMX587	-	P.09	-	05-Feb-77		(became MM587/MMP009) AMI, Cameri, recruiting aid
MMX588	IDS	P.14	-	09-Jan-79		(became MM588/MM7001) On display, Vigna di Valle
MM7002	IDS	IS.001/065	5003/2	22-Dec-81		AMI, 154° Gruppo/6° Stormo, Ghedi [6-10]
MM7003	IDS	IS.002/073	5004/2	28-Jan-82		AMI, TTTE, RAF Cottesmore, UK [I-93]
MM7004	IDS	IS.003/086	5006/2	23-Feb-82		AMI, 156° Gruppo/36° Stormo, Gioia del Colle [36-46]
MM7005	IDS	IS.004/094	5007/2	23-Mar-82		AMI, 154° Gruppo/6° Stormo, Ghedi [6-05]
MM7006	IDS	IS.005/102	5008/2	06-Aug-82		AMI
MM7007	IDS	IS.006/114	5010/2	20-May-82		AMI, 155° Gruppo/50° Stormo, Piacenza [50-07]
MM7008	IDS	IS.007/119	5011/2	09-Jun-82		AMI, 155° Gruppo/50° Stormo, Piacenza [50-41]
MM7009	IDS	IS.008/125	5012/2	07-Jul-82		AMI, 155° Gruppo/50° Stormo, Piacenza [50-45]
MM7010	IDS	IS.009/133	5013/2	02-Jul-82		AMI, 102° Gruppo/6° Stormo, Ghedi [6-33]
MM7011	IDS	IS.010/139	5014/2	02-Jul-82		AMI, 156° Gruppo/36° Stormo, Gioia del Colle [36-32]
MM7012	IDS	IS.011/154	5016/3	07-Sep-82		Cr 21-Oct-92, on the Nellis ranges, USA (154° Gruppo)
MM7013	IDS	IS.012/158	5017/3	09-Oct-82		AMI, 156° Gruppo/36° Stormo, Gioia del Colle [36-40]
MM7014	IDS	IS.013/170	5019/3	25-Oct-82		AMI, 155° Gruppo/50° Stormo, Piacenza [50-43]
MM7015	IDS	IS.014/176	5020/3	22-Nov-82		AMI
MM7016	IDS	IS.015/187	5022/3	23-Dec-82		AMI, RSV, Pratica di Mare [RS-01]
MM7017	IDS	IS.016/195	5023/3	17-Jan-83		AMI, 154° Gruppo/6° Stormo, Ghedi [6-07]
MM7018	IDS	IS.017/207	5025/3	04-Feb-83		AMI, 154° Gruppo/6° Stormo, Ghedi [6-18]

Serial	Type	Build No/ Plane set	c/n Batch	First flt	Delivery	Operator, location or fate
MM7019	IDS	IS.018/213	5026/3	03-Mar-83		AMI, 155° Gruppo/50° Stormo, Piacenza [50-05] (conv to ECR)
MM7020	IDS	IS.019/225	5028/3	14-Mar-83		AMI
MM7021	IDS	IS.020/231	5029/3	18-Mar-83		AMI, 154° Gruppo/6° Stormo, Ghedi [6-21]
MM7022	IDS	IS.021/244	5031/3	14-Mar-83		AMI
MM7023	IDS	IS.022/250	5032/3	12-May-83		AMI, 156° Gruppo/3° Stormo, Gioia del Colle [36-31]
MM7024	IDS	IS.023/255	5033/3	03-Jun-83		Cr 14-Dec-95; damaged beyond repair on landing, Decimomannu (154° Gruppo)
MM7025	IDS	IS.024/261	5034/3	15-Jun-83		AMI
MM7026	IDS	IS.025/267	5035/3	16-Jun-83		AMI
MM7027	IDS	IS.026/274	5036/3	17-Jun-83		AMI, 102° Gruppo/6° Stormo, Ghedi [6-47]
MM7028	IDS	IS.027/280	5037/3	29-Jun-83		AMI, 154° Gruppo/6° Stormo, Ghedi [6-18]
MM7029	IDS	IS.028/286	5038/3	25-Jul-83		AMI, 154° Gruppo/6° Stormo, Ghedi [6-19]
MM7030	IDS	IS.029/292	5039/3	23-Aug-83		AMI, 102° Gruppo/6° Stormo, Ghedi [6-35]
MM7031	IDS	IS.030/297	5040/3	30-Aug-83		AMI, 155° Gruppo/50° Stormo, Piacenza [50-01]
MM7032	IDS	IS.031/303	5041/3	19-Sep-83		Cr 12-Jun-84, near Asolo, northern Italy after collision with another Tornado (154° Gruppo)
MM7033	IDS	IS.032/309	5042/3	23-Sep-83		AMI, 154° Gruppo/6° Stormo, Ghedi [6-11]
MM7034	IDS	IS.033/315	5043/3	14-Oct-83		AMI, 102° Gruppo/6° Stormo, Ghedi [6-30]
MM7035	IDS	IS.034/322	5044/4	16-Nov-83		AMI, 156° Gruppo/36° Stormo, Gioia del Colle [36-47]
MM7036	IDS	IS.035/328	5045/4	21-Nov-83		AMI, 154° Gruppo/6° Stormo, Ghedi [6-43]
MM7037	IDS	IS.036/333	5046/4	02-Dec-83		AMI, 154° Gruppo/6° Stormo, Ghedi [6-07]
MM7038	IDS	IS.037/338	5047/4	05-Dec-83		AMI, 156° Gruppo/36° Stormo, Gioia del Colle [36-41]
MM7039	IDS	IS.038/345	5048/4	22-Dec-83		AMI, 155° Gruppo/50° Stormo, Piacenza [50-03]
MM7040	IDS	IS.039/350	5049/4	13-Jan-84		AMI, 156° Gruppo/36° Stormo, Gioia del Colle [36-35]
MM7041	IDS	IS.040/357	5050/4	16-Feb-84		AMI, 155° Gruppo/50° Stormo, Piacenza [50-42]
MM7042	IDS	IS.041/363	5051/4	23-Feb-84		AMI, 102° Gruppo/6° Stormo, Ghedi [6-31]
MM7043	IDS	IS.042/369	5052/4	06-Mar-84		AMI, 154° Gruppo/6° Stormo, Ghedi [6-13]
MM7044	IDS	IS.043/375	5053/4	26-Mar-84		AMI, 154° Gruppo/6° Stormo, Ghedi [6-20]
MM7045	IDS	IS.044/381	5054/4	03-Apr-84		Cr 26-Jul-84
MM7046	IDS	IS.045/386	5055/4	12-Apr-84		AMI, 154° Gruppo/6° Stormo, Ghedi [6-06]
MM7047	IDS	IS.046/392	5056/4	18-Apr-84		AMI, 156° Gruppo/36° Stormo, Gioia del Colle [36-36]
MM7048	IDS	IS.047/399	5057/4	29-May-84		Alenia [36-54]
MM7049	IDS	IS.048/406	5058/4	25-May-84		AMI
MM7050	IDS	IS.049/413	5059/4	13-Jun-84		AMI, 156° Gruppo/36° Stormo, Gioia del Colle [36-44]
MM7051	IDS	IS.050/419	5060/4	17-Jul-84		AMI, 154° Gruppo/6° Stormo, Ghedi [6-01]
MM7052	IDS	IS.051/424	5061/4	29-Jun-84		AMI, 154° Gruppo/6° Stormo, Ghedi [6-32]
MM7053	IDS	IS.052/430	5062/4	20-Jul-84		AMI, 102° Gruppo/6° Stormo, Ghedi [53]
MM7054	IDS	IS.053/436	5063/4	27-Aug-84		AMI, 102° Gruppo/6° Stormo, Ghedi [6-54]
MM7055	IDS	IS.054/442	5064/4	31-Aug-84		AMI, 156° Gruppo/36° Stormo, Gioia del Colle [36-33]
MM7056	IDS	IS.055/449	5065/4	22-Sep-84		AMI, 102° Gruppo/6° Stormo, Ghedi [6-46]
MM7057	IDS	IS.056/456	5066/4	26-Oct-84		AMI, 102° Gruppo/6° Stormo, Ghedi [6-47]
MM7058	IDS	IS.057/461	5067/4	17-Nov-84		AMI
MM7059	IDS	IS.058/467	5068/4	17-Nov-84		AMI
MM7060	IDS	IS.059/473	5069/4	11-Dec-84		AMI, 155° Gruppo/50° Stormo, Piacenza [50-06]
MM7061	IDS	IS.060/478	5070/4			AMI, 156° Gruppo/36° Stormo, Gioia del Colle [36-41]
MM7062	IDS	IS.061/492	5072/5			AMI, 155° Gruppo/50° Stormo, Piacenza (conv to ECR)
MM7063	IDS	IS.062/498	5073/5			AMI
MM7064	IDS	IS.063/503	5074/5			AMI
MM7065	IDS	IS.064/514	5076/5			AMI, 154° Gruppo/6° Stormo, Ghedi [6-14]
MM7066	IDS	IS.065/520	5077/5			AMI, 102° Gruppo/6° Stormo, Ghedi [6-44]
MM7067	IDS	IS.066/526	5078/5			AMI, 156° Gruppo/36° Stormo, Gioia del Colle [67]
MM7068	IDS	IS.067/531	5079/5			AMI
MM7069	IDS	IS.068/537	5080/5			Cr 18-Nov-93, Mount Galero, near Cuneo (155° Gruppo)
MM7070	IDS	IS.069/544	5081/5			AMI, 154° Gruppo/6° Stormo, Ghedi [6-01]
MM7071	IDS	IS.070/550	5082/5			AMI, 102° Gruppo/6° Stormo, Ghedi [6-42]
MM7072	IDS	IS.071/556	5083/5			AMI, 102° Gruppo/6° Stormo, Ghedi [6-36]

Serial	Type	Build No/ Plane set	c/n Batch	First flt	Delivery	Operator, location or fate
MM7073	IDS	IS.072/563	5084/5			AMI, 156° Gruppo/36° Stormo, Gioia del Colle [36-43]
MM7074	IDS	IS.073/567	5085/5			Cr 18-Jan-91, during Gulf War
MM7075	IDS	IS.074/573	5086/5			AMI, 155° Gruppo/50° Stormo, Piacenza [50-04]
MM7076	IDS	IS.075/580	5087/5			Cr 31-Aug-95 into the Gulf of Taranto (102° Gruppo)
MM7077	IDS	IS.076/585	5088/5			Cr 20-Jun-89, near Ghedi (102° Gruppo)
MM7078	IDS	IS.077/591	5089/5			AMI, 155° Gruppo/50° Stormo, Piacenza [50-02]
MM7079	IDS	IS.078/597	5090/5			Alenia (conv to ECR)
MM7080	IDS	IS.079/603	5091/5			AMI, 102° Gruppo/6° Stormo, Ghedi [6-41]
MM7081	IDS	IS.080/609	5092/5			AMI, 154° Gruppo/6° Stormo, Ghedi [6-02]
MM7082	IDS	IS.081/615	5093/5			AMI, 155° Gruppo/50° Stormo, Piacenza [50-40] (conv to ECR)
MM7083	IDS	IS.082/621	5094/5			AMI, 102° Gruppo/6° Stormo, Ghedi [6-37]
MM7084	IDS	IS.083/627	5095/5			AMI, 102o Gruppo/6o Stormo, Ghedi [6-34]
MM7085	IDS	IS.084/634	5096/5			Alenia [36-50]
MM7086	IDS	IS.085/639	5097/5			AMI, 154° Gruppo/6° Stormo, Ghedi [6-04]
MM7087	IDS	IS.086/644	5098/5			AMI
MM7088	IDS	IS.087/650	5099/5			AMI
MM55000	IDS	IT.001/045	5001/2	25-Sep-81		AMI, TTTE, RAF Cottesmore, UK [I-42]
MM55001	IDS	IT.002/056	5002/2	20-Nov-81		AMI, TTTE, RAF Cottesmore, UK [I-40]
MM55002	IDS	IT.003/080	5005/2	05-Feb-82		AMI, TTTE, RAF Cottesmore, UK [I-41]
MM55003	IDS	IT.004/108	5009/2	16-Apr-82		AMI, TTTE, RAF Cottesmore, UK [I-43]
MM55004	IDS	IT.005/144	5015/2	10-Aug-82		AMI, 154° Gruppo/6° Stormo, Ghedi [6-15]
MM55005	IDS	IT.006/164	5018/3	29-Sep-82		AMI, 102° Gruppo/6° Stormo, Ghedi [6-40]
MM55006	IDS	IT.007/182	5021/3	17-Nov-82		AMI, 154° Gruppo/6° Stormo, Ghedi [6-03]
MM55007	IDS	IT.008/201	5024/3	27-Jan-83		AMI, 155° Gruppo/50° Stormo, Piacenza [50-51]
MM55008	IDS	IT.009/220	5027/3	23-Feb-83		AMI, 102° Gruppo/6° Stormo, Ghedi [6-45]
MM55009	IDS	IT.010/238	5030/3	03-May-83		AMI, 156° Gruppo/36 ° Stormo, Gioia del Colle [36-56]
MM55010	IDS	IT.011/485	5071/5			AMI, 155° Gruppo/50° Stormo, Piacenza [50-50]
MM55011	IDS	IT.012/507	5075/5			AMI, 156° Gruppo/36° Stormo, Gioia del Colle [36-55]

Now gaining an overall grey colour scheme, Italy's Tornado IDS aircraft previously had toned-down codes, reduced size (and re-located) national insignia and toned-down unit insignia, as seen on MM7035 of 6° Stormo. HARTMUT FELDMANN

TORNADO EXPORT PRODUCTION

Royal Saudi Air Force Tornado IDS 762 was delivered in May 1987 and is based at Dhahran with No 7 Squadron. PETER R MARCH

Serial	Type	Build No/ Plane set	c/n Batch	RAF Serial	First flt	Delivery	Operator, location or fate
701	IDS	BS.157/CS.001/483	3219/5	ZD997	17-Feb-86	26-Mar-86	RSAF, No 7 Sqn, Dhahran (became 751)
702	IDS	BS.158/CS.002/488	3221/5	ZD998	25-Feb-86	26-Mar-86	RSAF, No 7 Sqn, Dhahran (became 752)
703	IDS	BS.159/CS.003/490	3222/5	ZE114	05-Mar-86	26-Mar-86	RSAF, No 7 Sqn, Dhahran (became 753)
704	IDS	BT.045/CT.001/495	3224/5	ZE115	06-Mar-86	26-Mar-86	(became 754) Cr 05-Sep-95, Dhahran (7 Sqn)
705	IDS	BT.046/CT.002/522	3235/5	ZE120	04-Apr-86	28-Apr-86	RSAF, No 7 Sqn, Dhahran (became 755)
706	IDS	BT.047/CT.003/547	3246/5	ZE125	11-Apr-86	28-Apr-86	(became 756) Cr 28-Aug-89, on approach to Dhahran after rear fuselage fire (7 Sqn)
757	IDS	BS.161/CS.004/511	3230/5	ZE117	27-Nov-86	19-Feb-87	RSAF, No 7 Sqn, Dhahran
758	IDS	BS.162/CS.005/515	3232/5	ZE118	04-Dec-86	19-Feb-87	RSAF, No 7 Sqn, Dhahran
759	IDS	BT.048/CT.004/598	3267/5	ZE147	06-Jan-87	26-Feb-87	RSAF, No 7 Sqn, Dhahran
760	IDS	BS.163/CS.006/517	3233/5	ZE119	03-Feb-87	26-Feb-87	RSAF, No 7 Sqn, Dhahran
761	IDS	BS.164/CS.007/527	3237/5	ZE121	27-Feb-87	11-May-87	RSAF, No 7 Sqn, Dhahran
762	IDS	BS.165/CS.008/534	3240/5	ZE122	20-Mar-87	11-May-87	RSAF, No 7 Sqn, Dhahran
763	IDS	BS.166/CS.009/536	3241/5	ZE123	09-Apr-87	18-May-87	Cr 08-Dec-93 – mis-identified a ground target (7 Sqn)
764	IDS	BS.167/CS.010/540	3243/5	ZE124	24-Apr-87	18-May-87	Cr 09-May-93
765	IDS	BS.168/CS.011/557	3250/5	ZE126	29-May-87	29-Jul-87	Cr 19-Jan-91; total hydraulic failure (7 Sqn)
766	IDS	BS.169/CS.012/561	3252/5	ZE144	17-Jun-87	29-Jul-87	RSAF, No 7 Sqn, Dhahran
767	IDS	BS.170/CS.013/578	3259/5	ZE145	29-Jun-87	05-Aug-87	RSAF, No 7 Sqn, Dhahran
768	IDS	CT.005/632	3282/5	-	09-Jul-87	05-Aug-87	RSAF, No 7 Sqn, Dhahran
769	IDS	CT.006/635	3284/5	-	30-Sep-87	07-Oct-87	Cr 29-Nov-90, on Half Moon Bay range (7 Sqn)
770	IDS	BS.171/CS.014/588	3263/5	ZE146	26-Aug-87	07-Oct-87	RSAF, No 7 Sqn, Dhahran
771	IDS	CT.007/808	3384/7	-	-89	24-May-89	RSAF, No 7 Sqn, Dhahran
772	IDS	CT.008/809	3385/7	-	-89	24-May-89	RSAF, No 7 Sqn, Dhahran
773	IDS	CT.009/810	3386/7	-	-89	06-Sep-89	RSAF, No 7 Sqn, Dhahran
774	IDS	CT.010/812	3388/7	-	-89	19-Dec-89	Cr 18-Jul-94 (7 Sqn)
2901	ADV	AS.086/DT.001/740	3340/6	ZE861	-Dec-88	20-Mar-89	RSAF, No 29 Sqn, Dhahran
2902	ADV	AS.087/DT.002/744	3342/6	ZE882	-Dec-88	20-Mar-89	RSAF, No 29 Sqn, Dhahran
2903	ADV	AS.088/DT.003/746	3343/6	ZE883	-Dec-88	12-Sep-89	RSAF, No 29 Sqn, Dhahran
2904	ADV	AS.089/DT.004/747	3344/6	ZE884	-Dec-88	16-May-89	RSAF, No 29 Sqn, Dhahran
2905	ADV	AS.084/DS.001/737	3338/6	ZE859	01-Dec-88	20-Mar-89	RSAF, No 29 Sqn, Dhahran
2906	ADV	AS.085/DS.002/739	3339/6	ZE860	-Dec-88	20-Mar-89	RSAF, No 29 Sqn, Dhahran
2907	ADV	AS.090/DS.003/749	3345/6	ZE885	-Dec-88	19-Sep-89	RSAF, No 29 Sqn, Dhahran
2908	ADV	AS.091/DS.004/751	3346/6	ZE886	-Dec-88	05-Sep-89	RSAF, No 29 Sqn, Dhahran

Serial	Type	Build No/ Plane set	c/n Batch	RAF Serial	First flt	Delivery	Operator, location or fate
2909	ADV	AS.094/DS.005/758	3350/6	ZE890	-89	05-Sep-89	RSAF, No 29 Sqn, Dhahran
2910	ADV	AS.095/DS.006/760	3351/6	ZE891	-89	12-Sep-89	RSAF, No 29 Sqn, Dhahran
2911	ADV	AS.096/DS.007/761	3352/6	ZE905	-89	05-Sep-89	RSAF, No 29 Sqn, Dhahran
2912	ADV	AS.097/DS.008/763	3353/6	ZE906	-89	19-Sep-89	RSAF, No 29 Sqn, Dhahran
3451	ADV	AS.099/DT.005/768	3356/6	ZE909	-89	14-Nov-89	RSAF, No 29 Sqn, Dhahran (became 2913)
3452	ADV	AS.100/DT.006/770	3357/6	ZE910	-89	13-Mar-89	RSAF, No 29 Sqn, Dhahran (became 2914)
3453	ADV	AS.102/DS.009/773	3359/6	ZE912	-89	13-Mar-89	RSAF, No 29 Sqn, Dhahran (became 2915)
3454	ADV	AS.103/DS.010/775	3360/6	ZE913	-89	14-Nov-89	RSAF, No 29 Sqn, Dhahran (became 2916)
3455	ADV	AS.104/DS.011/777	3361/6	ZE914	-89	18-Dec-89	RSAF, No 29 Sqn, Dhahran (became 2917)
3456	ADV	AS.105/DS.012/780	3363/6	ZE935	-90	04-Jun-90	RSAF, No 29 Sqn, Dhahran (became 2918)
3457	ADV	AS.107/DS.013/782	3365/6	ZE937	-90	30-Apr-90	RSAF, No 29 Sqn, Dhahran (became 2919)
3458	ADV	AS.108/DS.014/784	3366/6	ZE938	-90	30-Apr-90	RSAF, No 29 Sqn, Dhahran (became 2920)
3459	ADV	AS.109/DS.015/785	3367/6	ZE939	-90	20-Aug-90	RSAF, No 29 Sqn, Dhahran (became 2921)
3460	ADV	AS.110/DS.016/787	3368/6	ZE940	-90	27-Aug-90	RSAF, No 29 Sqn, Dhahran (became 2922)
3461	ADV	AS.112/DS.017/791	3371/6	ZE943	-90	27-Aug-90	RSAF, No 29 Sqn, Dhahran (became 2923)
3462	ADV	AS.113/DS.018/793	3372/6	ZE944	-90	08-Oct-90	RSAF, No 29 Sqn, Dhahran (became 2924)
6601	IDS	CS.015/826	3398/7	-	-90	31-Jul-90	RSAF, No 66 Sqn, Khamis Mushayt
6602	IDS	CS.016/831	3401/7	-	-90	31-Jul-90	RSAF, No 66 Sqn, Khamis Mushayt
6603	IDS	CS.017/835	3404/7	-	-90	20-Aug-90	RSAF, No 66 Sqn, Khamis Mushayt
6604	IDS	CS.018/840	3407/7	-	-90	18-Jan-91	RSAF, No 66 Sqn, Khamis Mushayt
6605	IDS	CS.025/874	3427/7	-		18-Jan-91	RSAF, No 66 Sqn, Khamis Mushayt
6606	IDS	CS.026/878	3430/7	-	-91	09-Jul-91	RSAF, No 66 Sqn, Khamis Mushayt
6607	IDS	CS.027/883	3433/7	-	-91	09-Jul-91	RSAF, No 66 Sqn, Khamis Mushayt
6608	IDS	CS.028/885	3434/7	-	-91	05-Aug-91	RSAF, No 66 Sqn, Khamis Mushayt
6609	IDS	CS.029/888	3436/7	-	-91	26-Aug-91	RSAF, No 66 Sqn, Khamis Mushayt
6610	IDS	CS.030/892	3439/7	-	-91	26-Aug-91	RSAF, No 66 Sqn, Khamis Mushayt
6611	IDS	CS.031/895	3441/7	-	-91	23-Sep-91	RSAF, No 66 Sqn, Khamis Mushayt
6612	IDS	CS.032/897	3442/7	-	-91	23-Sep-91	RSAF, No 66 Sqn, Khamis Mushayt
6613	IDS	CS.033/901	3444/7	-	-91	24-Oct-91	RSAF, No 66 Sqn, Khamis Mushayt
6614	IDS	CS.034/905	3447/7	-	-92	15-Jun-92	RSAF, No 66 Sqn, Khamis Mushayt
6615	IDS(R)	CS.019/843	3409/7	-	-91	11-Nov-91	RSAF, No 66 Sqn, Khamis Mushayt
6616	IDS(R)	CS.020/846	3411/7	-	-91	18-Nov-91	RSAF, No 66 Sqn, Khamis Mushayt
6617	IDS(R)	CS.021/849	3412/7	-	-91	18-Nov-91	RSAF, No 66 Sqn, Khamis Mushayt
6618	IDS(R)	CS.022/852	3414/7	-	-91	25-Nov-91	RSAF, No 66 Sqn, Khamis Mushayt
6619	IDS(R)	CS.023/853	3415/7	-	-91	25-Nov-91	RSAF, No 66 Sqn, Khamis Mushayt
6620	IDS(R)	CS.024/857	3417/7	-	-91	11-Nov-91	RSAF, No 66 Sqn, Khamis Mushayt
6621	IDS	CT.011/861	3419/7	-		18-Jan-92	RSAF, No 66 Sqn, Khamis Mushayt
6622	IDS	CT.012/865	3422/7	-		18-Jan-92	RSAF, No 66 Sqn, Khamis Mushayt
6623	IDS	CT.013/867	3423/7	-		18-Jan-92	RSAF, No 66 Sqn, Khamis Mushayt
6624	IDS	CT.014/870	3425/7	-		18-Jan-92	RSAF, No 66 Sqn, Khamis Mushayt
6625	IDS	CT.021/936	3477/9	ZH911	-96	12-Dec-96	RSAF, No 66 Sqn, Khamis Mushayt
6626	IDS	CT.022/937	3478/9	ZH912	-96	09-Jan-97	RSAF, No 66 Sqn, Khamis Mushayt
6627	IDS	CT.023/938	3479/9	ZH913	-Jan-97	13-Feb-97	RSAF, No 66 Sqn, Khamis Mushayt
6628	IDS	CT.024/939	3480/9	ZH914	-Jan-97	13-Feb-97	RSAF, No 66 Sqn, Khamis Mushayt
6629	IDS(R)	CS.035/940	3481/9	ZH915	-Oct-96	16-May-97	RSAF, No 66 Sqn, Khamis Mushayt
6630	IDS(R)	CS.036/941	3482/9	ZH916	-Jan-97	16-May-97	RSAF, No 66 Sqn, Khamis Mushayt
6631	IDS(R)	CS.037/942	3483/9	ZH917	-97	13-Jun-97	RSAF, No 66 Sqn, Khamis Mushayt
6632	IDS(R)	CS.038/943	3484/9	ZH918	-Feb-97	13-Jun-97	RSAF, No 66 Sqn, Khamis Mushayt
6633	IDS(R)	CS.039/944	3485/9	ZH919	14-Mar-97	11-Jul-97	RSAF, No 66 Sqn, Khamis Mushayt
6634	IDS(R)	CS.040/945	3486/9	ZH920	04-Apr-97	11-Jul-97	RSAF, No 66 Sqn, Khamis Mushayt
7501	IDS	CT.015/930	3471/9	ZH905	-96	03-Oct-96	RSAF, No 75 Sqn, Dhahran
7502	IDS	CT.016/931	3472/9	ZH906	-96	03-Oct-96	RSAF, No 75 Sqn, Dhahran
7503	IDS	CT.017/932	3473/9	ZH907	-Aug-96	07-Nov-96	RSAF, No 75 Sqn, Dhahran
7504	IDS	CS.041/946	3487/9	ZH921	-97	21-Jun-97	RSAF, No 75 Sqn, Dhahran
7505	IDS	CS.042/947	3488/9	ZH922	-97	21-Jun-97	RSAF, No 75 Sqn, Dhahran

The Royal Saudi Air Force's Tornado ADVs equip No 29 Squadron, based at Dhahran.

Serial	Type	Build No/ Plane set	c/n Batch	RAF Serial	First flt	Delivery	Operator, location or fate
7506	IDS	CS.043/948	3489/9	ZH923	-97	24-Jul-97	RSAF, No 75 Sqn, Dhahran
7507	IDS	CS.044/949	3490/9	ZH924	-97	24-Jul-97	RSAF, No 75 Sqn, Dhahran
7508	IDS	CS.045/950	3491/9	ZH925	-97	08-Aug-97	RSAF, No 75 Sqn, Dhahran
7509	IDS	CS.046/951	3492/9	ZH926	-97	08-Aug-97	RSAF, No 75 Sqn, Dhahran
7510	IDS	CS.047/952	3493/9	ZH927	-97	11-Sep-97	RSAF, No 75 Sqn, Dhahran
7511	IDS	CS.048/953	3494/9	ZH928	-97	04-Oct-97	RSAF, No 75 Sqn, Dhahran
7512	IDS	CS.049/954	3495/9	ZH929	-97	11-Sep-97	RSAF, No 75 Sqn, Dhahran
7513	IDS	CS.050/955	3496/9	ZH930	-97	04-Oct-97	RSAF, No 75 Sqn, Dhahran
7514	IDS	CS.051/956	3497/9	ZH931	-97	30-Oct-97	RSAF, No 75 Sqn, Dhahran
7515	IDS	CS.052/957	3498/9	ZH932	-97	30-Oct-97	RSAF, No 75 Sqn, Dhahran
7516	IDS	CS.053/958	3499/9	ZH933	-97	21-Nov-97	RSAF, No 75 Sqn, Dhahran
7517	IDS	CS.054/959	3500/9	ZH934	-97	21-Nov-97	Cr 08-Dec-97 (75 Sqn)
7518	IDS	CS.055/960	3501/9	ZH935	-97	-Dec-97	RSAF, No 75 Sqn, Dhahran
7519	IDS	CS.056/961	3502/9	ZH936	-97	-Dec-97	RSAF, No 75 Sqn, Dhahran
8301	IDS	CT.018/933	3474/9	ZH908	-Sep-96	07-Nov-96	RSAF, No 83 Sqn, Khamis Mushayt
8302	IDS	CT.019/934	3475/9	ZH909	-96	09-Jan-97	RSAF, No 83 Sqn, Khamis Mushayt
8303	IDS	CT.020/935	3476/9	ZH910	-96	12-Dec-96	RSAF, No 83 Sqn, Khamis Mushayt
8304	IDS	CS.057/962	3503/9	ZH937	-97	12-Mar-98	RSAF, No 83 Sqn, Khamis Mushayt
8305	IDS	CS.058/963	3504/9	ZH938	30-Nov-97	12-Mar-98	RSAF, No 83 Sqn, Khamis Mushayt
8306	IDS	CS.059/964	3505/9	ZH939		26-Feb-98	RSAF, No 83 Sqn, Khamis Mushayt
8307	IDS	CS.060/965	3506/9	ZH940		26-Feb-98	RSAF, No 83 Sqn, Khamis Mushayt
8308	IDS	CS.061/966	3507/9	ZH941	03-Feb-98	17-Apr-98	RSAF, No 83 Sqn, Khamis Mushayt
8309	IDS	CS.062/967	3508/9	ZH942	-Feb-98	08-May-98	RSAF, No 83 Sqn, Khamis Mushayt
8310	IDS	CS.063/968	3509/9	ZH943	-Feb-98	08-May-98	RSAF, No 83 Sqn, Khamis Mushayt
8311	IDS	CS.064/969	3510/9	ZH944	-98	18-Apr-98	RSAF, No 83 Sqn, Khamis Mushayt
8312	IDS	CS.065/970	3511/9	ZH945	-98	30-May-98	RSAF, No 83 Sqn, Khamis Mushayt
8313	IDS	CS.066/971	3512/9	ZH946	-98	-Jun-98	RSAF, on order
8314	IDS	CS.067/972	3513/9	ZH947	-98	30-May-98	RSAF, No 83 Sqn, Khamis Mushayt
8315	IDS	CS.068/973	3514/9	ZH948	23-Apr-98	-Jun-98	RSAF, on order
8316	IDS	CS.069/974	3515/9	ZH949	20-May-98	-Jul-98	RSAF, on order
8317	IDS	CS.070/975	3516/9	ZH950	-98	-Jul-98	RSAF, on order
8318	IDS	CS.071/976	3517/9	ZH951	-98	-Aug-98	RSAF, on order
8319	IDS	CS.072/977	3518/9	ZH952	-98	-Aug-98	RSAF, on order

The third Tornado ADV prototype shows off its clean lines and low-drag SkyFlash installation, as well as the early single AIM-9 launch rails and small fuel tanks.

A No 23 Squadron Tornado F3 from Leeming in formation with a pair of Leuchars Wing Phantoms. Nos 43 and 111 Squadrons were destined to be the last to convert to the Tornado ADV. CPL JOHN CASSIDY

Carrying a TIALD laser designator below the belly, a No 14 Squadron GR1 dashes through a narrow Lake District pass. FRANK HOUSBY

A No 617 Squadron GR1B pulls into the vertical, despite the weight of two Sea Eagle anti-ship missiles mounted under the fuselage.

The Tornado F3's excellence as a long range BVR interceptor is widely acknowledged, although its superb performance is less publicised.

The markings of No 56 Squadron (on the nearest aircraft) now adorn the F3s operated by the ADV conversion and training unit. CPL JOHN CASSIDY

The Tornado F3 will be replaced by the quadrinational Eurofighter during the early years of the 21st Century. CPL JOHN CASSIDY

An overall grey colour scheme is rapidly replacing the original two-tone disruptive camouflage on all bomber and recce Tornados. FRANK HOUSBY

The RAF's GR4s will probably be further refurbished and modernised before their planned retirement between 2015 and 2018. SGT JACK PRITCHARD

A No 13 Squadron GR1A shows off the distinctive shape of its underfuselage TIRRS fairing.

A No 111 Squadron Tornado F3 ejecting IR decoy flares from its underfuselage Vinten dispensers.